Commercial Housekeeping and Maintenance

Commercial Housekeeping and Maintenance

Iris Jones FHCIMA
Cynthia Phillips

Stanley Thornes (Publishers) Ltd

First published 1984 by

Stanley Thornes (Publishers) Ltd
Old Station Drive
Leckhampton
CHELTENHAM GL53 0DN

Reprinted 1987
Reprinted 1989
Reprinted 1990

British Library Cataloguing in Publication Data

Jones, I
    Commercial housekeeping.
    1. Institutional housekeeping
    I. Title   II. Phillips, C.
    647′.9   TX321

    ISBN 0–85950–377–1

Photoset by A.K.M. Associates (U.K.) Ltd., Southall, Greater London.
Printed and bound in Great Britain at The Bath Press, Avon.

Contents

Preface

In compiling this book our aim has been to bring together specialised information for those who work, or are about to work, within the industrial housekeeping and maintenance sector. While giving up-to-date information it should be appreciated that with new technology, better training and staff awareness, work situations are changing. We hope this book will inspire the reader to ask questions, find answers and be better equipped to meet the new challenges, while at the same time retaining the many traditional skills found within our industry. This book has also been written to help and guide students through the relevant examinations, City & Guilds 764, 708, 705, BTEC and HCIMA (Part A).

At the end of each chapter we have included a selection of questions; the majority of these can be answered by using the text but a proportion of them will challenge the reader to carry out further individual research.

1984
I. JONES
C. PHILLIPS

Acknowledgements

CUPRINOL — for permission to use details on the key to common wood destroying fungi and the key to wood-boring insects.
HMSO — for details on dry rot, insulation of buildings and hospital building notes.
MR JACK STROUD FOSTER, FRIBA, and BATSFORD ACADEMIC & EDUCATIONAL LTD — for their kind permission to reproduce drawings for the chapter on basic information on building and planning, organisation, fabric construction and layout.
NATIONAL BEDDING FEDERATION — for use of diagrams and information on beds.
FIRE PROTECTION ASSOCIATION — diagrams and charts.
PROCTER & GAMBLE — for details on fabric care and labelling.
MR E WOOLLEY, FIPHE, CIBS, MRSH — sanitation details (Northwood Publications).
Our appreciation and gratitude is also extended to our families, colleagues and friends for their kindness and understanding while we were compiling this book; also to the typists who worked so efficiently on our behalf.

PART A: GENERAL CONSIDERATIONS

1 An Introduction to Housekeeping

THE IMPORTANCE OF HOUSEKEEPING

Housekeeping — the maintenance of a clean, pleasant and orderly environment —has always formed an essential part of civilised living. It is a labour-intensive activity, though less so now than in earlier times, when there were few mechanical aids and labour was so cheap and plentiful that its cost was not an important consideration.

Housekeeping, and cleaning generally, involves full-time, part-time and, sometimes, casual workers — either directly employed or recruited and paid by a contractor. Many of those engaged are of foreign or Commonwealth origin, and this sometimes leads to difficulties with regard to communication and cultural differences.

The importance of the role of the housekeeper in management is rarely fully recognised, and the consequences of poor housekeeping are not always appreciated. In common with other departments that are spenders of money rather than direct revenue-earners, housekeeping is too often the victim of penny-pinching economies when costs have to be reduced.

In hotels especially the standard of cleanliness and tidiness can make or mar the general impression retained by a guest. In institutions good housekeeping can make a substantial contribution to the comfort and welfare of the residents.

The image of housekeeping staff is often one embodying low intelligence, poor motivation, slipshod appearance and inferior status. There are a number of ways in which the concept conjured up by such expressions as 'charwoman' or 'Mrs Mopp' might be eradicated. These include inculcating a better understanding of the role of the housekeeping department by general management, the provision of efficient equipment and materials, the improvement of working conditions, and better facilities for training.

In order to avoid the development of an ageing work force unfamiliar with and unreceptive to the most effective methods of working, it is desirable to encourage the recruitment of young people to housekeeping; but this is unlikely to be successful without recognition of the importance of the housekeeping function and its status within the management team.

LIAISON WITH OTHERS

Housekeeping is the only department with legitimate access to the whole establishment, and it maintains regular liaison with other departments. Management relies in many ways on housekeeping staff for the first impression the guest receives of the establishment.

If surfaces and equipment are regularly cleaned and maintained, their life expectancy will be increased considerably. If equipment is not regularly maintained, it may not only use more power but will not work as efficiently and will cost more in worker-hours.

With the introduction of modern cleaning techniques, equipment, materials and finishes and with recent legislation such as the Health and Safety at Work Act 1974, people are now becoming aware that cleaning is a job for the expert. The staff employed need to be flexible to meet changing needs and services.

Each building to be cleaned is unique in design and layout, and space needs to be used to maximum advantage. It is essential that there is good cooperation between the architects, builders and domestic housekeeper/manager at the initial stages and development of a building. This will enable the establishment to be completed on time and in A1 condition using the budget to its best advantage. It also reduces the cost of maintenance and the need for replacement and redesign, and it provides a basis for good organisation in the day-to-day running of the establishment.

THE DUTIES OF THE HOUSEKEEPER OR DOMESTIC MANAGER

The duties of the housekeeper or domestic manager* vary considerably, depending on the type and size of the establishment, the number of staff employed, company policy, the number and extent of contract services used and the function of other departments (e.g. finance, purchasing, personnel, training, security and maintenance). The job can be very demanding and time-consuming, and 60–70% of the time may be spent dealing with personnel in all its aspects. Some of the main duties and responsibilities are indicated below:

- The recruitment and dismissal of staff within the department.
- Staff training and appraisal.
- Welfare of staff and customers.
- The control and supervision of staff.
- Implementing the policy of the company, organising work schedules, duty rosters, setting standards and achieving goals.
- The control and supervision of the linen room.
- Security of the establishment.
- Maintenance of the buildings and contents, e.g. equipment, furniture and fittings.
- The keeping of all relevant records on staff, finance, equipment, materials, redecorating, room occupancy, special functions.
- The purchasing of supplies and equipment.

In order to carry out the required duties effectively the housekeeper must delegate some of the tasks to assistants.

*In future when we refer to the 'housekeeper' we shall mean 'housekeeper' or 'domestic manager' or 'head of maintenance'. The term used obviously varies between establishments.

2 The Classification and Staffing Structures of Establishments

THE FIVE MODERN SECTORS

A housekeeping department's function in any establishment is as wide and varied as the many jobs it offers to trained and non-trained staff.

Because of an increased awareness of the importance of a well-run section and since the introduction of the Health and Safety at Work Act, most premises, whether commercial or non-profit making, employ or contract a person (or persons) responsible for the housekeeping department.

Classification of the types of establishment that need a housekeeping department used to fall into three sectors: hotels, hospitals and institutions. Today, however, there are so many different types of premises that they are very hard to classify. To understand the varied types of premises, it is better to categorise the sectors under: *industry, institutions, hospitals, welfare,* and *hotels.*

THE INDUSTRIAL SECTOR

Included in this sector are factories, shops and offices, and all forms of transport (e.g. ships, boats, planes and buses). It is considered one of the biggest sectors to employ contract labour. Factories, shops and offices, and transport all need special consideration in terms of cleaning and maintenance. Are the premises and/or equipment in use for 24 hours? Can night cleaning be done? Is there any specialised equipment, e.g. computers, paint shops, machinery? What standard is required?

The staffing structure is shown below:

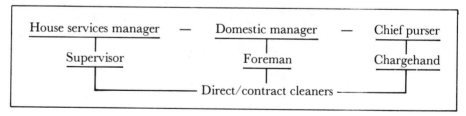

INSTITUTIONS

Institutions include prisons, armed services and non-residential schools.

Prisons use inmate labour and employ direct labour for supervision and training. Duties include all routine housekeeping duties and often laundry work.

Armed services. Most camps now employ civilian housekeeping labour to allow service personnel more time for specialised jobs, although it is expected that each such person is responsible for bed changing and general tidiness.

Non-residential schools   may use direct or contract labour. Local education authority schools normally use only direct labour, and staff are trained locally.

The staffing structure is shown below:

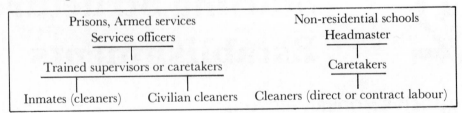

HOSPITALS

Hospitals fall into two types: (a) the private sector; (b) the National Health Service. Many private hospitals use contract cleaners, and usually standards are extremely high, as the level of costing for housekeeping is in proportion to the amount the patients pay. The specialised hospitals (e.g. psychiatric, geriatric and children's) require close attention because of the nature of the work, so too do operating theatres and intensive care units.

The staffing structure is shown below:

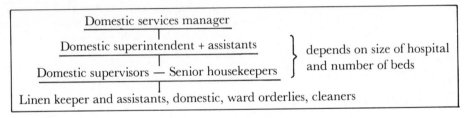

WELFARE ESTABLISHMENTS

Old people's homes, children's homes, halls of residence and conference centres are included here. The first two are usually administered by the local authority; caretakers, matrons, etc., are employed to recruit staff and train them on the job.

Halls of residence are usually administered by colleges and universities, and each is run by a different method. Some are run on a self-clean/catering basis, whereas others provide all amenities including food. During vacations most open their doors to conferences and visiting groups. This may pose special problems if extra staff are needed on a seasonal basis. The provision of extra linen can also be difficult.

The staffing structure is shown below:

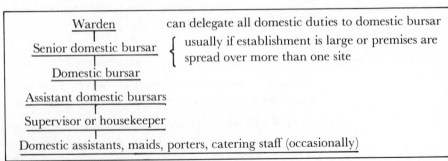

HOTELS

Included in this sector are the private and national hotels, motels and motor hotels, guest houses and boarding houses. The service offered by this group is the most diverse, according to the amount paid by its guests. The AA and RAC offer a 'star' system that is awarded according to a hotel's facilities (e.g. lifts, lounges, etc.). Most employ direct labour, but depending on the location and size of the premises this can be seasonal or non-seasonal. In the past 10 years, motels and motor hotels have grown in number. These offer either a limited service or no service except vending machines. Usually they are sited on or near main motorways or roads. Guest houses or boarding houses are normally privately owned and tend to have very individual standards and methods of cleaning.

The staffing structure is shown below:

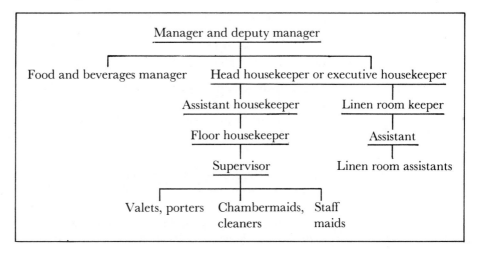

Small guest houses and boarding houses tend to be family businesses, and if staff are employed job specifications are often of a very informal nature. Each establishment delegates jobs very differently; one person may be responsible for all the cleaning, and this person is normally under the direct supervision of the owner. Only a small percentage of guest and boarding houses have bathrooms *en suite*, so the work tends to be finished quite quickly. Many of the staff double up and become waiters or waitresses during the rest of the day.

The staffing structure is shown below:

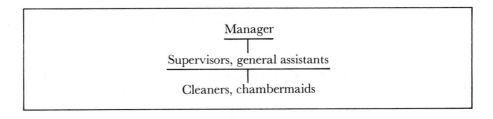

3 Accommodation Requirements and Personal Services

INTRODUCTION

All categories of commercial and residential accommodation must be clean, comfortable and warm. They must also provide an atmosphere in which the guest or resident can feel at ease. All types of accommodation will need careful designing, planning and staffing if the business is to be successful.

The needs and standards of accommodation vary widely within an area, especially in hotels. Hotels usually cater for either short- or medium-stay guests who use the hotel for business or pleasure. Hospitals have short-, medium- and long-stay patients, often within the same establishment. This can cause problems, as the needs of the patients vary (as does the level of nursing care, laundry, maintenance, etc.).

Most hostels belonging to colleges, schools and universities let rooms during vacation periods. These may need extra-careful planning and staffing to deal with the change-over, and with the difference in use, between, for example, students during term time and conference guests. Staff hostels require extra facilities, such as storage space, seating areas, laundry, social and entertaining rooms, and communal kitchens.

The amount of space needed in any area is calculated after the following have been established, and the results added together:
- The amount of space which each item of furniture or equipment uses.
- The amount of space needed to use it.
- The amount of space needed to reach it (access space).

INSTITUTIONS

There are three main types of accommodation within this group:
1. Hostels or homes providing total care and accommodation.
2. Those providing accommodation with facilities for self-catering and laundering.
3. Those providing living accommodation only.

All groups have been studied by various Government committees, and recommendations have been given as to area and facilities required.

As a very general guide a room for long-term residents needs to be a minimum of 10 m^2, but this may be modified by available space, facilities needed, money available, etc.

All hostels provide a bed and some extra furniture such as a desk, chair, storage and hanging space. Cooking and laundry facilities may be provided, although to what degree will depend on the residents' needs.

Communal facilities for hostels can be special entertainment rooms, quiet areas for study, bars and snack facilities, common rooms, dining rooms and chapels. Provision for illness within hostels is usually very basic: sick bays should only be used for minor ailments; more serious ailments should be referred to a doctor and treatments should be carried out in hospital. Because space is usually limited a sick bay often doubles up as a guest room as and when required.

College and university halls of residence have changed over the years in that most establishments now, where possible, provide single bedsit accommodation. There may, however, be shared accommodation within the same complex. Building, heating and maintenance costs have risen sharply, so hostel rooms now tend to be smaller. Space can be provided elsewhere for other amenities such as entertaining, eating, ironing, etc. This also cuts down the risk of fire and of overloading power points. Shared study bedrooms for colleges, universities, training colleges, etc., are common in the USA, but as yet are not as popular in other countries. They have the advantage of breaking down the feeling of isolation when a new student first arrives, but they can have disadvantages. One student may want to work while the other does not, especially if they have different timetables; also there may be personality differences. The sharing of facilities such as sinks, hanging space, etc., does cut down dramatically on resources and costs. The diagram below shows one possible scheme.

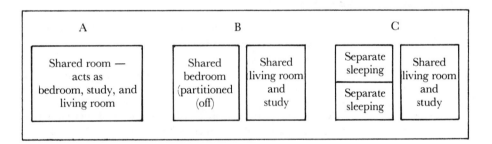

A	B		C	
Shared room — acts as bedroom, study, and living room	Shared bedroom (partitioned (off)	Shared living room and study	Separate sleeping / Separate sleeping	Shared living room and study

HOSPITALS

Hospital design and planning, and surfaces and materials used, have changed dramatically since the days of long wards, cramped areas, strict visiting times and inflexible routines for staff and patients.

Today with better architectural planning, new surfaces and cleaning materials, hospitals are more pleasant and more efficiently run. This change was partly brought about by the re-styling of wards, the need for higher standards of hygiene and cleanliness, and the introduction of new technology.

Most NHS hospitals have a selection of ward areas. These tend to be either open wards, open bays with three or four beds, or individual rooms.

Open wards or Nightingale wards consist of long 'corridor-type' areas. These wards can take up to 30 beds. The disadvantage of this type of ward is that it tends to be noisy, there is less privacy, and it may involve extra walking for staff and patients, especially for toilet areas. Also, it may not feel as 'homely' as a smaller unit, so it can be frightening for some patients, especially older people and children. The advantage of this type of ward is that it may be easier for the staff to observe patients, and it may be easier to clean because of only one continuous floor and wall surface.

Three-to-four-bedded open bays.   Many hospitals are now designed around the idea of having small units of beds, but within the same area as the open wards. Each bed is parallel to the window, giving each patient much more light and a view. Also any fresh air from the window blows laterally across the beds, rather than directly behind the head, so these wards can be more comfortable. The bays are divided by partitions, so each area is more private and makes the patient feel more at ease.

Individual rooms   are common in private hospitals and nursing homes, but in NHS hospitals they tend to be reserved for either:
- patients who are likely to infect others,
- patients who may disturb others while ill,
- patients who are seriously ill or dying,
- patients who need special or intensive care.

Hospital staff,   resident and non-resident, should be well catered for. Coffee lounges, day rooms, sleeping, washing and working facilities should all be carefully designed. (A local reference library will give up-to-date information on recommendations and examples of room layouts.)

WELFARE ESTABLISHMENTS

Hostels and housing for the elderly need careful planning and designing at all levels. There are two main types of dwelling:
1. Special housing and hostels providing total and limited care.
2. Sheltered housing, where residents have individual self-contained flats, with a warden.

Older residents are often infirm, crippled or bedridden, and many use wheelchairs. Extra space will be needed in rooms as most older residents like to have their possessions around them.

Floor surfaces should be non-slip; power points and plugs within easy access; lifts, ramps, handrails and gripping handles need to be plentiful. Common rooms, launderettes and small shops may be required.

HOTELS

Within newer hotels, especially groups, space allowances where possible tend to be standardised. This makes planning, cleaning and maintenance schedules easier, staff training more effective, and the purchasing of fittings and furniture cheaper, because of bulk ordering.

It is always advisable to check with a local reference library for current information on recommended space and size allowance as they do change and vary. As an *approximate* guide use the following dimensions:

- **A single room**: 3.8×2.6 m ($12\frac{1}{2} \times 8\frac{1}{2}$ ft) giving an area of 9.9 m^2 (106 ft^2).

- **A double room**: 4.4×3.8 m ($14\frac{1}{2} \times 12\frac{1}{2}$ ft) giving an area of 16.7 m^2 (178 ft^2).

- **An attached bathroom**: 1.6×2.2 m ($5\frac{1}{4} \times 7\frac{1}{4}$ ft) giving an area of 3.5 m^2 (38 ft^2).

Depending on the type, size, service and standard offered, a hotel room should provide a clean bed, bedside table, chair, table or desk, hanging and storage facilities — and possibly an attached bathroom.

A busy city hotel, or one that has a brisk conference trade, will usually be designed with the business person in mind and will provide extra desk space, conference areas, facilities for the use of visual aids, etc.

Hotels usually offer either traditional room service, a self-service system or a system which combines both the traditional and self-service methods.

With traditional room service, food, drink or other items may be obtained at most times by ringing reception or room service direct.

A self-service system provides kettles, sachets of tea, coffee, etc., and sometimes even continental breakfast, so the guest may obtain refreshment at any time without leaving the room. Alcoholic drinks may be provided by a stocked drinks dispenser within the bedroom. Each dispenser is checked daily and the total amount of drink consumed is then transferred to the guest's account. It is not always easy to ensure that only guests over 18 years old have the access key to drinks dispensers. In large hotels, vending machines, ice dispensers, shoe-cleaning machines, etc., may be found in designated areas. All these facilities are particularly useful in hotels near airports or motels where guests arrive and depart at unusual hours.

Many guests lament the passing of traditional room service with the introduction of the self-service system. The newer system may seem impersonal and also may not stock the items that are required. On the other hand, traditional room service is costly to operate, especially in quiet periods and during the low season.

The turning down of beds during dinner is another service that has been discontinued by many establishments. Often beds are made up with the cover already turned down, ready for use by the guest. This reduces the number of chambermaids required on evening duty.

Valets, who were originally responsible for the cleaning and pressing of gentlemen's clothes, are now employed only in the larger, more expensive hotels and their duties have widened to include porterage, linen exchange, room service, etc.

Radios, televisions and telephones are found in many hotel bedrooms. In the larger hotels, telephones connect the guest with reception where outside lines, links with telex machines and bookings for theatre and restaurants can be requested.

Many small personal items may be added to a hotel bedroom, for use by the guests. These include writing paper, tissues, hotel and local literature, fresh fruit and flowers.

QUESTIONS

1. What are the chief requirements of any residential accommodation?

2. Most hotels provide some staff accommodation. Indicate how this would vary from the main accommodation provided for the 'guests'.

3. What facilities would be needed in a hostel catering for both able-bodied and handicapped residents?

4. In intercontinental hotel groups, room design tends to be standardised. Point out the advantages and disadvantages to guests and staff.

5. Describe the advantages and disadvantages of:

(a) traditional room service,

(b) self-service.

6. Compare and contrast the staffing structure of a large city hotel (200 bedrooms, 4-star) and a small guest house accommodating 10 people.

4 Safety, Fire and First Aid

SAFETY

In 1974 the Health and Safety at Work Act was introduced (HASAWA). This Act now supersedes all previous safety legislation including The Offices, Shops and Railway Premises Act 1963. The new Act was brought about after a committee looked into safety conditions at work.

HASAWA is defined as 'an Act to make further provision for securing the health, safety, and welfare of persons at work, for protecting others against risks to health or safety in connection with the activities of persons at work'. The main aim of the Act is to protect by law all persons at work, and it extends protection to others who might be affected by activities at the work place, e.g. pollution in the form of contamination. Another objective is to increase the safety awareness of all. Unlike other Acts it lays down precisely the responsibilities of employers and employees. The Act also created a new Health and Safety Commission and Executive. Involved with the Commission and Executive are Inspectors who are responsible at 'grass roots' level for carrying out the provisions of HASAWA. In the case of hotels and catering establishments, the responsibility is delegated to the local authority and they provide Environmental Health Officers. Also incorporated in the Act are stricter, more powerful penalties.

Who is Covered by HASAWA?

Under the new 1974 Act an employer is held directly responsible for the health and safety of employees. Any break of the safety rules occurring by his/her neglect, or committed with his/her connivance or consent will render him/her liable to a fine or up to 2 years' imprisonment and/or an unlimited fine. The Act states:

- An employer must provide and maintain equipment and provide safe working practices.
- Articles and substances must be stored, handled and transported with maximum safety.
- Information, instruction, training and supervision must be provided to ensure the health and safety of employees.
- The place of employment must have a safe exit and access.
- The working environment must be without risks to health and have adequate facilities (toilets, staff rest rooms, etc.).
- A written Statement of General Policy (relating to HASAWA) must be displayed by all employers employing more than five people, and it must be revised and amended as necessary.

Although the Act is weighted with responsibilities for the employer, the employee also has specific areas of responsibility. These are namely:

- He/she must take reasonable care of himself and other employees and other persons on the premises.
- He/she should cooperate with his/her employer concerning health and safety.

Safety representatives are appointed in most medium- and large-sized establishments. Their responsibility is to check the safety of work places, equipment, staff rooms, etc., and to report back to management on how to maintain and improve working conditions. In very large establishments there may be a safety committee, and the whole range of topics dealt with in the Act is revised, maintained and implemented by this specialised group of people.

How is HASAWA Enforced?

If on inspection a fault is discovered, an official can issue a verbal or written Advice Notice, or an Improvement Notice can be given, whereby a set time is allowed for the fault to be remedied. If the fault is serious, a Prohibition Notice is issued and the area of risk is closed or sealed until action is taken by the employer to remedy the fault.

Finally, anybody contravening HASAWA can be prosecuted as well as being served an Improvement Notice or a Prohibition Notice.

Safety Records

By law, accident record books must be kept. Apart from recording all the relevant details they help to provide detailed information for insurance purposes. More importantly, they can give a good indication of the areas of possible danger. Up-to-date information regarding records can be obtained from the local Health and Safety Inspector.

The Major Causes of Accidents

1. Lack of information or training.
2. Failure of supervision.
3. Lack of knowledge or ability of those involved.
4. Human failing — failure to implement safety procedures.
5. Lack of organisation.
6. Lack of physical or mental attributes of those involved.
7. Design faults in machinery.
8. Breakdown of machinery or lack of maintenance.
9. Maliciousness and vandalism.

Specific Causes of Accidents

1. Incorrect handling of equipment and cleaning methods.
2. Falls — on the ground or from heights.
3. Badly maintained areas.
4. Inadequate lighting and ventilation, especially in key areas.
5. Incorrect method of lifting objects.
6. Failure to use guards on machinery.
7. Poor stores and stock control procedures.

8. Electrical, e.g. faulty wiring.
9. Health hazards — fumes, gases, etc.
10. Explosions — excessive noise.
11. Unsafe systems of work.
12. Carelessness, haste, horseplay.
13. Lack of food or excessive alcohol.

If an accident does occur, it should be reported immediately.

Example of Accident Report Form

This Form should be sent to the Company Health and Safety Officer.

ACCIDENT REPORT FORM

Name of Injured Person _____
Section _____
Supervisor _____
Time of Report _____
Date _____

Extent of Injury _____
_____
_____

Was Hospitalisation Required _____
_____

THE ACCIDENT

Time _____ Place _____
WHAT HAPPENED (include equipment/items etc., and other persons)
_____
_____
_____
_____

Witnessed by 1. _____
_____
2. _____
_____
Supervisor's Recommendations _____
_____
_____

Date _____ Supervisor's Signature _____

This Form should be sent to the Company Health & Safety Officer.

HOW TO AVOID DANGER

Floors. Avoid over-polishing and use a non-slip polish. Take extra care in hospitals and old people's homes. Secure all mats and rugs; avoid using these on polished floors.

Stair carpets must be placed firmly in position. Where two types of floor surface meet, it is better to use a metal joining strip or make sure the two surfaces are joined professionally.

Display warning signs to indicate that floor areas are being treated or washed, and train the staff to report any frayed carpets, uneven floors, missing tiles, etc. Canteen and kitchen floors are dangerous areas; there is always the risk of staff falling, burning and scalding themselves.

Equipment. When any equipment is not in use it should be returned to its designated position. If left unattended, it can easily cause a hazard. Only trained staff should be allowed to use dangerous equipment. Electrical equipment must be checked frequently for fraying flexes, overheating, etc. Any open fire must have a fireguard. Gas fires and boilers need servicing regularly and staff must be trained how to light gas equipment and pilot lights.

Human error in accidents. During staff training all grades must be aware of the dangers that are particular to the housekeeping section, e.g. trailing flexes, slippery floors, exposed equipment and the misuse of chemicals. Also it is necessary to show employees how to lift and move heavy objects to avoid straining the back and legs.

Routine cleaning tasks. Dust inhalation and infection, skin infections and eye injuries can occur during cleaning operations, especially during the periodic clean when a build-up of dust, dirt and grease can be difficult to remove. If the area to be cleaned is very dusty, a mask should be worn at all times. The efficient use of a vacuum cleaner is necessary to ensure dust is collected and not just moved to a different site. Dust can harm the eyes and, if inhaled, the lungs.

SAFETY MARKINGS AND SIGNS

A clearly marked danger area means fewer accidents and injuries and provides a safer working environment. British Standard 5378 of 1976 recommends that environmental danger zones, safety areas, and escape routes be identified by specific colours, and different shaped signs.

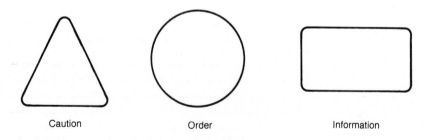

| Caution | Order | Information |

Shape of signs

Warning — Red. Use this colour with white as a contrast for STOP or DANGER signs. Red is also used for fire appliances, the location of fire-fighting gear, dangerous substances and the storage of explosives.

Safety — Green. This colour is for safety equipment, emergency escape doors and routes, and first aid posts. It is used with white as a contrast.

Caution — Yellow. Use this colour for all warning signs, such as dangerous contents, machinery, etc. Use with black diagonal stripes to indicate ramps and obstructions.

PIPE IDENTIFICATION

Pipes can be a hazard. Opening the wrong valve could produce explosive results. Pipe identification aids the emergency services in the event of an accident. British Standard 1710 of 1975 recommends the following:

Water — Green	**Acids and alkalis — Violet**
Steam — Silver grey	**Air — Light blue**
Oils — Brown	**Electrical services — Orange**
Gases (except air) — Yellow ochre	**Other fluids — Black**

The maintenance and operation of service pipes should be done only by authorised personnel. There must be a set isolation procedure in cases of emergency.

FIRE

Fire Protection

Every year, lost lives and damage estimated at millions of pounds, remind both management and employees of the danger of fire and toxic smoke.

Not all fires can be prevented, especially in public buildings, but with organised training on every level the hazards can be kept to a minimum. In all public places personnel should be aware of the possible causes of fire, and take appropriate steps to ensure the safety of guests, patients, etc. Since 1971 it has been a legal requirement to provide 'provision for the protection of persons from fire risks, and for the purposes connected therewith' (Fire Prevention Act 1971).

The Nature of Fire

Fire results when oxygen and fuel (combustible material) and ignition occur at the same time. Examples of combustible materials are paper, refuse, certain liquids and furniture. Matches, cigarettes or heat may be the ignition source. If the oxygen supply is reduced, the fire is restricted, but this may be difficult as oxygen is approximately 21% of air; fuel (combustible material) is nearly always present, so it is important to recognise and control the ignition source. With the production of smoke and hot gases, flames travel upwards and on meeting an obstruction (e.g. high fittings) they spread horizontally. Smoke and hot gases move quickly through open doors, unclosed staircases, lift shafts, rubbish chutes, etc.

Causes of Fire

It is difficult to give exact percentages to show the causes of fire because the sources of ignition are often unknown. However, it is thought that more than 30% of fires are caused by faulty or misused electrical installations and equipment. Only occasionally do industrial gas installations cause fire except by leaks or misuse. At least 20% of fires are started by careless smokers. Increasingly, fires are being started deliberately. The majority of fires in hospitals, hotels and other residential establishments start between midnight and 5 a.m.

Prevention of Fire   **Electrical equipment.**   All equipment should be professionally installed and then checked at least once every 5 years though most equipment will need more frequent checks, depending on use. All faults must be corrected by a qualified electrician. Notices should be posted on or near TV sets advising guests to switch off and unplug the set before leaving the room. *Check all frayed flexes.*

Smoking.   A plentiful supply of ashtrays is necessary. They must be emptied regularly into metal bins with metal lids. Smoking should be banned in as many areas as possible. Check public rooms after use for smouldering cigarette ends.

Kitchens.   Take care not to overheat oils and fats; carefully dry chips before placing them in oil. *Never leave frying food unattended.* Towels should not be left on stove tops to dry. Arrange for the regular cleaning of filter ducts and extractors. Notices have limited value, so good staff training and supervision are essential.

Workmen.   Check the area regularly after workmen have left. Look for smouldering wood chippings, flammable paint and canisters of gas.

Waste.   Do not let waste accumulate. Keep all areas clean and tidy.

Furniture and furnishings.   All new upholstered furniture must comply with The Upholstered Furniture (Safety) Regulations 1980.

Linen rooms.   All irons, calenders and steam irons must be switched off after use.

Fire Alarm System   Some establishments, e.g. theatres, cinemas and car parks, have to be left unmanned for large parts of the day and night, as do many residential areas; thus the need for automatic fire alarms is vital. In the last 20 years alarm systems have become more sophisticated.

They fall into the following groups:
- Pre-ignition systems.
- Combustion gas detectors.
- Smoke detectors.
- Flame detectors.
- Thermal air currents.
- Temperature change detectors.

All alarm systems must be checked regularly; faults must be recorded and corrected. The alarm must be clearly audible and recognised by everyone. Alarm systems can have bells, buzzers, or horns that are activated by one or more of the above detectors.

Fire-fighting   Fires are extinguished by:
- removing the fuel, or
- excluding the oxygen, or
- cooling the materials involved to below ignition level, and removing the source of ignition.

Fire-fighting equipment acts by excluding oxygen or cooling the materials. The equipment falls into two groups: (a) fixed equipment, (b) non-fixed (portable) equipment.

Fixed Fire-fighting Equipment

Fixed equipment sprinklers consist of a grid of water pipes fixed under the ceiling with delivery heads normally 3 m apart. When the temperature around the sprinklers reaches a pre-determined level, the enclosed liquid expands, which causes the glass to break and releases water to the area below. Bulbs can be set to break between 68-180 °C depending upon requirements. The spray usually covers an area of approximately 10 m^2. Also the sprinkler head sounds an audible alarm. If a special area needs to be protected, e.g. one with electrical equipment, professional help is needed in choosing and positioning the sprinkler head correctly.

Drenchers are similar to sprinklers but are used on the outside of a building. They are normally operated manually to avoid mishaps.

Audible alarm Unit. This is one of the cheapest and easiest systems to use. A small glass case is smashed on the outbreak of a fire and this connects to a large bell that sounds the warning. The alarm can also register at the local fire brigade head-quarters.

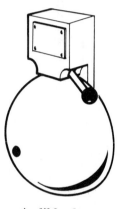

Audible alarm

Smoke or flame detectors are positioned on ceilings. As flames and gases are carried upwards, the detectors register and a siren or bell warns those in the building to follow the escape procedure. Normally the detectors operate over an area of approximately 20–100 m^2. Emergency lighting is operated when the main lights fail. It should operate automatically, lighting up corridors and escape route signs.

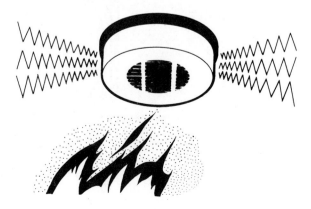

Fusible links. Two strips of brass are soldered together with low-melting-point solder. In the event of a fire the strip melts and automatically sends a signal to close the fire doors, close the air shafts and stop the lifts. There is usually no audible sound on the strip melting. Usually, when fire doors are released they shut tightly and form 'compartments' which contain the fire by stopping the flames and smoke spreading.

Non-fixed Fire-fighting Equipment

Extinguishers are of many different types, as shown below:

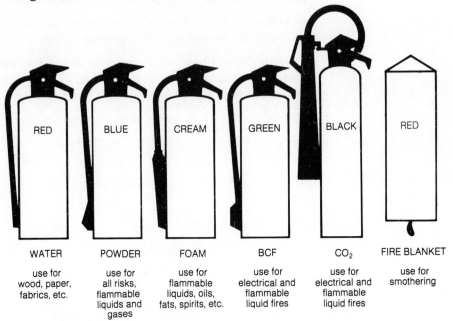

WATER	POWDER	FOAM	BCF	CO$_2$	FIRE BLANKET
RED	BLUE	CREAM	GREEN	BLACK	RED
use for wood, paper, fabrics, etc.	use for all risks, flammable liquids and gases	use for flammable liquids, oils, fats, spirits, etc.	use for electrical and flammable liquid fires	use for electrical and flammable liquid fires	use for smothering

Hoses used on larger fires are much more effective than buckets or soda-acid extinguishers. The hose can extend up to 36 m. The hose is wound on to a coil and is usually sited in a recess, on a corridor or stairs.

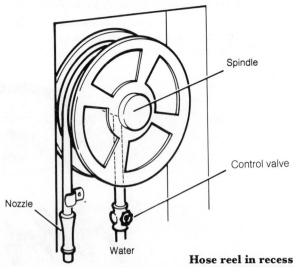

Spindle

Control valve

Nozzle

Water

Hose reel in recess

Buckets. *Sand* is non-conducting so can be used on small fires and those associated with electrical fires, but in the latter case, *it must be dry*. Sand has a limited use because it can only be used on flat surfaces; also it can cause permanent damage to equipment. *Water* is cheap and its use is well understood, but, unless the water level is checked regularly buckets may be empty in times of emergency.

ACTION IN THE EVENT OF A FIRE

- Raise the alarm, either by breaking the glass case of the alarm or by telephoning direct to the fire brigade, the reception area or switchboard.
- Warn occupants in the building. Shut doors and windows. Isolate dangerous supplies of gas, electricity, oil, etc.
- Assist in evacuation, especially the handicapped, elderly or children. Inspect rooms if safe to do so. Do not use lifts.
- Attack the fire if safe to do so.
- Carry out special allocated tasks.

Staff Training for Fire Drills

It is vital that all staff have a thorough knowledge of fire-fighting equipment and that that knowledge is always updated when necessary. Do not rely on notices. Officers of the fire brigade are always willing to come to premises and give demonstrations to staff on equipment, fire-fighting and safety procedures. Escape routes should be common knowledge and fire drills should be practised frequently. Staff are expected to take positive action in the event of a fire. Whenever possible, permanent staff should be employed so that they are able to take the initiative and keep calm in the event of a fire. Fire drills must be practical exercises and as near to the 'real thing' as possible.

GUEST INFORMATION

All fire exits and escape routes must be clearly marked and in each area a copy of the fire procedure should be displayed (a good example is shown below). Also it is wise to ask guests to inform receptionists of any disability they may have, e.g. deafness, physical handicap, etc., in case they need extra help if a fire occurs.

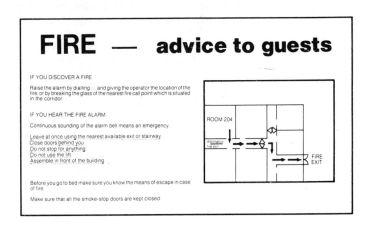

Fire Checklists   A typical fire checklist is shown below.

PRINCIPAL FIRE SAFETY MEASURES FOR HOTELS

CHECKLIST FOR MANAGEMENT

The law
Does the hotel comply in all respects with the conditions of its Fire Certificate under the *Fire Precautions Act?*
Is the fire brigade consulted on all matters which may affect the Fire Certificate?

Location and environment
Is there adequate access for the fire brigade?
Do you maintain regular liaison with the fire brigade?
Are hydrants clearly marked and readily accessible?

The building
Is the hotel so constructed that, in the event of fire, smoke and flames are prevented from rising from storey to storey or moving along corridors?
In connection with alterations, repairs and decorations are there procedures for making sure that:
suitable precautions are taken to prevent fires?
means of escape are not obstructed?
no reduction in fire safety will result from alterations?
Are there at least two escape routes available to occupants from all storeys?
Are all fire exits and escape routes clearly signposted and lighted, and kept free of obstructions?
If the hotel has external escape stairs, are these maintained in a safe condition?
Are floor plans displayed for the benefit of the fire brigade?
Can all doors leading from escape routes be opened outwards from the inside?
Are special hazards such as electronic data processors and basement car parks adequately separated from other areas and has suitable fixed fire protection been provided for them?
Has advice been obtained on any building materials (e.g. wall/ceiling linings) which could help fire to spread?
Is there an emergency lighting system in case of mains failure?
Has the electrical installation been inspected and tested within the last 5 years?

Furniture, furnishings and equipment
Is the fire risk fully considered when ordering any replacements or additions?

Fire protection equipment
Are there means of sounding an alarm which can be heard by all occupants?
Has an automatic fire detection system been installed?
Is there equipment for fighting fire: hose reels, portable extinguishers, sprinkler system?
Is all equipment regularly tested and maintained?

In the event of fire
Do you have a clearly defined procedure should fire break out?
Are fire instruction notices displayed for:
Guests?
Staff?

Those with special duties?

Has someone (e.g. switchboard operator) been instructed to call the fire brigade immediately a fire is reported — and to alert the management?

Have the night staff been instructed to do this at night?

Are you (or a deputy) ready at any time to assume responsibility for operating this procedure?

Are all staff trained as to what they must do in the event of fire?

Do they know that their first duty is to raise the alarm?

Are all staff aware that their main responsibility is to guide guests to safety?

Are all staff trained to operate fire alarm call points, and to use hose reels/extinguishers to put out a small fire?

Do they understand the importance of closing doors to check spread of fire and smoke?

Have you chosen an outside assembly point well away from areas where fire appliances may be placed?

Will the hotel register be easily available so that names can be checked in the event of fire?

Guests

Are there notices in all bedrooms and public rooms instructing guests in what they should do and where they should go in the event of fire?

Fire prevention

Are all staff given fire prevention instruction and told to report any potential fire hazards?

Are the smoke-stop doors kept closed at all times?

Are all public rooms inspected last thing at night to ensure that cigarettes have been extinguished and electrical appliances have been switched off?

Are large ashtrays provided in all rooms?

Is waste and rubbish collected regularly and placed in safe receptacles?

Are 'No smoking' rules rigorously enforced in such places as storerooms?

Are kitchen staff specially instructed in fire dangers?

Are fat deposits removed regularly from ovens, ranges, hoods and ducts?

Are records kept of routine inspections, maintenance, fire drills and training?

Are food service staff familiar with the fire hazards of flamed dishes?

Are maintenance workshops kept clean and tidy?

It is essential that completed forms are acted on. Therefore, provision should be made on a checklist for a signature from the inspector, the date, and time of the last check.

Access by the Fire Brigade

For a fire-fighting team to be efficient, knowledge of the layout of the building is essential. Regular meetings and discussions on better techniques and equipment, etc., will make sure that:

1. The team are aware of possible high risk areas, and how to cope on the outbreak of fire.
2. Access to the building is always clear for fire brigade engines, and that hydrants, dry risers and foam inlets are easily found.

3. A copy of the plan of the building is at the fire brigade headquarters and a duplicate is left at the premises for emergencies.

4. Management delegate certain staff to assist the fire brigade, informing them of missing staff or public, or where the fire is located.

High Buildings

When the price of land is high there is a tendency to erect high buildings. They can, however, cause fire hazard problems. In new buildings over 24 m high it is usual to have a 'fire tower' built in for every 1000 m² of floor space. In the initial stages of building, the lobby or entrance areas are constructed so that the main staircase and doors leading off are fire-resistant. Also this area incorporates wet and dry risers. A wet riser runs vertically through the inside of the building and is basically a pipe for carrying water to fires (it is not used for other purposes). A dry riser runs on the outside of a building over 45 m high. It is connected to the water hydrants in the event of a fire, and supplies water instantly to all floors through various valves.

FIRST AID

The application of first aid takes into account a whole range of medical areas, which would be too vast to cover in one section. The basic idea of first aid is to:

- sustain life (by cardiac massage, resuscitation, etc.),
- prevent the casualty's condition from becoming worse,
- help recovery.

Both the St. John Ambulance and the Red Cross provide excellent, basic, first-aid courses. In large establishments there are staff who take direct responsibility for first aid, this also includes keeping the first-aid box replenished. The responsibilities of the first aider are as follows.

Assessing the problem.   Try to determine the severity and cause of the accident, reassure the casualty if conscious. Make sure the area is safe for yourself and the casualty. Where there is more than one casualty, the first aider must assess quickly which person needs priority treatment. The requirements of a First Aider are to:

- be confident, do not hesitate,
- be caring and reassuring,
- be quick in emergency situations,
- be able to delegate any given instructions to others when necessary.

Check breathing.   Make sure the airway is clear, if the casualty has stopped breathing, commence artificial respiration (the kiss of life).

Mouth to Mouth Resuscitation

- Loosen clothing, remove any debris from mouth, (teeth, vomit, etc.). Tilt the head backwards and the chin upwards, often this is enough to make the casualty start breathing again, if it is the tongue that is blocking the airway.
- Open your mouth wide and breath deeply.
- Pinch the casualty's nostrils with your fingers, place your lips around the casualty's mouth to form a seal.
- Blow into the lungs until the chest rises.
- Repeat inflations to your natural breathing rhythm and continue as long as necessary.

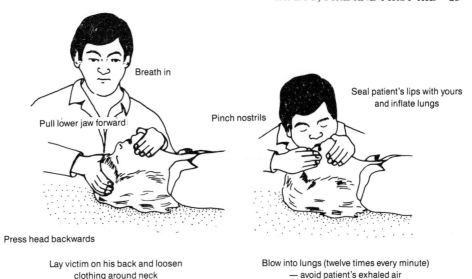

Breath in

Pull lower jaw forward

Press head backwards

Lay victim on his back and loosen
clothing around neck

Pinch nostrils

Seal patient's lips with yours
and inflate lungs

Blow into lungs (twelve times every minute)
— avoid patient's exhaled air

Diagram showing artificial respiration

Unconsciousness   Place casualty in the recovery position if unconscious, see the diagram below. This
allows the airway to remain free and any vomit, blood, etc., to flow away.

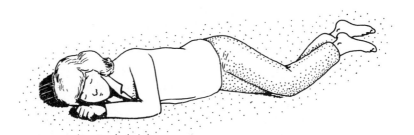

Diagram showing the recovery position

Recovery Position
- Kneel beside casualty and put both his arms closely by his side.
- Turn him gently on to his side and place the head slightly forward so that the air
  passage remains clear and any blood, vomit, etc., is emitted.
- Draw up the upper arm until it makes a right angle with the body. Bend the elbow.
- Draw up the upper leg so that it makes a right angle with the body. Bend the knee.

Controlling Bleeding

- Pad and pack the wound.
- Do not try to remove large deeply embedded objects.
- Try and raise the affected part, if possible, if no fracture is apparent.

Treatment — Bleeding and Cuts

- Apply some form of padding and apply pressure by pressing with fingertips to the
  wound for at least 15 minutes.

- Clear off any dirt or foreign bodies and apply a sterile padded dressing. Secure it firmly.

Shock

This arises when there is a lack of blood supply to the vital organs and functions of the body. Shock usually occurs with severe pain, injuries or sudden illness. It is associated with many conditions and injuries and it can be very severe and cause death.

Causes of Shock

- Severe bleeding — external and internal.
- Loss of plasma — due to burns etc.
- Heart failure.
- Severe abdominal emergencies — ruptured appendix.
- Loss of body fluids — vomiting, diarrhoea.

Possible Signs and Symptom of Shock

- Cold clammy skin, pallor, sweating, blurred vision.
- Vomiting.
- Thirst.
- Shallow, rapid breathing.
- Patient may be unconscious.

Treatment

- Lay casualty down and give reassurance.
- Deal with the underlying cause of shock.
- Get casualty to hospital.
- Keep the head low and turned to one side and if possible raise lower limbs. If the head is injured, support the shoulders slightly and move head to one side.
- Loosen clothing, especially at neck and waist.
- Do not give casualty anything to drink; if thirsty, just moisten lips with water.
- Try not to move the casualty, but cover with a blanket.

Burns and Scalds

Burns are caused by dry heat, e.g. fire flame, friction and radiation. Scalds are caused by moist heat, e.g. boiling water, hot oil, steam, tar, etc.
Treatment is the same as for bleeding and cuts.

- Always check for shock. If necessary, call for an ambulance.
- Reduce the heat around the affected part as quickly as possible, either by immersion into cold water or by dabbing the part with ice and water for at least 15 minutes.
- Remove any rings, belts, etc., to allow for swelling.
- Remove wet clothes but leave dry ones.
- Lay casualty down and give small drinks of water.
- Place a clean dressing (not adhesive) on the area. Never apply oil-based lotions and creams to burns and scalds.

Fractures

A fracture is a broken or cracked bone. A fractured bone is usually apparent by swelling at the site of the fracture, tenderness, deformity of the limb, loss of movement. Shock is often present. If possible treat the fracture before moving casualty.

Treatment

- If an untrained person arrives at the scene of the accident, he must call for expert advice immediately.
- Avoid moving the casualty, place a blanket over him to keep him warm. If movement of the casualty is necessary, steady and support the injured parts before any lifting or moving takes place.

Heart Attacks

Shock is nearly always present. Often the casualty is giddy, short of breath, has a weak and irregular pulse rate and has severe pains in the chest and arms.

Treatment

- Loosen casualty's clothing at neck and waist, try and place him in a sitting position (it makes breathing easier).
- Call a doctor and arrange transport to hospital immediately
- Give artificial respiration and heart massage if necessary.

Stroke

Casualty can appear drunk. Often there is a sudden loss of power or sensation in a limb and speech may be slurred.

Treatment

- Make sure airway is clear and give breathing assistance if necessary.
- Call a doctor.
- Ensure there is plenty of fresh air.
- Place casualty in the recovery position and cover with a blanket.
- Do not give anything to drink and do not leave the casualty unattended.

Diabetic Coma

Quite often the casualty's breath smells of acetone (similar to the smell of nail varnish). They have a flushed face, sweat a lot and may appear drunk (slurred speech, etc).

Treatment

- If conscious ask if he/she is diabetic.
- Give a drink of heavily sweetened tea or any other sweet food, e.g. sweets or sugar lumps.
- If unconscious place in recovery position and call for help immediately. Most diabetics carry cards indicating what to do in an emergency.

Poisoning (General rules)

If the casualty is conscious ask for details of what happened. If there are signs of burning in and around the mouth give water or milk to drink. (Do not force the casualty to vomit.) Take to hospital immediately. In the case of non-acid poisons it may be safe to let the patient vomit but always try and check if possible.

If the casualty is not conscious, but breathing easily, place in the recovery position and send for an ambulance. If breathing is not free, start artificial respiration and send for help. When the casualty is seen by a doctor try and give as many details of the event as possible. This helps identify the poison (e.g. tablets etc.) and thereby aids recovery.

There are provisions laid down by law, the Health and Safety (first aid) Regulations, 1981, to the number of first-aid boxes that must be provided on premises. It is recommended that the markings of first-aid containers be a white cross on a green background. A general contents guide of such boxes would be the following items.

- Waterproof dressings (blue for food areas).
- Individually wrapped sterile adhesive dressings.
- Scissors, tweezers.
- Disinfectant.
- Safety pins.
- Bandages (preferably sterile) including at least one triangular.
- Sterilised eye pad.
- Assorted unmedicated dressings.
- Where tap water is not available, sterile water, or a sterile saline solution and disposable containers must be available for eye irrigation.

All accidents should be noted on an accident report form with details of time, place, witnesses, etc.

QUESTIONS

1. (a) List the four main aims of HASAWA 1974.

   (b) Draw up a code of safety to be issued to members of the housekeeping staff.

   (c) What are the main factors to be considered when calculating the cost of an accident?

2. Suppose the number of minor accidents has risen considerably in the last 6 months in your department. Indicate what investigations you would carry out to prevent further occurrences. Prepare a report with your findings and recommendations to be submitted to your supervisor or manager.

3. Design a poster for a code of safety using the following phrase: 'Think safety'.

4. Carry out a safety survey in your establishment. Indicate the major hazards and suggest possible remedies.

5. From the following list tick the essential ingredients for combustion to take place:

Flame	Gas
Air	Oxygen
Spark	Fuel
Heat	Solid material

6. There are three causes for the spreading of fire. What are they?

7. In the box below tick the extinguisher you should use for the types of fire listed.

TYPE OF FIRE	CO$_2$	WATER	BCF	FOAM	FIRE-RESISTING BLANKETS	Other means
Chip pan						
Electrical						
Paper and wood						
Petrol						
Gas leak						

8. You are employed as a chambermaid and discover a fire in a bedroom. Outline the procedure you should follow.

9. Why is it advisable that in the case of wet burns clothing should be removed, but in dry burns clothing can remain?

5 Security

INTRODUCTION

The security of premises can be both expensive and time-consuming, but more and more the public and staff are demanding a higher level of safety. Complete security of areas is difficult, but there are certain procedures and arrangements that can be adopted.

STAFF AND THEIR KEYS

It is advisable to ask prospective staff for at least two references (not testimonials) at their interview, one being from their most recent employer.

In most establishments there are various types of key, for example:

The grandmaster key. This double-locks a room so that nobody can enter until a senior member of staff opens it again. Such a key is normally used in a hotel or hostel where it is advisable that the door remains locked for a very specific reason, e.g. death of a guest, student, etc. This key is normally held by the duty manager, security officer or other responsible person.

Master keys. These will open all doors except where a door has been locked with a grandmaster. They are usually carried by junior managers or departmental heads. The loss of a master key requires the changing of all locks at once.

Submaster keys. These usually open a small section of rooms and are carried by the cleaner or chambermaid, porter, etc.

The knowledge of how to handle keys by all grades of staff is vital, not only for the protection of guests and residents, but also for the protection of staff. On no account must a key be lent to unauthorised personnel. At the beginning and end of each work period there should be a signature given to show the receipt and handing back of keys. Keys issued should be kept in a safe place, e.g. fixed securely on the belt, during work hours. If a key is lost, details must be reported immediately to the housekeeper or supervisor. There should be a record kept of all main key-holders, and keyboards should be positioned securely. Key numbers and hooks on boards must be clearly visible to make missing keys quickly identifiable. Nightwatchmen or security guards often have devices that register the time an area was checked. A key or card may be placed in a time-registering machine which records the time and place of the check.

STAFF CONTACT WITH 'GUESTS'

On entering a room the cleaner or chambermaid should follow a set security procedure for his/her own benefit as well as the guest's. A room door should not be closed while staff are inside cleaning. Many establishments now have special fittings on room doors that can be activated to let senior staff know that the room is being cleaned, (the device is known as 'staff or maid finder'). If a member of staff finds the room occupied by a gentleman on his own, he/she should try to leave the room until the end of the cleaning schedule then return. If this is not convenient he/she should enter with another member of staff or enter alone, but make sure the door remains open and that another member of staff is aware of the number of the room being cleaned.

Any jewellery, clothes, make-up, etc., belonging to guests should not be touched. Guests are usually told of the procedure for the safety of valuables. During conferences or at meetings extra security may be necessary as there can be a greater number of people than usual entering and leaving the building.

COMMUNICATIONS FROM STAFF

During staff training it must be stressed how important it is to report quickly and accurately anything or anybody looking suspicious. This includes unattended luggage, parcels and letters for residents, workmen who seem unsure of the job or area, or indeed anybody who is unknown and seems to be acting strangely.

On no account must an unauthorised member of staff open up a room at the request of a guest. On being asked to do so he/she must report to the housekeeper or manager. Larger establishments employ a security officer or house detective whose job it is to ensure that all aspects of security are checked.

BUILDING CHECKS

Most non-domestic buildings have built-in alarm and security systems of some kind. The new types of system include laser beam alarms or electrical 'trip' wires under carpets. Special alarms and locks on windows, doors, stockrooms and refrigerators can be fitted. Normally a strict, routine check is made as necessary on all ground floor doors and windows. Fire doors may cause a problem. They must remain closed from the outside but remain accessible from the inside because of the possibility of fire. For all premises the local Crime Prevention Officer will be glad to give advice regarding security.

THE BOMB THREAT

The aim of any establishment is to prevent bomb or incendiary attacks or, when this is not possible, to minimise their effects. In buildings to which members of the public must have access this must be done without imposing unacceptable restrictions on them, and the occupier must weigh the seriousness of the threat against the need to maintain business as usual and decide the extent to which countermeasures should be adopted.

The measures listed below are common sense suggestions and are not firm recommendations applicable in all cases. Some measures (e.g. intruder alarms and guard dogs) are expensive and may be applicable only at times when the threat is serious.

Security Responsibilities

A member of staff should be appointed security officer to co-ordinate all aspects of security, ensure that countermeasures are taken, and encourage security awareness and vigilance among the staff. He/she should be of sufficient seniority to command the respect of the staff and ensure that the necessary measures are implemented. Responsibilities for particular aspects of security (e.g. lock-up drill — see below) should be clearly established.

Survey of Buildings

A survey of the building and surrounding area should be made, if possible with the assistance of the police and/or fire authorities. The following physical security measures should be considered:

The surrounding area
- Covering open basement areas with wire mesh and/or illuminating them.
- Securing access points to underground parking or loading bays and ensuring their supervision when in use.
- Restricting parking to areas away from the building.
- Removing rubbish bins to a safe distance from the building.
- Cutting down undergrowth or shrubs immediately adjacent to the building.
- Securing manholes, ducts or other subterranean access points.

The external building face
- Securing ground floor doors and windows, including the sealing of letter boxes.
- Bevelling off, or removal of, window or other ledges, particularly in rear areas.
- Illumination of porches and basement areas.
- Leaving on ground floor lights at night.
- Removal of ladders which give access to the roof, and painting of drain pipes with anti-climb paint.
- Securing of skylights or other roof-top access points.
- Installation of intruder alarms, guards, or nightwatchmen with or without guard dogs.

Fire or explosive hazards
- Removal of rubbish which could hide explosive or incendiary devices, particularly on the ground floor or in the basement.
- Securing doors and windows or ventilators that give access to fuel storage, the central heating plant or boilers.
- Fire-fighting equipment and fire escapes should be checked.

Vital facilities
Identification of particularly important facilities, (e.g. computer installations) giving them additional protection (e.g. stout doors and good locks).

Restriction of Public Access

If possible, the areas of public access should be separated from the rest of the building. The rest of the building can then be made a secure area.

The secure area should be given an appropriate degree of physical security, and access to it should be controlled. Visitors should establish their identity and, if necessary, be escorted.

The public area. Entrances should be kept to a minimum. Doors and windows and other openings which are not in use should be secured internally. A thorough search should be made of the area to reduce to a minimum any hiding places for bombs and incendiaries. Cupboards should be kept locked. Good lighting with no areas of shadow is essential. Curtains may be shortened to clear the windowsills and floor.

Particular attention should be paid to lavatories and washrooms. Members of the public in this area should be kept under observation. This is best done by staff, who should be advised of the threat and asked to be particularly vigilant. Surreptitious observation can be maintained by closed circuit television, but this has the disadvantage that operator fatigue precludes continuous watching. One-way glass can also be used. Uniformed guards or commissionaires may be preferable, since they act as a deterrent. Guards and staff should be particularly alert for anybody entering with a case, parcel, or similar object and should challenge the bearer should there be an attempt to leave without it.

Flying Glass

Casualties from flying glass can be greatly reduced by securing polycarbonate sheets behind the glazing, or by reglazing with polycarbonate sheets or laminated security glass. Alternatively, transparent polyvinyl chloride (PVC) film or special shatter-resistant transparent adhesive polyester film, may be applied to the inner surface of the window. Additional protection can be provided by venetian blinds or, better, by a free-hanging transparent 250 micron polyester sheet weighted at the bottom with a sand-filled 'sausage' and suspended as close as possible behind the glazing.

Security Plans

A lock-up routine should ensure that no unauthorised persons remain in the building after working hours. Plans for action in the event of a fire or bomb threat are essential and should be rehearsed. In times of bomb threats, new stock should only be accepted from recognised sources. Precautions should be observed on entering the building at opening time if there is evidence of an intrusion during the night.

Communications

Alarm buttons, or preferably alarm strips that can be operated unobtrusively, may be installed in the public area, which will then ring at a manned control point, from which the police and fire authorities can be telephoned.

Evacuation

The responsibility for evacuation and/or search rests with the employer. A search party should be organised, each person having a particular area to check. The party should report directly to the person co-ordinating the search, carry out the search and report the result.

Do not touch any suspicious or unacccountable objects. When the police arrive they will take control of the situation and advise accordingly.

Planning in advance is the best course of action. If efficient 'self-help' searching and evacuation plans are prepared, much valuable time will be saved.

Persons who are required to evacuate the building should take their immediately accessible personal belongings with them (i.e. such items as handbags and briefcases).

A person should be nominated in each office or department who is familiar with the day-to-day appearance and contents of the office or department in order that any suspect parcel or package can be brought to his/her attention immediately.

Package Bombs

Postal bombs are not likely to be in large parcels, but rather in flat letters 145×100 mm ($5\frac{3}{4} \times 4$ in) weighing up to 113 g (4 oz), or in packets the size of a book.

Remember they may explode on opening, so look out for:
- *the postmark*, especially if foreign, and any name and address of the sender,
- *the writing*, which may be of a 'foreign' style,
- *the balance*, which if uneven is suspect,
- *the feel*, which if 'springy' or stiff with cardboard may indicate a trap,
- *the holes*, pinpoints that may be made by a wire,
- *the stains*, which could be 'sweating' explosives,
- *the smell*, some explosives have an aroma of marzipan or almonds,
- *the rattle*, which might indicate a loose part,
- *the booby trap*, which could be in an envelope within the packet.

Check *all* mail carefully — not only foreign mail, as there is always the possibility that extremist groups could use posting boxes in the United Kingdom itself. Finally, remember that such letters may be delivered by hand.
If there is any doubt –call the police.

Bomb Hoaxes and Threats

Unfortunately, 'bomb hoax' telephone calls are a common occurrence. All persons responsible for the management of their buildings or staff should instruct their telephone operator to report all such calls to them confidentially and immediately. Usually bomb threats come in anonymous telephone calls. Note that they could, however, be mailed or even surreptitiously hand-delivered.

As soon as it is clear that the caller is making a bomb threat, *let him finish his message without interruption.* If any response is essential as to a statement such as, 'This is about a bomb, are you listening?' keep it to one or two words. While the caller talks, get the message *exactly* and also listen for clues to:
- caller's sex and approximate age,
- noticeable condition affecting speech such as drunkenness, laughter, anger, excitement, incoherency,
- peculiarities of speech such as a foreign accent, mispronunciations, speech impediment, tone and pitch of voice,
- background noises audible during the call such as music, traffic, talking or machinery.

When the caller has given his message, try to keep him in conversation. The following are key questions and should be asked, if possible, *after the caller has given his message:*

- Where is the bomb located?

- What time will it explode?
- When was it placed?
- Why was it placed?

Note whether the caller repeated his message or any part of it. Note the exact time of its receipt. Write the message down *immediately* after the call. Immediately after that, notify the police. Repeat the message, *exactly as you received it*; then fill in the other details you were able to get.

Be calm. Listen carefully. Report exactly.

QUESTIONS

1. The question of security should be uppermost in the mind of the housekeeper, especially with the problems of today. Try to describe the facilities and procedures which must be established to ensure adequate security of:

   (a) employees' possessions,

   (b) guests' possessions,

   (c) the building and its contents.

2. During a conference how could you safeguard guests from unwelcome intrusions by outsiders?

3. How should a chambermaid or cleaner deal with a member of the public who demands entry to a locked room?

4. On receiving a bomb threat what action should the housekeeper take to provide for the safety of guests and staff?

5. Why is it necessary for members of staff to sign for keys as they take them, and then re-sign when handing them back at the end of the working period?

PART B: PLANNING AND OPERATION

6 Basic Information on Building and Planning

INTRODUCTION

Buildings, however modern looking, have usually been built by a traditional method that has been adapted. All buildings must fulfil the requirements of shelter, warmth, sound insulation.

Buildings are of two basic types. Some are solid structures made of brick, concrete, stone, etc.; others are made from metal or wood, with infills of brick, concrete blocks, which may or may not have surface cladding.

ROOFS

Roofs are necessary on buildings to provide shelter and protection from the elements.

There are two types.

Pitch roofs are constructed at an angle so that rain water is quickly shed. Traditionally they were made from thatch over timber trusses, but nowadays they are made of more modern materials such as concrete tiles, plain clay tiles, slates or other suitable materials over timber or metal supports.

Flat roofs are essentially easier and cheaper to construct than pitch roofs. Even so, they require a slight 'fall' to allow the rain to run off. Covering may be sheet felt or asphalt, laid over boards and supported by timber, metal or concrete beams.

Generally flat roofs are lighter in weight than pitch roofs. The roof covering needs protection from the adverse effect of sunlight. This is usually obtained by coating the surface with a reflective paint, or by applying stone chippings on the surface.

There are problems with flat roofs:
- Unless adequate support is given they tend to sag, causing pools of water on the surface.
- If stone chippings are used as the reflective medium, care must be taken when gaining access from the roof to adjacent structures for maintenance purposes so as not to force the stones through the waterproof covering.

FOUNDATIONS

The aim of a foundation is to distribute the load of the building over the largest practical area.

The choice of a foundation depends on the structure of the building, the type of materials used in its construction, and the type of surface on which the building is to stand.

Most foundations are now made of either mass or reinforced concrete; the various types of foundation fall into two groups:

- Shallow foundations, where the load of the construction is transferred as near as possible to soil level.
- Deep foundations, where the load is transferred to a very deep level below the surface of the soil.

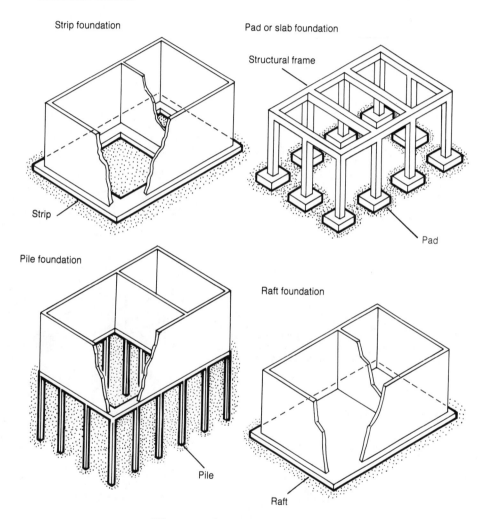

Diagram of types of foundation

Causes of Defective Foundations

- Problems can often occur when the foundations have not been laid deep enough.
- Roots of trees have been known to spread and cause cracking of the foundations.
- The changes in the moisture content of the soil can cause erosion of the foundations. Defective pipework, underwater streams or constant rain can bring about these changes.
- Incorrect mixing of concrete can cause defects: the concrete itself is weak, or the reinforcing is too near the surface and corrodes quickly, again weakening the structure.

CAVITY WALLS   Cavity walls are constructed of two 'walls' or 'skins' of brick or brick and concrete blocks, with a space of approximately 50 mm between each. This cavity prevents moisture (rain) entering through the wall from the outside; it also gives a greater degree of thermal insulation. The two walls or skins are held together by wall ties. Occasionally if pieces of debris have fallen on to the ties, or if mortar has dropped to the bottom of the wall cavity, a bridge will occur for dampness to pass over to the inner wall. If this happens bricks have to be removed and the obstruction cleared. The cavity usually extends to approximately 150 mm below the damp-proof course level.

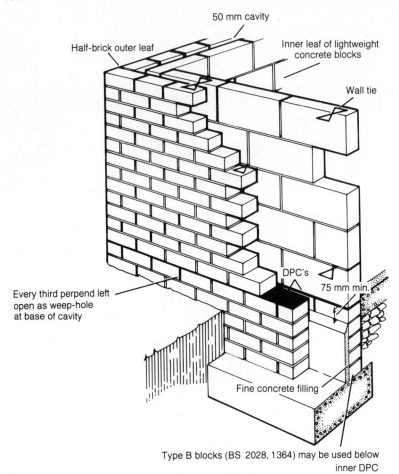

Cavity wall construction

COMMON PROBLEMS LEADING TO STRUCTURAL FAULTS

Tree roots   can cause extensive damage. Quite often an existing tree is incorporated into the design of a new building; before any structural work commences the location and length of the roots must be established. Tree roots can extend up to 7–8 m. They dry the ground in their need for moisture and often grow beneath brickwork and concrete and can wrap themselves around pipes.

Cracks are
usually stepped
diagonally

Diagram showing how tree roots can cause severe damage to buildings

Subsidence is usually caused by the movement of soil from either landslides or earthquakes. Normally the whole building is affected and long-term repair is needed.

Temperature changes. All building materials are affected to a greater or lesser degree by expansion and contraction. The most pronounced changes occur in the height of the summer and the middle of the winter. The most noticeable areas affected are doors and windows.

Frost damage mostly affects porous materials (e.g. stones, bricks, cement and soil) by contraction and expansion. Often, when the weather becomes warmer again, a salt deposit is left on the material.

PLANNING

Before any building can be designed and erected, a detailed feasibility study is required. The aim of planning is to produce premises with maximum benefits for staff and public at minimum cost. If at every stage the planning is thorough and well co-ordinated, the building should be erected with speed and precision.

In the planning stages the main areas that need to be considered are:
- details of site — ownership, local and national building regulations and bylaws, types of soil, access roads and existing buildings,
- type of business — number to be employed or catered for, various different specifications for offices, hotels, hospitals, etc.,
- standards required — to include: further provision for possible future extensions, durability, prestige, health and safety, and fire precautions,
- cost — breakdown into sectional and total.

Once all the above have been recorded it is up to the prospective clients to seek the help and advice of a professional team of architects, builders, surveyors, etc.

There should be a set pattern of building from the first pre-planning stage (the setting out of objectives) through to completion and occupation of the premises.

There are strict laws and building regulations governing the building and occupation of buildings. Among these are:
- Public Health Act 1936,
- Clean Air Act 1956,
- Public Health Act 1961,
- Fire Precautions Act 1974,
- Health and Safety at Work Act 1974,
- Building Regulations 1972 (first amendment),
- Building Regulations 1974 (second amendment),
- Building Regulations 1985.

SERVICES PROVIDED BY PROFESSIONALS

The architect is the agent, whom the builder or owner engages to design and advise, and to see the building through to completion, while keeping to the original cost and design.

The quantity surveyor is expected to give precise details of the amount of materials needed for the contract to start, and is also responsible for checking tenders and assessing prices.

The engineers are usually specialists (e.g. heating, sanitary, etc.). They give advice on areas relevant to the architect.

The building surveyor is employed by the building contractor to assist the quantity surveyor while working on the actual project. He may also assist in working out bonuses for the building personnel.

The contractor is employed directly by the building owner. Although he takes instructions from the architect, the contractor often subcontracts work which he is unable to carry out (e.g. electrical, painting, etc.).

The clerk of works is employed as an on-site representative of the architect to check most aspects of the construction, and to check co-ordination of the various teams of workers.

Others involved include environmental health officers, health and safety inspectors and fire officers. They are involved in new or existing building operations as well as alterations and extensions. Each will give free advice if called upon to do so.

QUESTIONS

1. Find out the meaning of the following abbreviations: RIBA, BRE, PVC, BS, CP, PA.

2. What factors influence the siting of a building?

3. In the planning of a new building the cooperation of the architects, builders, executive housekeeper or manager is essential. Explain why and detail the benefits it offers to all concerned.

4. Try to find out the names of parts 1-20 on the diagram below:

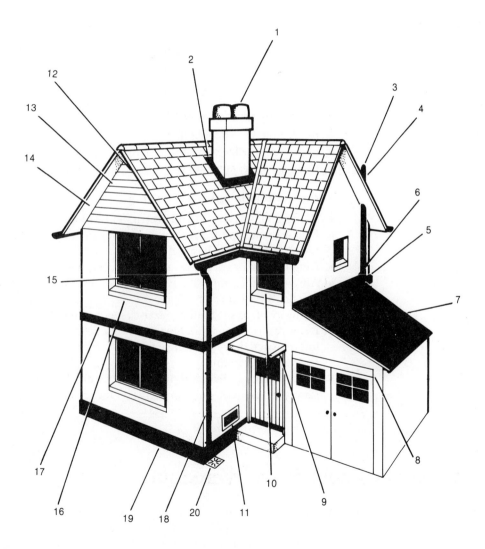

Components of a building exterior

7 Cleaning Principles and Procedures

INTRODUCTION

With costs always rising, cleaning procedures should be studied very carefully and updated from time to time so as to incorporate modern equipment, materials and techniques.

The reasons for cleaning are:
- to promote health and safety,
- to prolong the life of furniture, fixtures, fittings and surfaces,
- to improve the appearance of the establishment.

The general principles of cleaning are given in the following checklist:
- Remove all surface soil and obstructions before cleaning.
- Follow the least obtrusive and disturbing methods of cleaning, especially early in the morning and in hospital situations.
- Restore all surfaces to as near perfect condition as soon as possible.
- Always use the simplest method of cleaning and the mildest cleaning agent; if in any doubt seek further advice.
- Be aware of possible safety hazards, e.g. trailing flexes, loose carpets, wet floors.
- Remove all dust and dirt. Do not transfer them to another area, e.g. use chemically impregnated dust-collecting equipment, vacuums and attachments, and central-ised vacuum systems.
- Carry out each cleaning process in the quickest possible time, to the highest standard, and with due consideration for the convenience of guests.

CLEANING SCHEDULES AND TECHNIQUES

While it may not be instantly apparent, most commercial establishments, whether private, Government- or company-owned, have a set schedule for cleaning. The schedule includes daily cleaning tasks and more intensive periodic, or 'spring' cleaning operations (although this word should be avoided because in most establishments 'spring' cleaning is carried out at any convenient time).

The table opposite represents a summary of cleaning tasks in each of the groups. It must be realised, however, that each establishment uses its own plan to suit its own needs and peculiarities. The table on pp. 43–4 gives a more detailed analysis of cleaning techniques.

A Summary of Cleaning Schedules

TYPES OF CLEANING	DEFINITION	AREAS OF WORK COVERED	ADVANTAGES	DISADVANTAGES
Initial	Work carried out after area has been opened, redecorated, refurbished or updated	All areas, e.g. floors, walls, surfaces, furniture, fixtures and fittings, etc.	Gives 'fresh' appearance to the area. Removes any soil or dust left by workmen	Area may be required immediately. Can add extra cost to the schemes
Routine 1 Daily 2 Nightly 3 Weekly	Cleaning that is carried out on a regular basis, depending on the method used, e.g. conventional, block or team	Daily/nightly Public and frequently utilised areas, e.g. toilets, bars, bedrooms, corridors, lounges etc. Weekly Furniture polished, paintwork, doors and surfaces cleaned	A high standard can be maintained at quite a low cost if work is kept to a set schedule and not allowed to develop into a major task	Can be slightly disruptive to guests, especially in hotels with visitors who sleep at irregular hours
Periodic *Special* *Vocational* *Deep*	Usually work carried out at certain times of the year when the establishment is either closed, e.g. seasonal hotels or in schools and universities during holidays. Quite often work is subcontracted to industrial cleaners or an establishment's own maintenance department	Carpets and soft furnishings cleaned. Paintwork renewed and recleaned. Bedding (blankets and covers) washed or dry-cleaned. Kitchen walls and stoves cleaned thoroughly	All areas are given a thorough clean, and dirt and grease is not allowed to build up to an excessive degree. Work can be done when the building area is quiet and the section can be maintained at the same time, thus reducing costs	If an establishment has a non-stop trade, it can be costly to seal off an area or section

METHODS OF ORGANISING CLEANING

There are a number of ways in which cleaning can be organised.

Conventional Clean

With this method, work is done in a given area in a sequence. When completed the worker moves on to the next area.

Advantages

- Improved security.
- More job satisfaction.
- Standard of work may be higher.

Disadvantages

- Room or area out of action for a longer period.
- May be more expensive, because it takes longer.

- Method of organisation may be better.
- Training simplified.

- More equipment required.
- Some work may be incomplete.
- May be a too rigid system.

Block Method

With the block method, the work is organised in such a way that one particular job is done in one area, and then the worker carries out the same job in the next area, before moving on to a different job.

Advantages

- Less equipment required.
- Cheaper to operate.
- Fits well into an organised scheme.

Disadvantages

- Security weakened.
- More disturbance, including disturbance to guests.
- May be more expensive in terms of area; cannot be left for longer periods.
- May be monotonous for staff.
- Work may have to be left incomplete.

Team Cleaning

Team cleaning is done by two or more people in a given area. They either work together or carry out different tasks in one area.

Advantages

- Equipment may be shared.
- When heavy work is carried out members of a team can help each other.
- Can be used to train staff on the job, by putting them with an experienced person.
- Increased productivity — provides a more efficient system.

Disadvantages

- Shared equipment — who is responsible for its care, cleaning, etc?
- Standards could be reduced — who is responsible?
- If used for training, staff could easily pick up bad habits.
- Some work may be forgotten. Members may assume others have carried out the work.
- Staff may not work well together, talking and gossiping.

Where an establishment has a large turnover of 'guests', either in hospitals or hotels, it is necessary to plan carefully how the daily, weekly, periodic cleans, etc., can be incorporated into the schedule. Again each housekeeper must look at individual factors. For example, can weekly tasks be incorporated with the daily ones? A decision might have to be made between these two possibilities:

- Monday — Daily clean all areas and clean windows.
  Tuesday — Daily clean all areas and polish furniture.
- Monday — Daily clean all areas and weekly clean one room completely.
  Tuesday — Daily clean all areas and weekly clean one room completely.

Cleaning Techniques

CLEANING OPERATION	DEFINITION	*Advantages*	*Disadvantages*
Sweeping	The removal of surface dust and non-greasy soil by the use of a brush and collecting pan	Cheap and easy to accomplish	Tends to transfer dirt. Causes clouds of dust
Dry mopping	The light buffing of a floor, using a soft polishing mop or an impregnated mop	Easy to operate. Economical method of buffing	Useful only for polishing. Is not a method for dust or dirt removal
Wet and damp mopping	Usually confined to floor areas. Normally water used with detergent or other cleanser, best used with a wet pick-up machine	Only limited amount of equipment needed (mops, buckets, single, double or treble system, wringer type mop and cleanser)	Care must be taken not to allow too much water to remain on the floor for safety's sake, also some floors may be porous
Impregnated mopping	Mops, gloves, etc., can be impregnated with a light oil to allow easy pick-up of dust and soil	Very efficient. Collects rather than transfers dirt. Also can be laundered and resprayed on premises	Can be expensive if misused.
Vacuuming	A high-powered machine – either upright or cylindrical is used to suck up dirt and debris – needs good suction power or brush attached for efficient operation – also needs good filtration	Most efficient method of dust and soil removal provided machines are used correctly and well maintained. Can be used on most types of surface. Vacuums for water removal are also available	Expensive to purchase but cost soon recouped
Centralised vacuum system	This system consists of long hoses and attachments which are fitted into an outlet socket situated around the skirting board. The dust, debris, etc., pass along these hoses through a piping system to a collection area, which is situated in the basement, where it is collected and disposed of	Efficient if well maintained and used properly. Less storage space required by equipment	Expensive to install initially – better if system can be installed when premises are being built. May be noisy and hoses may be heavy for staff to use. Back-up equipment is necessary in case system breaks down

Cleaning Techniques *(cont.)*

CLEANING OPERATION	DEFINITION	*Advantages*	*Disadvantages*
Spray cleaning	Cleans and polishes in one operation. Can be used with a machine or independently. Mainly used for floor areas	Cuts down time saved on stain removal. Carpets become less static, floors are easier to clean	Expensive, may not be worth cost outlay on older surfaces
Dry dusting	Surface dust is removed with a soft cloth which is then shaken to remove excess dust, then washed	Very cheap. Only equipment needed is a soft dry cloth	If not carried out correctly, the dust is just flicked from one area to another
Damp dusting	Removal of grease, finger marks, etc., by using a cloth wrung out in water and mild detergent, then rinsed again and left to dry	Removes stains more efficiently than dry dusting, especially grease stains	If too much water is used, it can spoil the surface, e.g. wood veneer

A Systematic Approach

A systematic approach to cleaning is necessary to ensure the efficient and economical running of a housekeeping section. This planned organisation is vital if standards are to be achieved and maintained.

- All equipment and materials must be used to the optimum extent in economic terms.
- Time must be used fully to achieve high standards compatible with the acceptable cost.
- Work cards, job descriptions and rosters must be well planned to include individuals' needs, e.g. foreign workers (who may have language difficulties), holidays and sickness. (See pp. 225-40.)

Where management is concerned, a well-informed housekeeper can be a valuable asset when budgets and estimates are being drawn up.

A STANDARDISED CLEANING SYSTEM

This suggests a set of fixed procedures which are built up into a routine and put into practice for the cleaning and maintenance of a building or group of buildings. All the operations have been studied in detail and a set of standard or average times are produced for each particular job. In order for the system to be successful and cost effective the following should be standardised:

- Staff selection and training; type of supervisor.
- Cleaning areas (uniform in shape, layout and size).
- Equipment.
- Cleaning materials.
- Surfaces.
- Services.

Once the system has been established and maintained, it is possible to transfer staff to other departments or establishments within the group and still maintain the same standard of work.

STANDARDS OF CLEANING

There are different ways in which something can be clean:

Physically clean. The surface is apparently free from dust and dirt when the hand is wiped over the surface.

Chemically clean. Free from harmful chemicals on the surface and floating in the air.

Bacteriologically clean. Free from harmful bacteria which must be removed to prevent cross-infection, especially in hospitals.

Entomologically clean. Free from harmful insects, surface dust and dirt.

Osmologically clean (prestige). This refers to a very high standard of cleaning particularly in hospital theatres, intensive care units, etc.

A high standard of cleaning should be maintained in any given area irrespective of the type of establishment. Once this standard has been established it is always possible to reduce it slightly, but it may prove very difficult to improve a low standard of cleaning.

CHECKS FOR CLEANING

In order to produce and maintain cleaning standards it is important to establish a system for checking work done by staff. It is the responsibility of the supervisor to check cleaning standards from time to time, and this can be done systematically or spot checks can be carried out at random on a variety of surfaces. There are two methods used in the industry, namely the white rag test and the cleaning checklist.

White rag test. The supervisor uses a white rag and wipes over the surface to check that it is free from dust and dirt.

Cleaning checklist. A checklist is drawn up for a particular establishment and must be adapted for a given situation — two examples are shown, one below and the

AREA NO. 3 *(Toilet + Corridor)* **PERSON IN CHARGE** .... **DATE**				
	Poor	Satisfactory	Good	Remarks
Floor surface	✓			Still wet
Skirting board		✓		
Walls		✓		
Toilet			✓	
Washbasin			✓	
Toilet paper		✓		Paper holder
Soap		✓		broken
Toilet floor surfaces		✓		
Toilet wall surfaces		✓		

Hospital checklist

second is given here. It is extremely useful if maintenance checks are done at the same time. Then relevant information can be passed on to the maintenance department.

In the list on p. 45 there is perhaps a good case in favour of using a wet pick-up vacuum. Or could the area be sealed off until completely dry?

ROOM NO. *86* .... DATE .... PERSON IN CHARGE				
	Poor	Satisfactory	Good	Remarks
Bed-making				
Washbasin				
Wardrobe				
Window ledges				
Hotel brochures				2 missing
Radio/television				
Carpet				Frayed near door
Light switches				Bulb missing, bedside light

Hotel cleaning checklist

It would then be seen that the three areas that are only satisfactory could perhaps be improved upon by the person concerned. Also the two missing brochures could be replaced before the next guest arrives.

STANDARD TIMES FOR SPECIFIED CLEANING OPERATIONS

Standard times have been worked out for various cleaning operations in the average situation, but they can only be used as a guideline. They are dependent on the various factors indicated below:

The Worker

- Type and amount of training given to the individual.
- Amount of previous experience gained by the worker.
- Type and quality of supervision.
- Age, sex, physical build and strength; intelligence and literacy of worker.
- Health and limitations — degree of disability, fatigue, etc., level, degree of manual dexterity.
- Ability to work with other staff.
- General attitude to work and the work situation.
- Motivation and incentive.

The Surface to be Cleaned

- Total area to be cleaned.
- Type and amount of traffic.
- Type and degree of soil.
- Condition of the sub-surface, e.g. level, smooth, porous.
- Type, composition and age of the surfaces, e.g. floors, walls, furniture, etc.
- Whether the surface has been protected from heat, water, chemicals, etc.

Working Conditions

- Type and amount of obstruction in the area.
- Standard and frequency of work required.
- Method of doing the work.
- Type, size and condition of equipment available.
- Type and quality of cleaning materials.
- Distance to facilities, e.g. storage areas, linen, etc.
- Physical working conditions, e.g. evaporation rate, area of illumination, type and degree of heating.
- Attitude of employees in the presence of others in the work situation, e.g. guests, patients, etc.

As conditions change and staff become more experienced these times will have to be reassessed, especially with the introduction of more mechanised equipment and modern cleaning materials and techniques. Where trade unions are involved consultation will be necessary before any attempt is made to reassess standard times.

Some specific standard times are given in the following table.

GENERAL CLEANING PROCEDURES FOR INDIVIDUAL OPERATIONS (DOUBLE TIME FOR DAMP CLEANING)

OPERATION	TIME TAKEN (MINUTES/ SECONDS)	OPERATION	TIME TAKEN (MINUTES/ SECONDS)
Empty ashtray	15 s	Dust small table	25 s
Empty waste paper bin	20 s	Dust large table	60 s
Dust small desk	20 s	Dust picture	15 s
Dust large desk	50 s	Dust telephone	15 s
Dust small chair	15 s	Dust venetian blind	2½ min
Dust large chair	45 s	Dust filing cabinet	
Wash and polish desk	10 min	(4 drawer)	35 s
Dust table lamp	35 s	Vacuum upholstery	
Wash cafeteria chair	35 s	chair	1 min
Wash cafeteria table	90 s	Vacuum upholstery	
Clean lavatory	3 min	settee	2 min
Wash large mirror	60	Shampoo chair	7 min
Wash hand basin		Shampoo settee	20 min
and soap dispenser	2 min	Sweep one flight	
		of stairs (15 steps)	6 min
		Damp mop one flight	
		of stairs (15 steps)	5 min

CLEANING OPERATION IN MINUTES/1000 ft^2

WINDOW CLEANING

Single pane	125 min
Multi pane	170 min
Frosted single pane	190 min

WALL WASHING

	Manual	*Mechanical*
Painted walls	150 min	100 min
Tiled walls	150 min	100 min
Marble walls	92 min	
Wall dusting	15 min	

CEILING WASHING

	Manual	*Mechanical*
Painted ceilings	300 min	180 min

FLOOR CLEANING OPERATIONS IN MINUTES/1000 ft^2

Sweeping with a dry mop sweeper, impregnated mop or broom	10 min	
Vacuum sweeping	5 min	
Damp mopping	20 min	
Wet mopping and rinsing	30 min	
Scrubbing	35 min	37 cm (15 in) machine
	30 min	47 cm (19 in) machine
	20 min	60 cm (24 in) machine
Suction drying	25 min	
Scrubbing and drying	10 min	(combined machine)
Strip and rewax	180 min	
Polish application	30 min	
Buffing	20 min	37 cm (15 in) machine
	15 min	47 cm (19 in) machine
	10 min	60 cm (24 in) machine
Spray cleaning	30 min	37 cm (15 in) machine
	25 min	47 cm (19 in) machine
Carpet vacuuming	20 min	

In the case of obstructed areas it may be necessary to increase the time by up to 50% depending on the degree of obstruction.

FACTORS AFFECTING CLEANING AND STAFFING REQUIREMENTS

Each establishment has to assess its own frequency of cleaning, and the method to be used to carry out the tasks quickly and efficiently. In order to assess staffing requirements, certain factors must be considered as follows:

- Type, size, layout and use of the building — amount of time that it is in use or open.
- Number of people using the building, and the number of residents.
- Amount of work to be done, taking into account any work done by residents.
- Type and degree of soil — whether organic or inorganic — degree of pollution.
- Surroundings of the building.
- Type of surface, furniture, fixtures and fittings — whether standardised, fitted or free-standing.
- Amount of specialised work to be carried out, e.g. deep cleaning, maintenance.
- Amount and availability of labour, equipment and materials.
- Cover required for holiday periods, sickness and emergencies.
- Standard of finish required.
- Use of contract services, e.g. window cleaning, maintenance, linen and laundry work.
- Budget available to meet wages, cost of equipment, materials, recruiting and training staff, contract services, etc.

Once these factors have been considered, various methods can be used to ascertain the number of staff required to clean and maintain a given area:

- Establish the size of the buildings from plans or by pacing out the building. The average cleaner can clean 1000 ft^2 in 8 hours.
- Carry out a method study operation, using either experts or your own staff.
- Use standard or average times.
- Check the staffing allocation in other establishments equivalent in size and standard.
- Call in a firm of consultants.
- Do a sample of work in each area and multiply by the number of areas, e.g.:
  (a) Time the routine clean of a single, twin and double bedroom and multiply by the number of each type of room.
  (b) Time the damp mopping or spray cleaning of a given area of floor surface and multiply this by the total area.

THE COSTS OF CLEANING AND MAINTENANCE

The costs involved in cleaning and maintaining an establishment must be analysed very carefully and not just left to chance. Resources must be used efficiently to maintain standards without overspending.

Points To Be Considered

- Area of surfaces to be cleaned — size, type, condition, etc.
- Type and amount of soil, dirt and number of obstructions.
- Standard of finish required.
- Type and amount of equipment used.
- Type and amount of materials used.
- Frequency of cleaning and maintenance — e.g. daily, weekly, monthly, three monthly, six monthly or yearly.

- Type and amount of labour used — direct, contract or both.
- Overheads — e.g. rent, rates, fuel, depreciation, repairs, maintenance, etc.
- Degree of air pollution.
- Acceptable cost within budget (in the case of contract catering) — profit required.

The Aims of Costing

- To ascertain the cost of products, processes, etc.
- To control costs of all types, increase profits and prevent overspending.
- To provide guidelines for management policies.

It is vital for every establishment to know its actual costs, not merely estimated costs.

Basic Elements of Costing

- Materials — e.g. cleaning materials, equipment, etc.
- Labour costs — payroll costs, including fringe benefits, uniforms, etc.
- Overheads — rent, rates, depreciation, fuel, repairs, etc.
- Profit — this may or may not be made after all expenses have been accounted for — more applicable to contract cleaning and maintenance.

Division of Costs

Costs may be classified using two different methods.

Method A
1. **Fixed costs** — rent, rates, wages (except overtime), depreciation, insurance, etc. They are usually fixed over a period of time and will not vary with any change in the volume of sales.
2. **Variable costs** — cleaning equipment and materials. They will vary in direct proportion to the volume of sales.
3. **Semi-variable costs** — fuels, breakages, etc. If turnover is increased by (say) 10%, these costs might only increase by 1-2%

Method B
1. **Prime costs/indirect costs** — costs which are directly related to the work — e.g. cleaning materials, equipment, wages, etc.
2. **Overhead costs/indirect costs** — costs which are not directly related to the work — e.g. rent, rates, fuels, etc.

To assess the cost of time, labour and materials used for a particular task, use the following formula:

$$\frac{\text{Time Area in 1000 m}^2 \text{ (ft}^2) \times \text{Job in min per 1000 m}^2 \text{ (ft}^2) \times \text{Frequency (in hours)}}{60}$$

Total labour cost = Total time in hours × Hourly wage rate
Add the cost of cleaning materials.
The total cost is divided by the area cleaned to give the cost per m^2 or ft^2. Monthly comparative costs can be made and any unusual variances should be investigated immediately and corrective action taken.

Unusual Labour Cost Variances

- Non-productive time.
- Incorrect timings provided for a given task.
- Staff not fully utilised.
- Duplication of work.
- Overlong break periods.

Unusual Material Cost Variances

- Wastage of materials.
- Increase in purchasing price.
- Bad purchasing.
- Overcharging — clerical errors on invoices.
- Pilfering — poor stores and stock control.

Unusual Overhead Cost Variances

- Increase in costs of fuel, rent, rates, etc.
- Lack of maintenance.
- Wastage of fuel.
- Increase of maintenance costs.

Ways of saving on cleaning and maintenance costs

- Careful selection, induction and training of all staff.
- Standardisation of surfaces, furniture, fittings, equipment and cleaning materials.
- Use of mechanisation — providing sufficient equipment for all staff so that time is not wasted waiting for equipment to be available.
- Good planning and layout of premises.
- Good planning and organisation of staff.
- Good supervision and means of checking work standards.
- Use of standard times for various tasks — use of job analysis.
- Use of work study, method study and work measurement.
- Careful purchasing, stores and stock control procedures to prevent abuse and wastage of materials, etc.
- Use of contract services especially for very specialised work.
- Use of preventative and planned maintenance.
- Effective use of cleaning materials.
- Use of preventative devices — e.g. mats, bin liners, ashtrays, seals, etc.
- Good communications system.
- Keeping up to date with modern technology — being prepared to accept change.

QUESTIONS

1. What is the purpose of a cleaning checklist? Draw up a cleaning checklist for a bedroom with private bathroom.

2. Briefly explain the following terms: initial clean, routine clean, deep clean.

3. Discuss the points to be considered when choosing a particular method of cleaning.

4. Indicate the points to be considered when determining the number of staff required to clean an establishment.

5. Discuss the advantages and disadvantages of introducing a team cleaning method in your establishment.

6. Define a standardised cleaning system and indicate the factors affecting an efficient system.

7. As an assistant domestic bursar, in charge of a hall of residence, you notice that the standard of work carried out by the staff is poor. After discussion with the senior domestic bursar, to whom you are directly responsible, you have been given the task of looking into the matter.

   (a) Indicate what immediate investigations you would make.
   (b) Suggest possible (i) long-term changes, (ii) short-term changes.
   (c) Draft out a report to be submitted to the senior domestic bursar with your recommendations.

8. The organisation of the internal and external cleaning of premises is essential. Discuss this statement.

9. As a new supervisor how would you plan and organise the cleaning in your department?

10. Discuss the main principles of cleaning in a hospital.

11. Your senior is concerned with the rise in the costs of cleaning in your section:

    (a) Suggest ways of reducing costs without reducing efficiency.
    (b) Prepare a report to be submitted to your senior.

12. Calculate the daily cost of maintaining a corridor floor space having an area of 450 m^2.

TASK	FREQUENCY	TIME PER 100 m^2
Remove old floor wax by machine	Once every 10 days	60 min
Apply two coats of buffable floor wax	Once every 10 days	80 min
Sweep with 30 cm (12in) brush	Daily	10 min
Buff surface	Daily	15 min
Spray clean	Twice every 10 days	15 min

Labour costs £3.60 per hour including overheads.

13. Three rooms with wood block floors 16 m × 5 m, 15 m × 4 m and 14 m × 5 m were prepared and sealed with two coats of seal. The work was carried out by two men and two women and they worked as follows:

Friday	8 a.m. — 12 noon 1 p.m. — 5 p.m. }	All working
Saturday	8 a.m. — 12 noon	All working
Sunday	9 a.m. — 1 p.m.	Two men only

   (a) The staff are paid £1.75 per hour and they are paid time and a half for Saturday and double time for Sunday. Calculate the cost of labour.
   (b) The cost of 5 litres of seal is £6.00 and covers 70 m^2. Other cleaning materials cost £4.00. Calculate the total cost of materials.
   (c) Calculate the total cost of labour and materials.

8 Linen and Laundry Services

INTRODUCTION

The efficiency of the linen section in any establishment is necessary for the smooth running of the business.

The linen room usually covers the issuing, marking, collection and storage of: bedding, towels, uniforms, and kitchen and restaurant linen.

LINEN REQUIREMENTS IN INSTITUTIONS

Full or partial linen service is provided. Homes and hostels normally provide one sheet, one pillowcase and one towel per week. The top sheet is placed to the bottom and the new clean one goes on top.

Many halls of residence now require occupants to provide their own bedding, towels, etc. During vacations or conference periods linen hire may be necessary. Curtains and bedspreads may be laundered on the premises in a small commercial or domestic washer.

Kitchen linen is kept to a minimum due to washing-up machines, paper towels and napkins.

LINEN REQUIREMENTS IN HOSPITALS

National Health Service hospitals change sheets and pillowcases every two or three days, but extra supplies are always available in an emergency. On surgical and maternity wards paper sheeting is invaluable. Private hospitals may change the sheets more often. Patients provide and clean their own personal laundry except in special wards.

Staff have access to clean uniforms from the ward linen cupboard which is kept 'topped up' from the central linen room.

Table linen is kept mainly to disposable paper items. Kitchen staff may use disposable plastic aprons, paper hats, paper-weave cloths or surface wipes.

LINEN REQUIREMENTS IN HOTELS

Hotels change the sheets on beds as each guest departs. In the more expensive hotels, bedding may be changed every day. Normally, beds are changed after two to three days and towels are changed every day. Undersheets, under-pillowslips and mattress covers are removed for washing approximately twice a year. Net curtains are cleaned as necessary. Staff laundry, including uniforms, are changed as often as required, or exchanged on a set day of the week. Kitchen linen may only include oven gloves and uniforms. Surface cleaning cloths may be paper-weave; hand-drying is usually by paper or hot air; dish-drying is largely by steam from dish-washing machines. Dining room linen is either all fabric or fabric and paper.

BUYING AND OWNING LINEN

Linen can be purchased or ordered by the senior housekeeper, manager or senior bursar. It is essential that careful consideration is given to style, quality, price, durability and type of fibre before purchasing.

The following points are also important:
- Buy from a reputable dealer. Ask for samples of various colours, and qualities. Wash the sample and test for shrinkage, colourfastness and strength when wet. If purchasing a small quantity of linen, it is sometimes possible to check for quality and value for money from consumer magazines and articles.
- Check the style of the sample. Frills on pillowcases and fitted sheets can cause problems and may require extra strengthening.
- The quality of the sample should be apparent. Hems and selvedges should be well sewn. Fabric weave must be close and firm. Rub the material together over a dark surface to check the amount of fabric dressing. The larger the amount, the poorer the quality of fabric.

The life of commercial linen is usually calculated per number of washes rather than by the number of years in use.
- For purchases of large quantities of linen, the manufacturer may emboss or weave in the crest or emblem of the establishment (e.g. linen, glass). If storage space is limited, manufacturers may sometimes store quantities of linen for future orders.
- Buy the best quality that money will allow. The price can be an indication of the quality and durability. Compare the prices from various manufacturers, warehouses, etc.

Calculation of Linen Needed

If the establishment is residential, calculate your requirements remembering the following points:
- Calculate the number of beds and the amount of linen on each.
- Decide the number of times per week linen will be changed.
- Allow for at least one set of linen to be at the laundry, one set in the linen room or cupboard and one set on the bed.
- In many establishments there is a quick changeover of one-night guests, so it could be necessary to allow 5–8 sets of linen per bed. This then makes allowances for delays in delivery due to bad weather, holidays or strikes.
- Towels allowed are usually one or two per day.
- Table linen and kitchen linen is calculated differently. It may be that an allowance of clean linen is made for every meal, or every day, or week. Uniforms should be changed as needed.

- Hospitals have 4–6 sets of linen per bed plus an emergency stock including uniforms. The allowance is not so critical as in other establishments, as linen is often laundered on the premises and therefore a quick turnover ensures clean linen is always available.
- Non-residential establishments calculate linen needs according to the number of guests, standards required, etc., and type of operation carried out.

OBTAINING CLEAN LINEN

There are four methods of obtaining clean linen:
- An establishment has its own linen and this is sent to a commercial off-the-premises laundry.
- Linen is owned and cleaned on-site.
- Linen is hired, the rental company is responsible for its purchase, marking, collecting, cleaning and delivery.
- Linen is owned and cleaned on-site by a professional laundry company under contract.

We now look at the advantages and disadvantages of these methods:

Commercial Laundry

- Less capital outlay is required. Only linen is purchased, no machines or space for equipment are needed.
- The type of linen preferred is bought by the establishment rather than stereotype provided by linen hire.
- Only part-time help may be necessary for sorting, packing, inspection and mending.
- Floor space is fully used for business purposes rather than laundry machines.
- There is less control over washing methods by management when linen is sent elsewhere. Many older laundries find synthetic fabrics a problem.
- A greater stock of linen may be needed to cope with delays, holidays and shut downs.

How commercial laundries may calculate charges

- *Flat rate charge.* Each item is charged for individually. Invoices need checking carefully.
- *Price per 100 items irrespective of type*, e.g. the same price for double sheets as for tea towels.
- *Price per pound or kilo:* soiled linen is weighed before insertion into the machines. An agreed price is charged per pound or kilo.
- *Discounts* may be offered for totals over one hundred pieces or a specified number of pounds or kilos. An extra discount can be given for prompt payment. Laundry charges are subject to VAT.

On-site Laundering

- Stricter control of washing methods may bring about higher standards, especially in hospitals where there is a risk of cross-infection.

- There are no delays of collection or delivery.
- There is no loss of linen — worn items can be reused as needed.
- There is a quicker service for guests' laundry.
- With high land costs it may be considered that the area to be used allocated for on-site laundry would be better used as a saleable space, e.g. bedrooms, restaurant, etc.
- More trained staff are needed. Washing technology is a complicated science and needs to be supervised by experts.
- Large amounts of capital are needed for equipment, linen, maintenance, etc. It is possible to lease machinery. The business may not want the added responsibility of a laundry.
- Where premises are 'out of town', deliveries and collections are difficult. An on-site laundry may be the answer.

Linen Hire

- There is no initial or replacement cost of linen or equipment — a deposit may be required.
- Fewer staff are needed.
- Uniforms are stocked in a wider range of sizes.
- Linen hire may be suitable for businesses with spasmodic trade, seasonal trade, infrequent banquets, conferences, etc. It avoids capital expenditure and the need to store seldom-used linen.
- Quality is not always maintained. There could be frequent breakdowns in the service.
- There is no control over standards of wash. The linen sent is not necessarily the same linen returned.
- Linen hire may not undertake guests' washing and dry-cleaning, so staff could have extra work dealing with guests' laundry.

On-site Contract Laundry

- Close supervision of laundering methods is possible. The cost may be worked out per article, per kilo, or using a cover charge to take into account the all-year-round operation.
- Professional staff are provided by the hiring company so work loads, cost and supervision should be cut to a minimum. Standards of wash are high.
- Responsibility for day-to-day running, equipment and staff is given over to the hiring company. Close liaison between both parties is vital.
- This type of operation is suited to premises which are 'out of town'.

Linen Pools or Linen Banks

Linen pools or linen banks are to be found in many large groups of establishments such as hospitals or chains of hotels where large stocks of linen are needed. All small linen stocks are moved into a large linen pool. Linen is issued on a 'topping up' basis or 'clean for dirty'. If more linen is needed, it can be provided quickly. Stocktaking is done centrally, cutting down on time, staff, and the need for lots of books. Less space is needed as most of the stock is in one area. Repairs are done centrally. Bulk purchasing gives large discounts.

LINEN ROOM AND LINEN ROOM STAFF

The linen room is one of the busiest areas in an establishment as the diagram below shows. Its efficient running and liaison with other departments is essential. Because of rising fuel costs and other costs, it may be necessary to look carefully at the work carried out in the linen room and the responsibility of its staff.

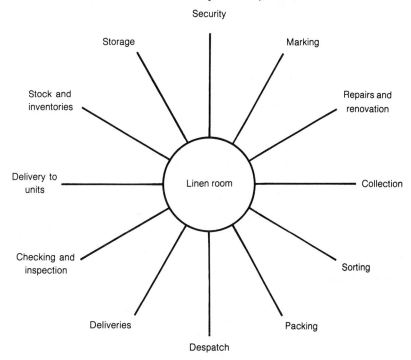

Liaison with the linen room

Marking.   Bedding, table linen, kitchen linen, etc. are marked with tapes, ink, identity tags, invisible marking or embroidery to denote use or area of ownership.

Renovation.   Torn sheets, blankets and uniforms are repaired and renovated if possible. If linen hire is used, no repairs or renovation are necessary.

Collection.   Used soiled linen is collected by porters, sent down a chute, or brought directly to the linen room. The soiled linen will be either exchanged 'clean for dirty' or the amount of linen in store will be 'topped up'.

Sorting.   Soiled linen, on reaching the linen room, is sorted into groups according to type. If there is a laundry on the premises, the linen will be sorted in washing cycles and finishes.

Packing.   Soiled items are counted and packed into hampers, chests or bags for despatch if using commercial laundries, linen hire or group laundries. In hospitals, containers are usually colour-coded to indicate the type or classification of dirty laundry, e.g. red for 'foul'.

Despatch.   Soiled linen should be labelled carefully with details of name of the establishment, the number of items sent, the date and time, and the despatch note signed as proof of sending.

Deliveries. Clean hampers should be kept separate from outgoing soiled ones to avoid confusion.

Checking and inspection. Clean linen should be counted and entered into a stock book. Look carefully for tears, stains and the standard of wash.

Delivery to units. Depending on the method of linen exchange, clean items are distributed. A few linen rooms are now making 'linen packs' for distribution; these consist of two sheets, two pillowcases and two towels for each guest. This cuts down on stocktaking, storage, and paper work.

Stock and inventories. Linen is usually counted once a month. Although this varies, strict control is necessary. To aid counting, sheets, pillowcases, towels, table-cloths and napkins are stored with the folded side outwards.

Storage. The linen rooms often keep a percentage stock of available clean linen in addition to unit requirements. All stock must be kept in dry, well-ventilated, moth-proofed areas. Slatted shelves are used to allow circulation of air. All fresh linen should be placed underneath or at the back of other clean linen to ensure the correct rotation of stock. It is stored in piles of ten for ease of checking, folded side outwards.

Security. Because of the value of linen and equipment, the linen room must be closed at all times when not in use. An authorised person should have access in times of emergency after normal working hours.

The Linen Room Staff

The linen room is perhaps the most physically demanding area of an establishment. Therefore the personnel concerned must be fit and have been trained in the art of lifting and carrying. The larger premises have a linen keeper whose job it is to oversee all the staff within the linen room. If a laundry is attached there is often a laundry manager. Where linen is sent to a commercial laundry or where linen hire is used, a linen keeper or housekeeper may have overall responsibility.

The number of staff needed will be determined by:
- the size and type of operation and the standards required,
- the quantity of items requiring cleaning.
- the type of fabric to be cleaning — newer synthetic fabrics or blends of fabrics require less finishing, therefore fewer staff are needed.
- where linen hire is used, renovated items will not be available, so a seamstress will not be needed.
- the method of internal collection and delivery — is the linen exchanged in the linen room or is it done on a small unit basis by members of staff?

SITING AND PLANNING OF A LINEN ROOM AND LAUNDRY

The size of the area is dependent on the type of operation.

The careful positioning of a linen room with a possible laundry attached is important if the operation is to be successful. The following points have to be considered:
- Easy access for collection and delivery both internally and externally.
- The area should be well ventilated and heated to prevent dampness and mildew; also to provide better working conditions for staff. If a laundry is to be below ground level, the factory inspector must give permission for the use of the rooms.

- If there is an on-site laundry, some structural alterations may be needed to comply with Section 174 of the Factories Act.
- Lighting must be well planned, incorporating as much daylight as possible. Refer to IES Code for interior lighting for advice. Avoid glare.
- The surface and floors should be easily cleaned. Checking and sewing tables must be covered with a coloured finish to avoid eye strain.
- Shelves for storage should be sturdy, slatted and easily reached for storage and stock taking.
- Fire and safety precautions must be well planned. Linen is a highly combustible material, as are cleaning chemicals used in the laundry.

Equipment Used in Linen Rooms and Laundries

Most laundry and linen equipment in use is expensive and, if of foreign origin, spare parts may be difficult to obtain. If breakdowns do occur it would cause serious problems for all departments.

Washing machines   should only be used by trained staff. Servicing and oiling at intervals is important. The careful following of washing programmes, also chemical and detergent dilution rates, is necessary to obtain standard results.

Tumble dryers and hydro extractors   must be situated in a well-ventilated area to extract all the moisture. They must be cleaned regularly and serviced as planned.

Flat bed presses   are used for finishing small flat work, e.g. pillowcases, aprons, napkins, pyjamas, etc.

Calenders   are used for pressing flat items, e.g. sheets and tablecloths.

A small iron and ironing board are usually provided for pressing non-flat items and for guests' laundry.

Tunnel driers   are used mainly for finishing easy-care uniforms.

Sewing machines   are used only in premises using a commercial or on-site laundry. They are used for repairing and renovating. They require oiling and servicing regularly.

Trolleys   are used for moving soiled and clean linen for smaller units or for internal movement of washed linen.

Laundry bags   are used to transfer dirty or clean linen to and from the laundry. They are usually made of nylon and are normally colour-coded for hospital use.

Tables   are needed for checking, inspection and book-keeping.

DRY-CLEANING AND GUESTS' LAUNDRY

Most dry-cleaning is contracted out to specialist firms. It would be too costly to operate a dry-cleaning unit on site. Guests' dry-cleaning is labelled by the owner, cleaned and returned. A copy of the invoice may go to the accounts office or the invoice may go to the guest for direct payment. Dry-cleanable articles, such as blankets, curtains, etc., are charged by weight or number by the cleaners.

For a code of practice, see p. 64.

Types of linen

The following tables give an indication of the fabrics used and the sizes and characteristics of all types of linen.

LAUNDERABLE	SIZE (approximate)	CHARACTERISTICS
Sheets (a)　Linen	Single bed 180 × 255 cm (70 × 100 in)	Very expensive, but extremely durable. Cold to touch and creases badly. Shrinks after washing up to 7% on average
(b)　Cotton	Double Bed 230 × 255 cm (90 × 100 in) 230 × 275 cm (90 × 108 in)	A wide variety of quality and prices available. Cheaper than linen. Absorbs moisture. Many establishments using a commercial laundry or on-site laundry use cotton. Gives a 'crisp' finish to a made-up bed. Withstands frequent hot washes. Most hospital laundry is cotton. May shrink initially up to 5%
(c)　Percale 　　　cotton		Soft, smooth and lightweight, but more expensive than ordinary cotton sheets
(d)　Flannelette	King size bed 275 × 295 cm (108 × 117 in)	Brushed cotton that is warm and absorbs moisture. Cheaper to purchase than the two other types. Not often used in hotels or hospitals but may be used in old people's or children's homes, especially in winter. Can shrink considerably; tends to become thin after frequent washings
(e)　Poly-cotton 　　　and 　　　cotton and 　　　Terylene		Very widespread use in small establishments and in on-site laundries because of ease of washing, care, drying and non-iron properties. This blend of fibres cannot be washed at high temperatures as the resin used in manufacture would break down, cause creasing, and make ironing necessary. Careful washing and folding is essential to reduce anti-static, which may cause fluff and hairs to adhere to the sheet. Less likely to tear than cotton
(f)　Nylon		Inexpensive. Not often used in commercial premises. Cold and slippery and can be very static. Best types have fitted corners. Easily washed and dried. Does not require ironing

LAUNDERABLE	SIZE (approximate)	CHARACTERISTICS
Pillowcases	50 × 76 cm (20 × 30 in) Can be bigger, depending on size of pillow	Made in the same fibres as sheets, so have the same characteristics
Pillows (a) Feathers or feather and down	48 × 74 cm (19 × 29 in)	Difficult and expensive to clean, very comfortable. Guests can be allergic to them. Both are liable to moth or vermin attack if stored incorrectly. Feathers are slightly cheaper than down
(b) Terylene or other synthetic fillings		Allergy-free. Can be washed by machine. Comfortable. Not as expensive as feather or feather and down
Pillow covers		Heavy-quality material used to keep the filling in place. Normally white or striped ticking is used. A second pillowslip may also be used to keep the pillow clean
Blankets (a) Pure wool	Sizes normally the same as sheets	Available in many different weights and qualities. Very warm. Newer blankets may be machine washable. In storage woollen blankets can be attacked by moths
(b) Mohair		Very expensive but light and warm. The blanket is usually brushed. Normally too expensive to be considered for large-scale use
(c) 100% Acrilan or 100% Courtelle		Good substitutes for wool. Both can be made 'cellular' for extra warmth. Strong and hard wearing. Often expensive
(d) Cotton		Used mainly by hospitals, old people's homes or clinics. Can be washed at very high temperatures. Usually made in cellular weave for extra warmth. Check label for flame retarding guide

LAUNDERABLE	SIZE (approximate)	CHARACTERISTICS
Under blankets		Used for extra warmth and to protect the mattress from stains. Can be made from old sheets or blankets
Towels (a) Bath towels	Wide range of sizes. Approximately 70 × 150 cm (28 × 59 in)	Made of 100% cotton or cotton and Terylene mix. The cotton and Terylene mix cannot be washed at very high temperatures, so are not suitable for hospital situations. Turkish or terry weave are the most common. The loops should be close together for greater absorbency and extend to the end of the towel
(b) Hand towels	48 × 100 cm (20 × 40 in)	These may be of terry weave or linen huckaback. Often white towels are provided for guests so the establishment's standard of cleanliness can be judged
Bathmats	60 × 90 cm (24 × 35 in)	Can be Turkish towelling. Many establishments now provide disposable bathmats
Roller towels	45 cm (18 in)	Usually these are provided by a specialist hire company. Each user is allocated a set amount of towels for use. They are available in either blue or white
Table Linen Table cloths and Napkins	Depends on the size of the table	Made from either linen, cotton or blends of natural and synthetic fibres. Linen is expensive but gives a crisp appearance and napkins fold more easily. Cotton is popular as it is cheaper and gives an acceptable finish. Synthetic fibres and blends are easier to launder, but often they appear creased and limp unless special precautions have been taken

CONTINENTAL QUILTS, DUVETS

Continental quilts have become increasingly popular for the commercial market. They are light and warm and make bed-making easier. They consist of a filling, sandwiched or stitched in a fabric case.

The fillings can be duck down, feather mix or a combination of the two, polyester or other synthetic fillers. The natural fillers are expensive, heavier than polyester but very warm. Unfortunately professional cleaning is necessary, so this may limit their use. Polyester fillers are light and mothproof, and can be washed in large-capacity machines. They tend not to be so warm as the natural fillers but they are cheaper to purchase. They can be very useful for guests who are allergic to the natural fillers.

Casings can be either cotton cambric or soft synthetic material; both types are closely woven to keep the filling in place.

Tog ratings are printed on each quilt and these give an indication of warmth. The higher the tog value or rating the warmer the quilt will be. 10.5 tog is an average tog rating.

The quilt should always be protected by an outside cover. To save laundry costs and labour it may be advisable to provide a top sheet in conjunction with the quilt cover, so changing of the quilt cover is not necessary after each guest departs. The quilt cover, bottom sheet and valance usually form a part of the overall colour decoration of the bedroom.

Advantages and Disadvantages of Using Quilts in Residential Establishments

Advantages
- They can make bed-making easier and quicker.
- Quilts, with careful planning and use, can cut down on laundry costs.
- They may be popular with younger guests.
- In orthopaedic hospitals, they may be helpful for patients who do not want the weight of blankets.

Disadvantages
- They do not give so neat an appearance to the bed as blankets.
- They are bulky to store.
- They can be expensive to purchase but can compare favourably with the purchase of two or three blankets.
- Natural fillings for quilts are expensive to clean.
- Guests may be used to blankets at home and may not readily agree to using quilts.

It may be easier for staff and guests if an establishment is provided with either all blankets or all quilts, although this is often not practical as some guests may request a different form of bed covering from the one provided. This problem can be difficult to solve unless a choice is given on arrival, when alterations can be made.

CODE OF PRACTICE FOR LAUNDERERS AND DRY-CLEANERS

The Association of British Launderers and Cleaners (ABLC), with the Office of Fair Trading, has produced a Code of Practice which lays down the standards of service its members should give. The main areas covered are cleaning, laundering, dyeing and repairs; the Code does not apply to launderettes or coin-operated dry-cleaners.

A laundry or dry-cleaners displaying the sign below is bound (though not legally) to the Code of Practice recommended by its association.

CARE LABELLING

The diagram below shows the labelling used in garments to denote the appropriate cleaning treatments.

Some garments imported from certain continental countries may carry symbols which indicate the treatment the garment requires. The most widely used are as shown here.

TREATMENT	Minimum precaution necessary	Some caution necessary	Special care necessary	Treatment prohibited
Washing	95	60	30	⊠
Bleaching (with chlorine)	Cl			⊠
Ironing	•••	••	•	⊠
Dry cleaning	Ⓐ	Ⓟ	Ⓕ	⊠

EXPLANATORY NOTES

1 WASHING: The figure shown in the washtub symbol represents the temperature of the washing solution in Centigrade. No indication of the amount of agitation required is given.

2 BLEACHING: The symbol refers to chlorine bleach only. It does not refer to the safe oxygen bleach, sodium perborate, which is incorporated in most heavy-duty washing products.

3 IRONING: The dots in the iron symbol represent the temperature of the iron.
  1 Dot • Cool iron
  2 Dots • • Warm iron
  3 Dots • • • Hot iron

4 DRY CLEANING: The letters in a circle indicate the type of dry-cleaning fluid which can be used on the fabric.
  A = Can be cleaned in any dry cleaning solvent.
  P = Clean in perchlorethylene or white spirit only.
  F = Clean in white spirit only.
  F30 = Use white spirit only at a temperature not exceeding 30°C (86°F).

QUESTIONS

1. What are the advantages and disadvantages of having a set day of the week for changing staff linen?

2. State why in an on-site group laundry, some items of linen would require identification.

3. Outline the various methods for linen exchange in:
   (a) a 180-room hotel (4 floors),
   (b) a large general hospital,
   (c) a cruise liner,
   (d) an old people's home.

4. Design a fire and safety poster for:
   (a) a linen room using a commercial laundry,
   (b) a linen room using an on-site laundry.

5. What type of bed linen would you choose for:
   (a) an 80-bed hostel;
   (b) a 100-bed children's hospital;
   (c) a prestige conference centre?

6. List the characteristics of the fibres and weaves used in bedding and table linen.

7. What are the advantages and disadvantages of linen pools?

8. You have been asked to advise on the provision of bed and table linen for a new residential conference centre. Bearing in mind new trends together with the cost of laundry facilities:
   (a) Discuss the reasons you would consider for this new establishment.
   (b) Giving reasons to support your recommendations, prepare a report to be submitted to your employers offering your advice.

9 Contract Services

It is possible to run an establishment almost entirely on contract, hire or leasing services. Some establishments only use these services for specialised work, e.g. deep cleaning, linen hire, etc.

TYPES OF CONTRACT SERVICE

The following types of contract service are available:

Contract cleaning — consultancy basis or specialist work (e.g. deep cleaning, carpet or floor maintenance, building maintenance and transport cleaning) or full cleaning services.

Linen hire — full linen hire service or specialised items (e.g. uniforms, towels, banqueting items, etc.).

Laundry — complete or part.

Flower arranging — redecorating, decor, etc.

Personal services — e.g. shoe-cleaning machines, dispensers for drinks, towels, soap, etc.

Dust control, pest control, refuse collection.

The method used to assess the cost of the contract depends on its type and size, the policy of the company and the establishment, and services required, as described below:

Management fee, consultancy basis. The customer provides his own labour, equipment, materials, etc., and the contractor provides the management expertise and possibly supervisory staff.

A fixed periodic cost may be made, either as a total cost or cost per unit of work, based on the quality of the work or the frequency with which work is carried out. This is the most commonly used method and available in two forms:

- **Uncontrolled input.** The contractor agrees to provide a service of a given nature for a specific cost. There is no indication of the number of worker-hours worked nor type of equipment and materials used. Therefore, it is essential that the specification is very detailed indeed.
- **Controlled input.** The contract also indicates the minimum number of worker-hours provided.

A cost plus percentage profit basis. This has the advantage of providing a perfectly viable, flexible programme, as the customer is free to determine his own needs as things change (e.g. occupancy, weather conditions and production). This also provides incentive for the contractor to increase his basic costs in order to earn more profits.

Cost plus fixed fee basis. The contractor is reimbursed for all costs (e.g. equipment, materials and labour) and is also paid a fixed fee for the management of the programme. This provides a flexible programme along with the elimination of any incentive to spend more money. The contractor is guaranteed a reasonable profit as long as he continues to perform a good service.

CONTRACT CLEANING

The contract cleaning industry came into being at the beginning of this century, but for various reasons it has still not reached its potential. In recent studies it has been shown that the cost effectiveness of using contract cleaning as opposed to direct labour could produce savings of up to 25% — so we should be asking ourselves why do all parts of industry not use contract services?

Unfortunately there is no simple answer. Before deciding on the use of contract services the following procedure should be adopted:

- Prepare a detailed specification indicating exact number of workers hours, areas, processes used, frequency, time factors and any special projects.
- Put out tenders to at least three contractors and compare quotes. Don't necessarily choose the cheapest quote, because the standard of work may be poor; also the contractor may be back asking for more money.
- Ask to see other contracts being carried out by the contractor — make sure you talk to the client as well as the contractor.
- Consider the length of contract — preferably at least 2 years — and the notice of termination of contract.
- Look carefully at the type and method of payment.
- Try to select a contractor with a local office (where possible). There is more risk of being let down if a contractor has to travel a long distance.
- Read the small print in the contract before you sign it — check with your solicitor if in doubt.
- Check on type and amount of supervision — make sure you know the names of people to contact, e.g. supervisors and managers.
- Check on security arrangements and identity passes — arrangements for meals, lockers, storage space, etc.
- Consider the effect on existing direct labour with regard to possible redundancy and redeployment. In some cases a contractor may be prepared to offer your own staff employment with the company.
- Once the contract has been signed, then make spot checks — check that the specification is being adhered to.

Some large establishments employ house services managers and direct labour but also contract out some of the services to possibly more than one company. This provides healthy competition and prevents standards dropping. It is essential that the house services manager (or bursar or administration officer) works very closely with the contractor to provide an efficient service for all.

An example of a contract cleaning specification for ten offices and adjoining areas is shown overleaf.

Work to be carried out daily

Offices

- Dust and clean all furniture, fittings, window ledges, radiators, clean and polish all metal work.
- Vacuum carpets — carry out any spot cleaning.

Corridors

- Sweep, buff or spray clean.

Stairs

- Damp mop all steps and landings.
- Clean metal handrails with a metal cleaner.

Lavatories

- Remove all waste paper and litter.
- Scour and disinfect lavatory bowls, w.c.s, urinals.
- Damp wipe tiled surfaces and window ledges, cisterns, fittings.
- Damp mop floors.
- Replace toilet rolls, soap dispensers, towels.
- Damp wipe mirrors and pipes.
- Clean hand basins and taps.

Waste paper

- Empty all waste paper baskets and receptacles in bins as directed (all waste paper must be retained for 24 hours before destruction) clean and replace linings.

Ashtrays

- Empty, damp wipe and/or polish.

Work to be carried out weekly

Offices

- Damp wipe all glass fittings, skirtings, etc.

Corridors

- Sweep and spray clean floors. Damp wipe all skirtings, glass fittings.

Lavatories

- As daily operation, but a very thorough and complete clean in every respect.

Work to be carried out periodically (as arranged)

Offices

- Damp wipe venetian blinds, electric light fittings.
- Spot clean and shampoo carpets.
- Spot clean and shampoo upholstered chairs.

Corridors

- Strip off old wax and replace with 2 coats of emulsion wax.

Windows

- Clean thoroughly inside and out.

An example of a cleaning contract specification at County Buildings

Advantages of Using Contract Services

- A budget can be worked out accurately — i.e. a price known for a given period. Contract services may be more economical than direct labour and services.
- The contractor is responsible for recruiting, training, paying and dismissing staff.
- Contract services alleviate many of the problems between management and the unions (or at least passes them to someone else).
- The contract cleaning company may be able to offer higher rates of pay than firms employing direct labour and therefore attract more highly qualified and competent staff.
- It alleviates the necessity to buy or hire specialist equipment. Contract services permit extra work without the increase of staff.
- Specialised services may be able to cope more easily in the case of an emergency.

Disadvantages of Using Contract Services

- The cost may be too high for the standard of services offered.
- It weakens management's authority over the quality and loyalty of the personnel working in the establishment.
- The housekeeper loses control over the operation.
- There may be poor supervision with the standard of work below par.
- There is a natural tendency for contractors to use poorer-quality products which could cause damage to a building and its contents.
- The specification must be clearly defined and detailed.
- Security may be weakened because of labour turnover — supervision and selection problems.
- There is often no redress if a contractor does not carry out appropriate work — the only alternative may be to cancel the contract.

QUESTIONS

1. List six types of contract service available to the housekeeper.

2. Discuss the advantages and disadvantages of employing contract labour as against direct labour.

3. Briefly outline why it is necessary to work out a detailed work specification for a contractor.

4. Discuss the main points to be considered prior to negotiating a cleaning contract.

5. Outline a checking system for a contractor to use.

6. Briefly explain the following:
   (a) Fixed periodic cost with uncontrolled input.
   (b) Cost plus percentage profit basis.
   (c) Cost plus fixed fee basis.

10 Work Study and its Applications

DEFINITION OF WORK STUDY

Work study is a generic term for 'those techniques which are used in the examination of human work in all its contexts and which lead systematically to the investigation of all factors which affect the efficiency and economy of the situation being reviewed in order to effect improvement'. It involves the study of such factors as people, machines, equipment, tools, materials and layout, with a view to increasing productivity by improving the efficiency and effectiveness of each factor involved. Work study has been described as 'organised common sense'. Unfortunately common sense has not always been in evidence; management has often installed very expensive equipment without really studying the implications in terms of either the job or the labour available. Today, work study is highly sophisticated and uses complex systems for analysis. It is essentially a tool of management, especially in the present economic climate, and it is essential that ways are found to be more efficient by:

- utilising labour, equipment, tools, machinery and facilities,
- detailed planning and control of work,
- improving methods and standardisation, etc., without forcing staff to work beyond their physical capabilities.

Work study can be carried out by managers and supervisors in the work situation or by outside experts on a consultancy basis. Before carrying out a work study it is essential to:

- plan the operation very carefully,
- consult with trade unions,
- consider the staff — they may resent the introduction of work study techniques because they are aware that it is likely to lead to redundancies or redeployment of staff,
- inform the staff so that some of the fears may be alleviated and to provide them with a sense of security.

Once the work has been planned and the staff have been informed, then make sure the work to be studied is done in as normal a way as posssible.

Work study is not a subject immediately associated with cleaning and maintenance, but if we accept that cleaning is a science, then why not use the application of scientific principles to make better use of resources? The diagram below indicates the two main techniques used to carry out a work study operation. They may be used separately, but will prove more successful if used together.

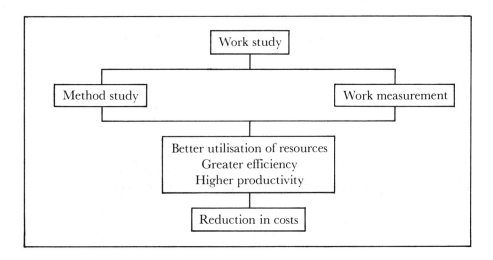

WAYS IN WHICH WORK STUDY CAN ASSIST THE MANAGEMENT/SUPERVISOR

- By improving methods of work and work processes, i.e. flow of work.
- By improving the layout of the working area.
- By improving the design of equipment and plant.
- By assisting in staffing requirements — hours of work required to clean, service and maintain the establishment.
- By reducing costs generally.
- By developing a better working environment.
- By reducing fatigue among staff.
- By reducing labour turnover and excess overtime.
- By utilising staff, equipment and materials to their fullest.
- By introducing standardisation into the work situation.
- By reducing the accident rate.
- By improving standards of work.
- By reducing complaints and grievances on the part of the employee and customer.
- By reducing wastage in all areas.

The two most common techniques of work study are *method study* and *work measurement*, but other techniques can be used, namely:

- cybernetics,
- operations research,
- ergonomics,
- suggestions — value analysis.

METHOD STUDY

Method study may be defined as: 'the systematic recording and critical examination of existing and proposed ways of doing work, as a means of developing and applying easier and more effective methods and thus reducing costs'.

The aim is to make improvements with the minimum of modification and expense. Method study is 'organised common sense' coupled with some specialised techniques.

The procedures in method study consist of the following stages:

Stage 1. Select the work to be studied.

Stage 2. Record the facts.

Stage 3. Examine the facts.

Stage 4. Develop a better method.

Stage 5. Introduce and maintain the better method.

STAGE 1. SELECT THE WORK TO BE STUDIED

Usually routine or repetitive tasks are chosen, e.g. dusting, bed-making, spray cleaning, mopping, etc., where some of the following problems or signs occur:
- Poor quality work.
- Bottlenecks in production.
- Delays.
- High fatigue level.
- Low or erratic output.
- High number of complaints and grievances.
- High labour turnover.
- Unnecessary movements of materials.
- Excessive breakages.
- Reduced profits.
- Wastage of materials.
- Frequent accidents.
- Excessive paper work.
- Low morale.
- Inefficient use of space.
- Excessive absenteeism.
- Excessive overtime wages.
- Poor working conditions.

STAGE 2. RECORD THE FACTS

The facts gathered can be recorded by using one of the following techniques, or a combination of more than one, for comparison and ease of understanding:
- Charts — in the form of process charts, time-scale charts, etc.
- Diagrams — in the form of flow diagrams and string diagrams.
- Models — three-dimensional, two-dimensional drawn to scale, cut-outs or templates.
- Filming — using cine or still films.

TYPES OF CHART

There are several different charts available, each with its own special purpose. The two main types are process charts and time-scale charts.

Process Charts

An outline process chart gives a broad picture of the process and the two principal activities used are 'operation' and 'inspection'.

These are represented by the following symbols:

O   Operation — the main steps in the process, method or procedure.

□   Inspection — indicates when something is examined or inspected for quantity or quality.

An example of such a chart is shown below.

JOB:	Damp mopping an area of floor 2 × 4 m (6½ × 13 ft)	Date:
CHART BEGINS:	Commencement of mopping	Time: 9.30
CHART ENDS:	Floor has been mopped	Time: 9.35

DISTANCE		SYMBOL	MOVEMENT
		O	Place mop into bucket
0.5 m	(1½ ft)	O	Wring out mop and remove from bucket
5.0 m	(16 ft)	O	Mop over a strip of floor using figure 8 action
0.5 m	(1½ ft)	O	Place mop into bucket
0.5 m	(1½ ft)	O	Wring out mop and remove from bucket
5.0 m	(16 ft)	O	Mop over a second strip of floor
0.5 m	(1½ ft)	□	Inspect the area
2.0 m	(6½ ft)	O	Move bucket to the end of the floor
0.5 m	(1½ ft)	O	Place mop into bucket
0.5 m	(1½ ft)	O	Wring out mop and remove from bucket
5.0 m	(16 ft)	O	Mop final strip of floor
0.5 m	(1½ ft)	O	Place mop into bucket and wring out mop
		□	Final inspection of floor
20.5 m	(65 ft)		

Number of operations   11
Number of inspections   2
Distance walked   20.5 m (65 ft)
Time taken   5 min

An outline process chart for damp mopping

A flow process chart   indicates in detail all the activities carried out and uses five symbols as follows:

O   Operation — the main steps in the process, method or procedure.

□   Inspection — indicates when something is examined or inspected for quantity or quality.

→   Transport — used when something or somebody is moved. Direction of arrow indicates direction of movement.

△   Storage — indicates controlled stage when something is issued from the stores, laid aside or kept.

D   Delay — indicates a delay in the process.

There are three main types:

- A man type records what the worker does.
- A material type records what happens to material.
- An equipment type records how equipment is used.

An example of a flow process chart is shown below.

JOB:	Damp mopping an area of floor 2 × 4 m	Date:
	$(6\frac{1}{2} \times 13$ ft)	
CHART BEGINS:	Commencement of mopping	Time: 9.30
CHART ENDS:	Floor has been mopped	Time: 9.35

DISTANCE		SYMBOL	MOVEMENT
		O	Place mop into bucket — wring out
0.5 m	$(1\frac{1}{2}$ ft)	→	Remove mop from bucket
5.0 m	(16 ft)	O	Mop over a strip of floor using figure 8 action
0.5 m	$(1\frac{1}{2}$ ft)	O	Place mop into bucket — wring out
0.5 m	$(1\frac{1}{2}$ ft)	→	Remove mop from bucket
5.0 m	(16 ft)	O	Mop over a second strip of floor
0.5 m	$(1\frac{1}{2}$ ft)	□	Inspect the floor
2.0 m	$(6\frac{1}{2}$ ft)	→	Move bucket to the other end of the floor
0.5 m	$(1\frac{1}{2}$ ft)	O	Place mop into bucket — wring out
0.5 m	$(1\frac{1}{2}$ ft)	→	Remove mop from bucket
5.0 m	(16 ft)	O	Mop final strip of floor
0.5 m	$(1\frac{1}{2}$ ft)	O	Place mop into bucket — wring out
		□	Final inspection of floor surface
20.5 m	(65 ft)		

Number of operations	7	
Number of transports	4	
Number of inspections	2	
Number of delays	Nil	
Number of storage	Nil	
Distance walked	20.5 m (65 ft)	
Time taken	5 min	

A flow process chart for damp mopping

Two-handed Process Charts

These charts record in detail the activities of the operator's hands or limbs in relation to one another.

The charts usually use the following four symbols:

O   Operation.
→   Transport.
△   Storage.
D   Delay.

An example of the two-handed process chart is shown below.

JOB:	Replacing a cartridge fuse into a flat pin plug	Date:
TYPE:	Manual type — two handed process chart	
CHART BEGINS:	Removing plug from socket	Time: 9.30 am
CHART ENDS:	Checking that the plug is functioning satisfactorily	Time: 9.32 am

LEFT HAND	SYMBOLS	SYMBOLS		RIGHT HAND
		O		Removes plug from socket
		O		Transfers plug to left hand
Holds the plug	O	O		Picks up screwdriver
Holds the plug	O	O		Unscrews top cover
Holds the plug	O	O	△	Puts down the screwdriver
Supports the plug	O	O		Turns the plug over
Holds the plug	O	O	△	Removes the cover and places it on to a flat surface
Holds the plug	O	O		Removes and discards the dead fuse
Holds the plug	O	O		Picks up the replacement fuse
Holds the plug	O	O		Replaces new fuse in plug
Holds the plug	O	O		Picks up cover and places on to plug
Supports the plug	O	O		Turns plug over
Holds the plug	O	O		Picks up screwdriver
Holds the plug	O	O		Secures cover to plug
Holds the plug	O	O	△	Puts down screwdriver
Transfers plug to right hand	O	O		Holds plug and replaces it into socket
		O		Checks that the plug is functioning satisfactorily

Number of storage	△	3
Number of operations	O	31
Number of transports	⇄	nil
Delay	D	nil
Total time for operation	2 min	
Distance walked	Nil	

Time-scale Charts

These charts record the activities and movements of more than one subject, e.g. worker/workers, machines or equipment; each is recorded on a common time-scale.

The different types of time-scale chart are:

- Multiple activity chart.
- Sims chart.
- PMST chart.
- Travel chart.

A multiple activity chart is shown below.

Multiple activity chart

PURPOSE:	To load, run and unload six washing machines in a group laundry
LOADING AND UNLOADING TIME:	10 min each
MACHINE RUN:	Ordinary wash (OW) 30 min Foul wash (FW) 50 min

		WASHING MACHINES					
TIME MINUTES	MAN	1 (OW)	2 (OW)	3 (OW)	4 (OW)	5 (FW)	6 (FW)
0		Machine					
10	Load machine 1	stopped	Machine	Machine	Machine	Machine	Machine
20	Load machine 2	Machine	stopped	stopped	stopped	stopped	stopped
30	Load machine 3	running	Machine				
40	Load machine 4		running	Machine			
50	Load machine 5	Machine		running	Machine		
60	Load machine 6	stopped	Machine		running		
70	Unload machine 1		stopped	Machine		Machine	Machine
80	Unload machine 2	Machine		stopped	Machine	running	running
90	Unload machine 3	idle	Machine		stopped		
100	Unload machine 4		idle	Machine			
110	Load machine 1			idle	Machine	Machine	
120	Load machine 2	Machine			idle	stopped	Machine
130	Load machine 3	running	Machine				stopped
140	Unload machine 5		running	Machine			
150	Unload machine 6	Machine		running		Machine	
160	Load machine 4	stopped	Machine			idle	Machine
170	Load machine 5		stopped	Machine	Machine		idle
180	Load machine 6			stopped	running	Machine running	

A multiple activity chart for washing machine operation

DIAGRAMS

Flow Diagrams

These are flow process charts which have been superimposed on a scale drawing of the work area. They indicate the movement of men, materials or equipment between specific locations during a process and by using the five charting symbols, indicate the activity carried out at these points. Templates to the scale of the equipment, machinery, etc., can be used on the diagram and moved about to assist in improving the layout. Usually, the flow process chart is examined in conjunction with the flow diagram.

An example of a flow diagram is given below. It shows the layout of a group laundry and follows the path of movement of soiled flat linen (sheets, pillowcases, etc.) from the receiving bay through the various processes to the linen bank ready for the redistribution of clean linen.

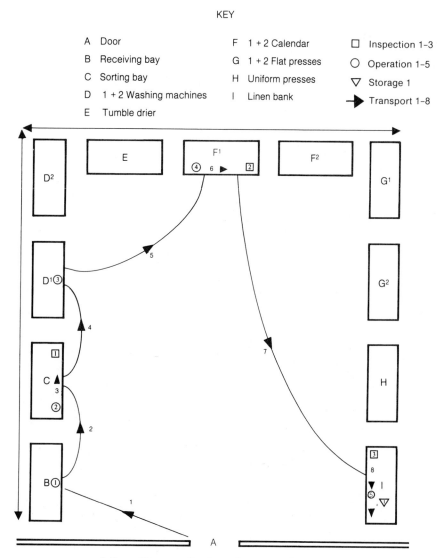

KEY

A	Door	F	1 + 2 Calendar	□ Inspection 1–3
B	Receiving bay	G	1 + 2 Flat presses	○ Operation 1–5
C	Sorting bay	H	Uniform presses	▽ Storage 1
D	1 + 2 Washing machines	I	Linen bank	➤ Transport 1–8
E	Tumble drier			

A flow diagram for laundry operations

String Diagrams   A string diagram is a scale plan or model on a piece of board — pins are inserted where the various operations are carried out or changes of direction occur. String or thread is then attached to these pins to trace and measure the path of the operator, materials or equipment during a specified sequence of events. Different coloured threads can be used to indicate the movements of different people carrying out the operation. After completion the string or thread is removed and measured, and then this will indicate the total distance travelled. Templates can also be used to determine improved layouts and thus reduce the number of journeys or distance travelled. They provide a very striking way of comparing an old and new layout or work process.

Examples of a string diagram follow.

KEY

A	Door		H	Toilet soap
B	Seals		I	Swabs
C	Floor polishes		J	Dusters
D	Strippers		K	Toilet rolls
E	General purpose cleaners		L	Literature and disposables
F	Furniture polish		M	Table
G	Scouring powder			

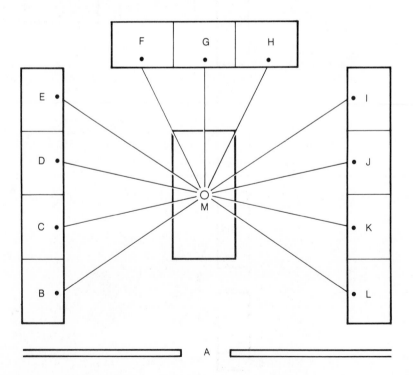

A string diagram for the issue of cleaning materials to domestic staff (original method)

KEY

A Door	H Toilet soap
B Seals	I Swabs
C Floor polishes	J Dusters
D Strippers	K Toilet rolls
E General purpose cleaners	L Literature and disposables
F Furniture polish	M Trolley
G Scouring powder	

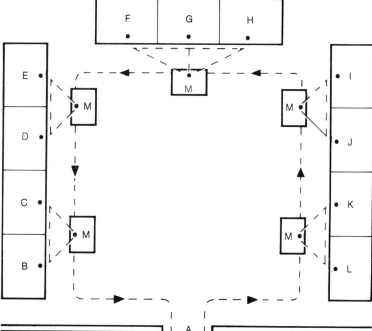

A string diagram for the issue of cleaning materials to domestic staff (improved method)

Models

Scale models have many advantages: they can be easily understood and changes can be visualised more accurately. However, they can be very expensive, especially if fully scaled three-dimensional models are produced/purchased and used. A cheaper method is to use toys, dolls' furniture or toy building bricks, as they can give a three-dimensional view. The expense involved can be justified, especially if they can be reused at a later date. A cheaper and more popular method is to use two-dimensional models in the form of cut-outs or templates using wood, cardboard, felt, magnets, self-adhesive materials, etc. The models can be used to indicate the positions of machines, equipment, working surfaces, etc.

Filming

Permanent records of processes, operations, and movements of staff and materials can be produced using cine film or still film in the form of slides, reels or 'Polaroid', at various speeds and in black and white or colour. Video and closed circuit television may also be used. Filming can be used in conjunction with charts, diagrams and models.

STAGE 3. EXAMINE THE FACTS

When all the facts have been obtained and represented by one of the charting or recording techniques, the facts must be examined systematically and analytically in an objective manner. The first step in the analytical process is to divide the operation into the following groups:

- Make ready or prepare.
- Do — the key operation.
- Put away.

The 'Do' operation will affect the 'Prepare' and 'Put away' and therefore the 'Do' operation must be analysed first. When analysing try to:

- eliminate,
- combine,
- simplify,

each operation or activity by systematic questioning, using the critical examination techinque as found in the chart below.

Critical examination

P U R P O S E	What is achieved?	Is it necessary? Why?	What else *could* be done?	What *should* be done?
P L A C E	Where is it done?	Why there? Advantage Disadvantage	Where else *could* it be?	Where *should* it be?
S E Q U E N C E	When is it done? After? Before?	Why then? Advantage Disadvantage	When else *could* it be done? Advantage Disadvantage	When *should* it be done?
P E R S O N	Who does it?	Why that person? Advantage Disadvantage	Who else *could* do it?	Who *should* do it?
M E A N S	How is it done?	Why that way?	How else *could* it be done?	How *should* it be done?

STAGE 4. DEVELOP A BETTER METHOD

Once the facts have been examined and questions have been answered then try to develop a better method by using one or more of the following factors:
- Elimination — eliminating certain activities or unnecessary parts of the job.
- Combination — combining activities together.
- Simplification — simplifying processes or activities.
- Change of sequence — the order of work carried out may be changed to improve performance, etc.

STAGE 5. INTRODUCE AND MAINTAIN THE BETTER METHOD

In order to complete the process of introducing a better method it is essential to carry out detailed planning and preparation, gain the assistance and cooperation of all staff, and monitor its progress very carefully, especially in the first few days. Extra supervision, guidance and training may be required to give staff confidence and alleviate fears, particularly if the change is considerable. If problems do occur, they should be investigated and corrected immediately.

At the development stage it is a good idea to contact suppliers of equipment and materials and visit similar types of establishment to acquire up-to-date information, which may assist in developing a better method. It is also important at this stage of the investigation to prepare and submit clear, concise reports, either oral or written or both, to back up proposals made.

MOTION ECONOMY

Motion economy is concerned with the economy of movement. Fatigue will be reduced and time fully used if movements can be eliminated, reduced or simplified.

The seven principles of motion economy are:
- minimum movements,
- simultaneous movements,
- symmetrical movements,
- natural movements,
- rhythmical movements,
- habitual movements,
- continuous movements.

In carrying out a task, these movements may be made individually or two or more may be combined together (e.g. habitual movements and rhythmical movements) in order to reduce fatigue. They are studied in order to develop better working methods, increased flow of work and improved design of tools and equipment.

WORK MEASUREMENT

Work measurement is the application of techniques designed to establish the time for a qualified worker to do a specified job at a defined level of performance. It is concerned with investigating, reducing, and subsequently eliminating ineffective time. People tend to work at different rates, depending on a number of factors:
- The type of job involved.
- The amount of mechanisation.

- The working environment.
- The amount of job satisfaction.
- The rate of pay and value of incentive.
- The ability and attitudes of fellow workers.
- The amount of rest periods.
- Is the job full-time or part-time, etc?

It is possible to work out a standard time for a job by calculating the average time it would take a number of operators to perform it.

The Procedure to be Applied When Carrying Out Work Measurement

- Select the work to be measured.
- Record all the relevant information.
- Define the job in detail.
- Measure the work.

The Two Main Techniques of Work Measurement

- Time study.
- Activity sampling.

TIME STUDY   The job is observed while it is being done. A stop-watch is used to measure the elements of the job accurately. A standard rating scale is used which runs from 0–100, based on the BSI recommendations. A performance of 100 is considered 'normal', a slow worker may achieve only 90 or 85, and a fast worker may achieve 110 or 120. A 'standard' hour is made up of 60 'standard' minutes.

The observer will judge the operator's rating relative to a standard rating scale. A standard or basic time for the job can be worked out by using the following formula:

$$\frac{\text{Observed rating time} \times \text{observed time}}{\text{Standard rating}} = \text{Standard or Basic}$$

e.g. $\dfrac{80 \times 10}{100} = 8$ min

Hence the standard or basic time for the operation is 8 minutes.

ACTIVITY SAMPLING

Work or activity sampling is easy to apply and follow. It involves random observations of activities during a normal shift or period of work, including waiting or idle time. Each observation records the work occurring at that instant and is expressed as a percentage of all the observations which record that activity. This then provides an idea of the percentage of time spent on that particular activity, so that:

$$\frac{\text{Number of observations where operator was carrying out one particular task}}{\text{Total observations carried out}} \times 100 = \text{The percentage of time for that particular job}$$

If, for example, a worker is observed 50 times and on 10 occasions he/she is polishing the floor, we do this calculation:

$$\frac{10}{50} \times 100 = 20$$

Hence 20% of the time was spent polishing the floor.

This can be taken a stage further by taking each work-element rate and determining the total work content required.

ERGONOMICS

This is the study of the relation of the worker to the environment, tools and equipment so as to avoid unnecessary strain and tension and thereby make the best use of human resources. Naturally it is impossible to provide ideal conditions for every individual worker, but every effort should be made to make conditions as pleasant as possible.

Ergonomics is a recognised science and at a simple level is very similar to motion economy. It is concerned with the following:
- Environment.
- Space layout.
- Design of tools and equipment.

Environment

The type of environment plays a very important part in the amount of stress, strain, tension and fatigue the worker endures in relation to the efficient use of human resources. Factors include:
- *lighting* — intensity, colour, method of lighting, amount of light emitted and glare,
- *heat, humidity and ventilation* — type used, temperature control in working environment, effect of sufficient air changes, etc.,
- *Noise* intensity and its effect on the worker.

Space Layout

Each worker needs a well-laid-out working situation. It is important to take into account the amount of working space and the height of working surfaces in relation to the size of the individual worker (e.g. height of beds, sinks, cupboards) in order to provide good posture with minimum physical effort.

The Design of Tools and Equipment

Equipment and tools should be well designed, well balanced, not heavy, easy to use and manoeuvre, and not inclined to 'run away' with the operator. It is also important that attachments are easy to connect and remove after use.

INCENTIVE BONUS SCHEMES

Incentive bonus schemes are being introduced into housekeeping and maintenance in some establishments to give workers added incentive to increase productivity, to produce a more efficient service, to reduce staffing ratios, and to give the individual workers more money in their pay packets.

There are two strongly opposing views on incentive bonus schemes. One view is that staff should be paid a realistic rate for the job so that there is no need for incentive bonus schemes. The other view is that by introducing incentive bonus schemes, productivity will be increased and wastage reduced. If an incentive bonus scheme *is* introduced, it is essential that standards are maintained and staff utilised to their fullest.

There are five main types of incentive bonus scheme.

Piece Work

With piece work, payment is directly proportional to output and is made against a rate per article which is set by rate fixing or work measurement. This system depends on the particular job, skill and speed of the operator, the availability of work, and other factors. As long as there is plenty of work, high bonuses can be paid, but if work is scarce the bonus will drop in proportion or be non-existent.

Group Bonus Schemes

The amount of bonus paid in such a scheme is dependent on the combined output of the group above a laid-down initial output. The workers record all their work. This is added up, and they are all dependent on each other's work to gain the bonus.

Individual Job Bonus Schemes

With this scheme the individual worker or group of workers who carry out a specific job are paid a percentage bonus over and above the fixed rate for the particular job. They are not dependent on other workers carrying out other activities or parts of the job. The onus is on the individual or small group to increase productivity. Close supervision may be necessary to ensure standards are maintained.

Profit Sharing

There are a number of different types of profit-sharing scheme, but basically they are each dependent on the amount of profit or savings made by the company.

One of the main ideas behind profit sharing is to encourage employees to stay with the firm for longer periods and to consider the long-term prospects of the company. The bonus paid to employees may be in the form of company shares issued once or twice a year. The bonus will fluctuate depending on profits made by the company.

Points System

In some establishments a points system for a bonus scheme operates whereby a point represents part of a job. If the job is completed satisfactorily in less time, the operator will be awarded bonus points which can be converted to extra wages, holidays, etc. This acts as an increased incentive to work.

QUESTIONS

1. Briefly define the following terms:
   (a) work study,
   (b) method study,
   (c) work measurement,
   (d) ergonomics,
   (e) motion economy.

2. Outline the main stages used when applying work study.

3. Illustrate, with examples, two of the main techniques used to record method study.

4. Briefly explain how method study might assist the supervisor in the housekeeping department.

5. How can the supervisor ensure that after a new method has been introduced the staff do not revert to the old method?

6. Outline the points to be considered before introducing an incentive bonus scheme.

7. A group bonus scheme is to be introduced in your department. How can you, as a supervisor, ensure that all the staff work to their fullest capacity to gain a high bonus for all workers?

PART C: TECHNICAL ASPECTS

11 Cleaning Agents

INTRODUCTION

It is essential that the housekeeper be familiar with the different range of products available, has a knowledge of the shelf-life of products, and keeps up to date with modern technology. Choosing which products to use can be very difficult especially with the conflicting claims of the manufacturers. It is useful to acquire samples and make comparisons of costs, suitability, durability, ease of application, and compare the amount of labour and equipment required.

The actual cost of detergents, seals, polishes, disinfectants, etc., may be only 5% of the total cost of cleaning and maintenance, but the use of unsuitable products will undoubtedly lead to a waste of time and energy, damage surfaces, possibly cause accidents and as a result increase overall expenditure. Where possible, products should be standardised, thereby effecting savings on materials and labour.

Solid dirt is relatively easy to remove and does not create too many difficulties, but problems can occur when dirt is mixed with grease or oil.

HOW TO SELECT A CLEANING AGENT

General Points

- Cheap products may be a false economy because they may increase labour costs considerably.
- Choose the best product for the money available.
- Wrong choice may damage surfaces and injure the user or cause accidents, thereby frustrating and demoralising the staff.
- Always use the least harmful cleaning agent first before resorting to harsh products.
- Never mix products together — they may cancel each other out or give off toxic gases.
- The dilution rate and working strength of the product should be checked.

pH Scale

The pH scale indicates the acidity or alkalinity of products. The scale ranges from 1 to 14. 1 to 6 is acid, 7 is neutral and 8 to 14 is alkali.

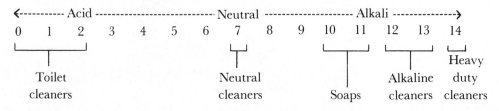

DETERGENTS A detergent is a substance which detaches particles of foreign matter (dirt) from an article, thereby cleaning it. Its efficiency depends on some type of mechanical action (e.g. mopping, scrubbing, agitation). Detergents are available in liquid, cake and powder form.

A detergent should:
- be readily soluble in water,
- be effective in all types of water and act as a water softener — produce no scum,
- have good wetting powers, so that the solution penetrates between the surface and the dirt particles,
- have good emulsifying powers, so that grease and oil are broken up and to some extent dissolved,
- have good suspending powers, so that the dirt particles when removed are suspended in solution and not redeposited on to the article,
- be effective over a wide range of temperatures,
- be harmless to the surface, article or skin,
- cleanse reasonably quickly with minimum agitation,
- be easily rinsed away,
- be bio-degradable.

It will depend on the type, quality and strength of the detergent whether or not it contains some or all of the above properties.

Types of Detergent Types of detergent are determined by the pH value of the product as follows:

Soap is manufactured from a combination of natural fats or fatty acids and an alkali. Soaps are not used a great deal as general cleaners because they are not very effective in hard water or cold water — they tend to leave a scum and a film on the surface. They are manufactured in a variety of shapes and sizes: toilet soap and liquid soap for personal washing; scrubbing soap for heavy cleaning and laundry work; flake and powder soap for laundry work.

Synthetic detergents are made up of: 'surfactants' (surface-active agents); inorganic builders or alkaline salts (e.g. soda, phosphates, sodium silicate) to assist in water softening; a synthetic gum to help their suspending powers; sodium perborate, an oxidising bleach; foam boosters to increase and stabilise the suds; brightening agents and perfumes; enzymes to help remove protein stains (e.g. blood, egg, perspiration); germicides and solvents with emulsifying powers to help the removal of grease from the surface.

Neutral or non-alkaline or anionic detergents are manufactured from strong alkalis and weak acids with a pH of 7-9. They are safe for all purposes and will not harm the skin or materials. They are by far the most widely used of all the detergents (80% of total usage) and are available as general purpose cleaners, washing-up liquids, carpet shampoos, window cleaners and for laundry work. Care should be taken over the amount used because the high foaming power could produce rinsing problems. The dilution rate is approximately 1:40. They can also be affected by extremely hard water.

Cationic or germicidal detergents   are manufactured from weak alkalis and strong acids with a pH of 6. They contain ammonia compounds, possess good germicidal and antistatic properties, and will kill certain groups of pathogenic bacteria. The main cationic detergents are the quaternary ammonium compounds (Quats or Qacs). These are used where hygiene is of paramount importance (e.g. in hospitals and food factories). They are available as cleaning gels, dish-washing detergents, deodorants, aerosol sprays (air-fresheners) and fabric softeners. They are mild in their action and have indifferent foaming powers. The dilution rate is 1:10, depending on use.

Amphoteric detergents   are basically neutral with a pH of 6–8 and some contain germicidal properties. They are specialised products and tend to be very expensive compared with other detergents. They are available as medicated liquid detergents, aerosol shampoos and metal cleaners.

Alkaline detergents   are manufactured from alkalis with a pH value of 9–12.5. They are used for heavy cleaning jobs to remove grease, heavy dirt accumulation, carbon black marks and a build-up of emulsion floor wax (the main use). The dilution rate is 1:8. Care should be taken over use; damage can be caused to surfaces so it is important to rinse surfaces well and neutralise them using a small quantity of vinegar in the final rinse of water. The product should not be allowed to remain in contact with the skin for long periods and hands should be washed after use. If a very concentrated solution is used from a spray, it may be necessary to wear full protective clothing.

Caustic detergents   are manufactured from caustic soda in either flake or liquid form and have a very high pH value of 12–14, depending on the concentration of the product, e.g.:
   5 litres water, 150 g caustic soda: pH = 14,
   5 litres water, 15 g caustic soda: pH = 13,
   5 litres water, 1.5 g caustic soda: pH = 12.

They are used for cleaning blocked drains and very dirty ovens, but should not be used on floorings because they can have a very harmful effect.

Detergent crystals and alkaline degreasers   are manufactured from sodium metasilicate blended with other surface-active agents. They provide a strong alkaline solution of pH 11–13, depending on the dilution rate. They are soluble in hot or cold water and are used mainly for removing an accumulation of oil and grease from floors, particularly from asphalt and concrete. They may also be used for removing a heavy build-up of emulsion floor wax where normal or fortified alkaline detergents are not effective. Care must always be taken to protect the skin and eyes.

Solvent-based detergent wax removers   are not strictly detergents, but are manufactured from a solvent (often of the white spirit type), water, a wetting agent and other additives. They are used mainly to remove solvent-based waxes and oils from floors, and oil and grease from equipment and machines. To use them, apply a solution to the surface, leave it to penetrate for up to 2 hours to loosen grease and hold it in suspension; then scrub the surface, rinse and dry. Do not use on floors which will be affected by solvents (e.g. PVC, rubber and lino).

OTHER CLEANING AGENTS AVAILABLE

Water is the cheapest and simplest cleaning agent available and will dissolve some forms of dirt, but it is not a very effective cleanser. It does not wet the surface satisfactorily unless another agent is added, e.g. a detergent, to break down the surface tension.

Abrasive cleaners The efficiency and effectiveness of an abrasive cleaner will depend on the type of abrasive material used in its manufacture and the size and shape of the particles.

TYPE OF ABRASIVE	GRADE	USES
Jewellers rouge	Very fine	Cleaning silver and gold
Precipitated whiting	Slightly coarser	Cleaning brass, copper
Powder pumice in liquid or paste form	Slightly coarser, depending on quality	Cleaning baths, hand basins, surfaces, etc.
Powder pumice in liquid, powder or paste form	Coarser grade	Heavy cleaning
Nylon, polyester or metal	Fine — coarse	Floor cleaning, e.g. buffing, spray cleaning and stripping
Sanding pads	Fine — coarse	Sanding down wood surfaces
Glass, sand and emery paper	Fine — coarse	Rubbing down surfaces
Steel wool (plain or soap impregnated)	Fine — coarse	Heavy cleaning or removing seals or waxes

Abrasives can be mixed with synthetic detergents, soaps, alkalis, solvents, bleaches, etc. They are available in natural, liquid, paste or powdered form. Always use the correct type of abrasive. The wrong choice can cause irreparable damage to the surface. Also make sure of the right dilution rate or quantity for the particular cleaning task and rinse surfaces thoroughly. After use, remove all deposits of the cleaner.

Window-cleaning agents are made from a water-miscible solvent (e.g. isopropyl alcohol, detergent and an alkali) to increase the cleaning efficiency of the product. A fine abrasive may also be added. They are available in liquid, cream or spray form and should be applied with a cloth and then rubbed off with a clean cloth to remove all the product. Water, water and methylated spirit, and water and vinegar can also be used: they tend to be cheaper, but require more effort to use effectively. A large number of establishments do not use a proprietary brand of window-cleaning agent especially for external surfaces, but employ contract window cleaners who use water — with the addition of a small quantity of detergent — sponges and squeeze blades.

Sweeping compounds are manufactured from inexpensive blends of organic and inorganic fillers (e.g. sand, wood flour or clay, etc., mixed with oil or wax). They are applied to the floor surface to absorb oils, fats and grease and are then swept up to remove build-up and dust.

Metal cleaners are made from fine abrasive grease solvents and in some cases from acids. They are available as liquids, powders, impregnated wadding or impregnated cloths. Some proprietary brands also contain 'long-life' elements which help to improve efficiency by preventing surfaces from tarnishing quickly. Always make sure that the correct product is used for the particular metal to remove the tarnish and scratches.

Hard metals (e.g. copper and brass) can be cleaned with a compound based on acid, generally vinegar or lemon, mixed with a fine abrasive such as pumice or salt. The acid must be washed off quickly to prevent further staining. This method will remove stains, but will not provide a shine. If a shine is required, polish with a proprietary brand of product.

Soft metals (e.g. silver and silver plate) can be cleaned using a proprietary brand of product or an impregnated cloth. When cleaning large quantities of silver use either:
- a hot solution of soda, water and aluminium strip or plate, or
- a burnishing machine, by using highly polished steel balls immersed in hot water and a detergent in a special container. The steel balls roll against the surface of the silver, remove tarnish and restore shine. Silver should be rinsed and dried after burnishing.

Toilet cleaners are available in crystalline form and liquid form.

Crystalline-form toilet cleaners are manufactured from sodium acid sulphate (a mild acid) and an anti-caking agent, pine oil and a detergent to help prevent corrosion of the surface.

Liquid-form toilet cleaners contain hydrochloric acid and must only be used as directed. The cleaner should be sprinkled on the pan and into the water, and left as long as possible before cleaning the toilet. They should never be used for cleaning any other area and should never be mixed with other cleaning agents because a harmful gas may be produced.

Shoe cleaners are made from special blends of waxes, spirit solvents and dyes. They are available as pastes, creams or liquids and used to clean leather footwear. They should be applied with a cloth, sponge or brush to a dry, dirt-free surface, then rubbed to a shine with a clean brush and soft duster. Never try to apply too much cleaner to the surface because more time and labour will be required to produce a good finish.

The majority of establishments no longer provide a shoe-cleaning service, but supply impregnated paper shoe wipes in the rooms or shoe-cleaning machines at strategic points in the establishment.

Furniture polish is made from special blends of waxes and a spirit solvent. Often, a silicone is added, which makes the polish easier to apply, reduces the amount of buffing needed and gives added protection from heat and moisture. Furniture polish is available in paste, liquid and cream forms.

Paste wax contains a high proportion of wax to solvent and may include silicones. The polish should be applied sparingly with a soft cloth and rubbed up with a clean duster. In most establishments paste wax has been superseded by spray polish unless the establishment has a lot of antique furniture needing several layers of wax.

Cream wax contains a lower proportion of wax and a higher proportion of solvents and silicones than paste wax. It should be applied with a cloth and rubbed up with a clean duster. Because of its make-up it will provide some cleaning action as well. It is suitable for a wide range of furniture, but if a build-up of wax is required it will take longer than paste wax.

Liquid or spray polish contains much more solvent and silicone and less wax than paste or cream polish. It can be sprayed directly on to the surface (e.g. furniture, glass or chrome) and wiped off immediately to remove dust and marks, etc., and to provide a shine. Care should be taken over the amount used because it is expensive and can be very wasteful. It may be more economical to spray the polish on to a cloth rather than directly on to the surface.

Teak surfaces should not be cleaned and polished with a conventional furniture polish, but with a teak oil, cream or spray to clean the surface and leave the furniture with a matt finish.

SEALS

A floor seal can be defined as a 'semi-permanent' material which is applied to the floor to prevent the penetration of dirt, stains, liquids and foreign matter. The purpose of a seal is to render a porous floor non-porous, but it is important to remember that all seals must be removed periodically and then renewed. Before a seal is applied it is essential that the floor surface is clean and dry otherwise the seal will not 'key' to the surface.

Requirements of a Seal

- To prevent dirt penetrating the floor surface.
- To provide a good appearance.
- To protect the surface from spillages (e.g. water, chemicals) and stains.
- To have good anti-slip properties.
- To be durable.
- To have good adhesion and not flake off the surface.
- To resist scuff marks.
- To have good levelling and floor properties.
- To be easy to apply, repair, remove and recoat.
- Not to alter the colour of the floor surface.
- To be quick-drying.
- To have a good shelf-life.
- To be realistically priced.
- To have a pleasant odour.

No one seal will provide all these requirements, but many contain most of them.

Factors to be Considered Before Selecting a Seal

- The type of surface (e.g. wood, PVC or concrete).
- The reason for sealing.
- The current method of maintenance — is the surface already sealed with a particular product?
- The use of surface, amount of traffic, durability required.
- The availability of surface for resealing at a later date.

- The subsequent method of maintenance.
- The cost — initial and long-term.
- The appearance.
- The speed of drying.
- The odour.
- The ease of applying seal.

Types of Seal

There is a wide range of seals available on the market today, but manufacturers are always aware of the need to produce more efficient and effective products to meet the demands of new technology.

Five main types of seal are in general use today.
- Oleo-resinous.
- One-pot (ready-for-use) plastic seals.
- Two-pot plastic seals, made up of a base (main body of the seal) and an accelerator or hardener.
- Pigmented seals (coloured).
- Water-based seals.

Other seals include: epoxyesters, styrenated alkyds, modified nitrocellulose, two-pot polyesters, two-pot epoxy resins, styrene butadiene lacquers, and shellac lacquers.

For a detailed analysis of the different types of seal see the table on pp. 94-5

Applying Floor Seals

- Always make sure the floor surface is clean, chemically neutral and dry before applying a seal.
- Ideally, sealing should be carried out at room temperature, 18.3 °C (69 °F) If the temperature is lower, the seal will take longer to dry.
- Good ventilation is required to give the best results.
- Prepare seals, especially two-pot seals, in readiness. However, do not mix too large a quantity of two-pot seal because it may deteriorate before being used.
- Prepare the applicators and room in readiness. Remove all furniture where possible.
- Apply several thin even coats rather than thick coats, to give a good finish.
- Try to prevent dust, flies, etc., from settling on the floor before it is dry.
- Do not allow people to walk on the surface until it is completely dry and finished. Put up notices or warning signs, e.g. 'Sealing in process — keep off'.
- Immediately after the completion of sealing, clean the applicators, trays, etc., using an approved solvent cleaner.

Types of Seal Applicator

Brushes   are very useful for sealing small areas or the edges of a floor which cannot be reached with another type of applicator. A 5 cm (2 in) brush is an ideal size. Never attempt to use a brush for large areas because it will be very time-consuming and may not give a very good finish.

Mops.   Good-quality cotton mops can be used to apply oleo-resinous or water-based seals to the surface. Do not apply too much seal. Pour a small amount of seal on to the surface and spread it over a small area — repeat until the whole area is sealed.

Lambswool bonnets may be used to apply seals to large areas. Seal is poured on to the floor and spread lightly and evenly over the surface. Lambswool bonnets are suitable for applying most types of seal except two-pot plastic seals — use roller applicators instead.

Roller applicators may be used for sealing large areas; they are usually made of mohair and used in conjunction with an applicator tray. The roller is dipped into the seal and any surplus removed by using a grille on an applicator tray. The roller is then applied to the floor until the surface has been sealed. It is very suitable for use with two-pot plastic seals, but should not be used to apply water-based seals.

Turk's-head brushes may be used to apply seals such as pigmented seals to concrete floors. Because concrete floors are often uneven and pitted, the seal can initially be applied with a roller or lambswool bonnet to a small area and then the Turk's-head brush is used to spread the seal into the pitted areas to prevent gaps appearing on the surface.

FLOOR WAXES

The application of a floor wax not only improves the appearance of a floor, but also facilitates maintenance by protecting the surface from wear, thereby prolonging the life of the floor. There are two main types of floor wax in use today:

Solvent-based waxes are made from blends of natural or synthetic waxes, synthetic resins, colourings, perfumes and silicones. Available in paste and liquid form, paste waxes contain a higher proportion of wax than do liquid waxes and are more expensive. They may be used to form a protective layer on wood, wood composition, cork, linoleum and magnesite floors. Do not use them on PVC, thermoplastic or rubber surfaces, which will be damaged by the solvent. Apply thin coats of wax to a clear dry surface with an applicator (liquid wax can be sprayed on to the floor surface). If too thick a coat is applied, this can cause problems (e.g. slipperiness). Build-up requires a great deal of buffing, etc. The frequency of application depends on the type and volume of traffic. Possibly one application per week would be sufficient, followed by buffing. Also, buff from time to time in between applications.

To remove solvent-based waxes use a solvent-based detergent wax remover. Spread the solution over the area to be treated, using a brush or mop, allow it to penetrate into the wax, and then scrub the surface. Rinse the surface well (do not use too much water), allow it to dry, and then apply further coats of wax.

Water-based waxes are made from synthetic waxes, alkali-soluble resins, polymer resins and additives. During manufacture, the wax solidifies into fine particles and remains dispersed in the water. Water-based waxes are widely used because they can be used on a variety of surfaces, including PVC, thermoplastic, rubber, asphalt, terrazzo and marble, as well as sealed wood, wood composition, cork and linoleum.

There are three main types of water-based wax:

Fully buffable. Normally dries with a low sheen which can be increased to a high gloss with buffing. These products contain approximately 50% wax and require buffing not only to give a gloss, but also to harden the film of wax — to increase durability. They are fairly resistant to scuff marks, but need to be buffed up regularly to renew gloss and remove marks.

Semi-buffable. The floor dries to a subdued gloss, but this can be increased by buffing. These products contain approximately 30% wax. Buffing will harden the wax and

Seals

TYPE	COMPOSITION	USES	DURABILITY	SHELF-LIFE	ODOUR	NO. OF COATS	DRYING TIME	METHOD OF REMOVAL
(1) Oleo-resinous	Linseed/dehydrated castor oil, resins, solvents and driers. Penetrating seals and surface-coating	Wood group. Wood. Wood comp. Cork. Magnesite	Moderate. Dark in colour. Not particularly resistant to chemicals. 1–2 years	Good. Several years if unopened	Mild	2–3 depending on surface and amount of traffic	Slow — 24 hours. Generally hard in 8–10 hours. Leave for at least 6 hours between coats	Easy to remove — use abrasive pads on machine or sand-down. Clean surface, allow to dry and apply new coats
(2) One-pot plastic seal (a) Urea formaldehyde	Urea formaldehyde resin with acid catalyst, solvents (e.g. alkyd resin). A finishing seal does not penetrate surface	As (1)	Quite good, even under heavy traffic	Reasonable but depends on formation of seal. Few months –2 years	Rather strong. Good ventilation required because strong solvents used	As (1)	Quite good — 6–8 hours. 6 hours between coats	More difficult to remove than (1). Use a sander or abrasive pads. May require a chemical stripper. Clean and dry surface and apply new coats
(b) Polyurethane	Pre-reacted polyurethane, small proportion of oil, solvents and additives. A finishing seal. Oil-modified or moisture-cured	As (1)	Quite good — 1–2 years	Reasonable — 1–2 years depending on composition and storage conditions	Mild	As (1)	Good. Oil-modified: 3–4 hours, 3 hours between coats. Moisture cured 6–8 hours, 6 hours between coats	More difficult to remove than (1). As above
(3) Two-pot plastic seals (a) Urea formaldehyde	Similar to one-pot urea formaldehyde seal	As (1)	Quite good, depends on traffic. 2 years plus	Very good. Indefinite if stored in good conditions	As (2)	2–3	Quite good — 3–4 hours. 6 hours between coats	As one-pot urea formaldehyde

						COATS	TIME	REMOVAL
(b) Polyurethane clear seals	A polyester and an isocyanate accelerator and solvents	As (1)	Very good. 3–4 years depending on traffic and condition of seal	Very good. Several years if stored in good conditions	Very strong until the seal has dried. Good ventilation required during use and drying time	3	3–4 hours. 2 hours between coats	More difficult to remove than most seals. Use sand to remove. Clean and dry floor. Apply new coats
(4) Pigmented seals (reasonable paint in appearance) (a) Synthetic rubber pigmented seal	Rubber resins and pigments (e.g. red, blue, green, purple)	Concrete and magnesite.	Quite good — 1–2 years.	Very good — several years.	Mild.	2–3	3–8 hours, depending on formulation of seal. 6 hours between coats	Use abrasive pads or sander. Solvent can be used to remove small difficult areas. Its use should be well controlled. Clean and dry floor. Apply new coats
(b) Two-pot polyurethane pigmented seals	Similar to two-pot polyurethane and pigments	Concrete, magnesite and some stone floors	Good — 2–3 years	Quite good. Base — indefinite. Accelerator — very susceptible to moisture	Strong until dry. Good ventilation required	3	Very good — 2–3 hours. 2 hours between coats	Difficult — remove by sanding or abrasive pads
(5) Water-based seals	Acrylic, polymer resins and plasticisers to assist flexibility. Provides a 'plastic skin' over surface	PVC, thermoplastics, rubber, porous linoleum, terrazzo, marble and asphalt	Depends on type and volume of traffic — 1–3 years	Reasonable — 1 year	Mild	1–2	Very good, 20–30 mins	Fortified alkaline detergent or abrasive pads. Clean and dry surface. Apply new coats

increase durability. They are more resistant to water, stains and scuff marks than fully buffable waxes.

Dry bright. The floor dries to a high initial gloss and buffing will not improve this. These products contain approximately 10–15% wax and more additives. They are durable and create a good appearance initially, but deteriorate under heavy traffic. They have very good resistance to stains, water, etc., and have very good anti-slip properties. They are more difficult to remove than semi-buffable or buffable waxes because of surface film.

Most water-based waxes on the market today are a combination of more than one type so that the surface can be buffed to renew its appearance without applying more wax. Hence the problem of build-up is reduced.

To remove wax use an alkaline detergent; in some cases a fortified alkaline detergent may be necessary.

SPECIALITY PRODUCTS

In recent years speciality products have been introduced to meet specific requirements.

High solids emulsion floor waxes have a high solids content and are used where very good durability is required (e.g. busy traffic areas in main corridors). They have excellent dry-bright properties, and only one coat is needed, whereas two or three coats of ordinary water-based wax are needed to give the same results. They can be buffed and have excellent slip-resistant properties. Care must be taken not to apply too much, otherwise there will be a heavy build-up very quickly. To remove wax, use an alkaline or fortified alkaline detergent.

Wash-and-wax emulsions (clean and shine) consist of a combination of wax and detergent. They are used to clean and wax floor surfaces in a single operation. They are not designed to remove heavy soilage, but to maintain light, normal traffic areas. They are very sensitive to water and have a tendency to water-spot. These products are easy to remove because there is little build-up. There is a wide range of these emulsions on the market. Some have very good dry-bright properties; others require buffing.

Acid-sensitive emulsion floor waxes are not used to a great extent, having been largely superseded by metallised waxes. They are resistant to detergents, so floors with heavy dirt deposits can be cleaned without the detergent affecting the wax. They give a very durable finish, but a special acid stripper must be used to remove wax from the surface.

Detergent-resistant emulsion floor waxes consist of metal-containing polymers — the metal component is usually zinc. They are hard-wearing and contain dry-bright and buffable properties. They are used quite considerably, but care should be taken over their use and the amount used. They are resistant to detergents and therefore a special stripper must be used (containing ammonia) to remove them. In some cases the surface may become very hard in a short period of time, and even the special strippers will not remove this wax. Therefore a coarse abrasive pad must be used.

Factors to be Considered Before Selecting a Floor Wax

- Type of surface, condition and amount of traffic.
- Size of surface.
- Use of surface and location.
- Ease of application, recoating, touching up and removing.
- Frequency of cleaning.
- Present and future methods of maintenance.
- Availability of labour.
- Availability of equipment.

Each factor should be considered carefully and priorities assessed before a final selection is made.

Requirements of a Floor Wax

- Good anti-slip properties.
- Durability.
- Resistance to carbon black heel marks.
- Good anti-scuff properties.
- Good levelling and flow properties.
- Being easy to apply, recoat, touch up and remove.
- Good adhesion to the surface.
- Being buffable to renew gloss.
- Reasonable cost.
- Good dry-bright properties.

The Reasons for Applying a Wax to a Surface

- To protect the surface.
- To improve safety.
- To improve the appearance of the surface.
- To assist in the cleaning process.
- To improve hygiene.

SOLVENTS

For some cleaning purposes, detergents and water alone are not sufficient. Recently solvents have been added to detergents to aid cleaning and remove fats, oils, grease, etc. Where these are still not effective, solvents alone can be used, but they should be used carefully under very strict conditions because they may have adverse effects on the skin or the surface, and they may be a fire hazard — good ventilation is required with their use.

The most common types used for general cleaning are now described.

Ethyl alcohol and methylated spirits are used to dissolve resins, waterproof inks, biro, iodine and colouring matters of many plants and fruits, e.g. blackcurrant. They are reasonably mild to the skin, but their vapours are intoxicating and could be dangerous in high concentrations, so good ventilation is required. They are highly flammable, so care must be taken.

Acetone is used to dissolve resins, paints, lipstick, nail varnish, many dyestuffs and plastics. Being very flammable and volatile, it tends to be rather overpowering, so good ventilation is necessary.

White spirit is also highly flammable. It is used to dissolve tar, rubber, fats, oils, waxes and pitch, but has little effect on paint, resins or plastics. It is relatively harmless to the skin, but its vapour can cause dizziness after long periods of use, so good ventilation is necessary.

Petrol dissolves tar, rubber, wax and pitch, but has little effect on paints and resins. A very volatile product; it should be avoided where possible because of fire risk.

Paraffin dissolves tar, rubber, wax and pitch rather slowly, but has little effect on paints and resins. It is less volatile than petrol and will not ignite in bulk.

Trichloroethylene is a chlorinated solvent which was developed to supersede carbon tetrachloride. It dissolves fats, oils, waxes, tar, pitch, paint, resins, rubber and many plastics, so should not be used on rubber, vinyl or bitumen surfaces. It is not flammable. Trichloroethylene may cause some degreasing of the skin and should be used with good ventilation.

Methylene chloride is a very volatile product which tends to evaporate at room temperature. It dissolves fats, waxes, paints, plastics and rubber, and is mainly used in the production of paint strippers.

Tetrachloroethylene perchloroethylene is very similar to trichloroethylene. It dissolves paint, resins, fats, oils, waxes, tar, rubber and plastics.

DISINFECTANTS

Disinfection is the removal or destruction of harmful microbes, though not usually including bacterial spores. It is the process of destroying sufficient numbers of micro-organisms to avoid danger to health. *A disinfectant* is an agent used to disinfect a surface or object.

Methods of Disinfection

Disinfection by heat, called *pasteurisation*, is the cheapest method available. Hot water or steam is used at a temperature of 65 °C for 10 minutes or 100 °C for 5 minutes. This will kill viruses, fungi and non-sporing bacteria, but will not kill bacterial spores. This method can be used to disinfect soiled, foul and infected laundry (especially in hospitals), equipment (e.g. mop-heads, sponges, cloths, buckets, etc.), bedpans (although in most hospitals disposable pans and bottles are now used), for dish-washing crockery, cutlery, etc., and disinfecting walls and surfaces.

Disinfection by cleaning can be very effective, but constant supervision is necessary to make sure cleaning staff are not simply transferring dust from one place to another. It is essential that staff are well trained to do their tasks to high standards and that checks are made from time to time to ensure that the standards do not drop. All equipment and materials should be chosen very carefully to improve efficiency and prevent the risks of cross-contamination. It is also essential that equipment is regularly cleaned and maintained to prevent the spread of germs, etc., to other areas. Mats should be placed in strategic positions to encourage people to walk on them and thereby help to prevent dirt and dust entering buildings.

Disinfection by chemicals. There is a wide range of chemical disinfectants available on the market today, and they should be chosen very carefully. They should only be employed if the use of heat is impossible and cleaning is not efficient. A chemical disinfectant should never be used to mask unpleasant smells. The source and cause of the smells should be found and removed.

The Main Groups of Chemical Disinfectants

Alcohols may be used to disinfect working surfaces, but they are not suitable for very dirty surfaces. Often they are used in conjunction with iodine for the general disinfection of all areas.

Aldehydes may be used in the form of a colourless gas with an irritating smell; the main type used is formalin. It is used for large-scale fumigation of areas.

Ampholytes are good as detergents but of very little use as disinfectants because they are inactivated by a wide range of materials.

Diguanides are used mainly to disinfect the skin in the form of Hibitane. It is not suitable for surfaces.

Halogens include chlorine and iodine. Their compounds are used as disinfectants for a variety of surfaces. Some are used in conjunction with detergents to give greater efficiency.

Phenolics are widely used as disinfectants for most areas, and available in the form of Dettol and white fluids (e.g. Izal, Clearsol, etc.,).

Pine fluids have a very pleasant smell, but they are not very efficient disinfectants for industrial use. They are used more frequently in the home.

QACs (quaternary ammonium compounds) are more suitable as detergents with germicidal properties than as disinfectants, because they are inactivated by a wide range of materials.

QACs combined with diguanides are used mainly as skin disinfectants, but are not usually very effective for disinfecting surfaces, because they are inactivated by a wide range of materials.

Omnibus disinfectants are disinfectants that are manufactured from chemicals belonging to several other groups. They tend to be rather expensive and are not used widely in the industry because cheaper and more effective products are available.

All chemical disinfectants are inactivated by certain materials, e.g. soap, detergents, hard water and synthetic products (as in plastics, sponges, mops, brushes, etc.). Some are inactivated by several materials. This reduces the efficiency and effectiveness of the disinfectant. Disinfectants should not be mixed because they may inactivate each other.

To use a disinfectant effectively adopt the following procedure:
- Measure the disinfectant very carefully and use the correct dilution rate.
- A disinfectant must come in direct contact with the organisms. That is the main reason why aerosol disinfectants are not very effective.

- A disinfectant must remain in contact with the organism long enough to destroy it or render it harmless.
- Always clean a surface before disinfecting it.
- Always dispose of disinfectant solutions when they have been finished with.
- Never top up disinfectant solutions.
- Do not leave cleaning equipment (e.g. mops) immersed in a disinfectant solution overnight.
- Do not allow staff to bring their own disinfectants to work. Use only those supplied by the establishment.
- Always be aware that the disinfectant may be inactivated by other materials.
- Disinfectant must be stored in the correct conditions if it is not to become ineffective.

QUESTIONS

1. What do you understand by the pH scale?

2. What are the requirements of:
   (a) a detergent,
   (b) a seal,
   (c) a polish/wax?

3. Why is it important that a floor surface is clean, dry and neutral before a treatment is applied?

4. What procedure would you use to remove the following from a floor surface:
   (a) a solvent-based wax,
   (b) a water-based wax?

5. Indicate what causes a build-up of seal or wax on a floor surface and suggest how it can be prevented.

6. Explain what points must be considered before selecting a treatment for a floor surface.

7. (a) What are the three main methods of disinfecting a surface?
   (b) Explain how disinfectants can be inactivated.

8. Why is it necessary to label cleaning materials and what information should be included on such a label?

9. A thermoplastic floor in a restaurant appears to be slippery. Indicate the possible causes and methods of prevention.

10. Care should be taken when using solvents for cleaning. List the instructions which should be given to staff with regard to their use and control.

12 Cleaning Equipment

INTRODUCTION

Mechanical cleaning equipment is one of the modern aids to cleaning, and manufacturers invest considerable amounts of cash, time and know-how into research in order to produce more efficient, compact and versatile machines. It is a well-known fact that 90–95% of the cost of the cleaning function is spent on labour and only 5–10% on machines and consumables. Of this 5–10%, 85% is spent on consumables and a mere 15% on equipment. As the need for cost control increases, owing to increased productivity, the need for greater automation will become evident. Establishments are tending to use more combined scrubbing, polishing and drying machines in order to help achieve this end.

The circumstances of every building are different in terms of:
- total area to be cleaned and maintained,
- size, shape and layout,
- type and nature of surfaces,
- degree of congestion,
- type and amount of soiling,
- standard of finish required,
- type and amount of labour available.

HOW TO SELECT EQUIPMENT

When one is considering equipment it is advisable to select the largest size that can be fitted into the site, thus providing savings in cost per hour of the equipment.

General Points to be Considered

- Cost — initial, running, maintenance and depreciation.
- Hire as opposed to purchase.
- Safety in operation of both mechanical and electrical equipment.
- Type of work and area; amount of obstruction and cleaning frequency.
- Suitability of equipment for the job to be performed.
- Durability.
- Size and loading (wattage) of equipment.
- Size, weight and height of machine, ease of handling and operating.
- Portability between floors.
- Robust construction, availability of spare parts.
- Correct speed for the job performed (e.g. scrubbing, buffing).

- Versatility of the machine so that it may accommodate various tasks (e.g. scrubbing, buffing, stripping).
- Noise level, particularly in hospital wards.
- Storage — is it easy to store? What space is required for storage?
- Protection and edging to prevent damage to furniture and fittings.

Ideally staff should be consulted when selecting equipment because they are the people who are going to use it. It would be disappointing if the equipment had been purchased and it was discovered unused a month or two later in the store room for the following reasons:

- It was not suitable for the job involved.
- It was too difficult to operate.
- Staff were afraid to use it.
- Staff were not trained to use it.

Once a decision has been made with regard to the type and amount of equipment required, the next decision is which supplier to choose. This can be achieved by:

- visiting exhibitions and conferences,
- studying trade journals for the latest equipment available,
- contacting similar types of establishment and comparing the reliability of different types and sizes of equipment,
- contacting suppliers, manufacturers and distributors of equipment and inviting their representatives to demonstrate a selection of equipment. Most reputable firms will allow the establishment to keep the equipment for a trial period to make comparisons.

Time and labour can be wasted by staff if they have to wait to use a piece of equipment. Where possible provide sufficient equipment to overcome this problem. Staff will also tend to care for equipment if they feel that they are personally responsible for it.

There are advantages and disadvantages of selecting one make of equipment, such as:

- more competitive prices,
- fewer problems of maintenance,
- machines and attachments may be interchangeable,
- spare parts may be more readily available.

A CARD INDEX SYSTEM

A card index system is a useful method of collating all information about each piece of equipment in use in a particular establishment. It is of great value to the manager or supervisor for the following reasons:

- It gives up-to-date information concerning the equipment.
- It indicates the location of the equipment.
- It indicates who usually operates the equipment.
- It contains a record of what servicing has been carried out, costs, new parts supplied, etc.
- When new equipment is being considered the information can be used to assess reliability.

Opposite is an example of an index card.

Type of machine Cleanco 450mm (18″) brush High-speed machine	*Serial number* CHS 1234
Date of purchase 13 January 1987	*Date first used* 27 January 1987
Cost of machine £xxx	*Life expectancy* 8 years
Period of guarantee 12 months	*Insurance* Alliance Insurance Co Ltd

User and location of machine Mrs T Smith, Ward Male 26

Supplier Cleanco Co Ltd, 151 High Street Birmingham

Local representative Mr J C Roberts, Tel No. 021-123-4621

Servicing and Maintenance

Date	*Work carried out*	*Parts cost*	*Total cost*

MANUAL EQUIPMENT

A list of manual equipment appears in the tables below. Some of these are illustrated on pp. 111-17.

TYPE	SELECTION	USE AND CARE
(1) *Applicators* – sponge, lambswool, cotton, nylon, bristle	Size, shape, ease of attaching to head	For the application of seals, polish, paints, etc. Wash after use, rinse and dry
(2) *Applicator trays* – metal, plastic	Size, shape	For seals, polishes and paints. Empty after use. Wash, rinse and dry
(3) *Brushes and brooms* — bass, bristle, horsehair, nylon	Size, shape	Remove fluff, hairs, etc., after use. Wash, rinse and dry frequently

TYPE	SELECTION	USE AND CARE
(4) *Carpet sweepers*	Size, ease of emptying	To remove surface dust, fluff, crumbs, etc., from floor surface. Empty frequently. Wipe with a damp cloth. Clean brushes periodically — lubricate as necessary
(5) *Chamois leather* — natural, synthetic	Size, quality — this is indicated by amount of stretch not thickness	For cleaning mainly glass surfaces. Rinse well after use — do not use hot water. Periodically wash and rinse
(6) *Dusters and mitts* — cotton or disposable, impregnated or untreated	Size, quality	Use in form of a pad for dusting surfaces to prevent dust scattering. Used for dry or damp dusting. Wash frequently, rinse and dry
(7) *Dustpans* — metal, plastic	Size, shape — pan should fit flush to the surface for efficiency	Used in conjunction with a hand brush to pick up dust, debris, etc. Empty frequently. Wash, rinse and dry after use
(8) *Edging tools* — nylon, polyester, mesh	Size, shape, reliability	For removing a build-up of polish or removing carbon heel marks, or for buffing small areas where a machine is not suitable. Change pads frequently. Wash, rinse and dry
(9(a)) *Mops, dry* — cotton, nylon, lambswool. Disposable	Size, shape, ease of attaching and removing mop-heads. impregnated or untreated	To sweep floor surface. Wash frequently, rinse and dry — re-treat if necessary or return to supplier for cleaning and treating
(b) *Mops, wet* — cotton, cotton and jute, cotton and nylon. Linen mixture. Sponge — natural/ synthetic. Disposable	Size of mop-head. Type — round-headed. Long, Treble Life, Kentucky, Minit	Used for damp/wet mopping surfaces. Rinse frequently while in use. Wash, rinse and dry after use — do not leave overnight soaking in a solution. Renew mop-heads as required

TYPE	SELECTION	USE AND CARE
(10) *Mop buckets—* galvanised, polypropylene, plastic/fibrolene	Size, mobility, method of extracting water, e.g. wringer, sieve, rollers, etc. Single/double bucket system. Size and type of mop	Change cleaning solution frequently. Empty, clean, rinse and dry after use. Store carefully
(11(a)) *Pads for normal speed machines —* nylon, polyester	Size, colour, thickness	Beige — buffing, green — scrubbing, black — stripping, bright green — for heavy cleaning. Make sure pads are secured to machine and change pads frequently. Remove dry dirt with centre of pad. Wash frequently, rinse and dry. Store flat
(b) *Pads for high speed machines —* nylon, polyester	Size, colour, thickness	White — super buffing, red — buffing, blue — spray cleaning, brown/maroon — heavy cleaning. Care and cleaning as for (11a)

The lighter the colour pad the less abrasive and vice versa. Most establishments use a combination of (11(a)) and (b) to keep the number of different coloured pads to a minimum

TYPE	SELECTION	USE AND CARE
(12) *Sprays —* plastic	Size — 1 litre (1¾ pints) 1½ litre (2½ pints)	For application of polish, paint, etc. Empty after use. Clean frequently to prevent clogging of jets
(13) *Squeegees—* straight-edged, curved	Size. Easy to fit replacement blades. Easy to manoeuvre	To remove excess water from surface. Clean, use and store carefully
(14) *Step ladders —* metal, wooden	Lightweight metal preferred — no rust. Platform type to take buckets, equipment, etc.	For ease of access to heights. Keep clean. Inspect regularly. Store in a secure place
(15) *Trolleys —* metal, polypropylene	Consider design, construction, size. Ease of manoeuvre	For the transport of equipment, linen, etc., to place of work. Clean regularly. Lubricate when necessary

MECHANICAL APPLIANCES

There is a large variety of mechanical appliances available in addition to the familiar vacuum cleaner. These will now be examined in detail. Some of them are illustrated on pp. 111-17.

VACUUM CLEANERS

Vacuum cleaners work on the principle of suction and are used to remove dust and debris from any surface —hard or soft. The dust, dirt, debris and air are collected into a container and then the air is filtered through a system of two or three filters back into the atmosphere. There are two main types of cleaner available on the market today: suction only, and suction plus mechanical action, e.g. brushes. Vacuum cleaners are available upright or cylindrical with an enclosed bag or with a bag on the outside. They are also available in different sizes and shapes. When selecting a vacuum cleaner the main point to look for is efficiency in operation, and not size, shape or colour.

Points to consider

- Is the suction powerful enough to dislodge dirt as well as removing dust and debris?
- If suction power on its own is not efficient enough, should you select a machine with a rotating brush?
- Can the suction power be directed where it is needed?
- Is the machine portable enough for the staff and layout of the building?
- Is the dust trapped inside the bag before the air is released?
- What type of filter system is used?
- What types of attachment are available?
- How easy is it to empty the contents of the machine?

Care and Maintenance

- The dust bags must be emptied regularly to prevent putting extra strain on the motor.
- The machine itself should be well maintained — any hair, fluff, etc., must be removed from the brushes.
- Never attempt to pick up objects which are large or made of metal, e.g. pins or grips — they could damage the machine, particularly the filter.
- Lubricate the machine occasionally.
- Store carefully and rewind the flex.
- Throw away dust bags and change the filters periodically.
- Generally keep the equipment clean. Time should be allowed each day for this and inspection.
- Periodic maintenance should be carried out by the contractor or service engineer every 6 months.

SCRUBBING AND POLISHING MACHINES

These machines are used for scrubbing, buffing, spray cleaning, scarifying and carpet shampooing. There is a wide range of machines on the market and they are manufactured as 'Normal speed 200–300 rpm' or 'High speed 400 rpm+'. The efficiency of the machine depends on the weight on the brush and the machine's speed. For scrubbing and scarifying the weight is the most important element, but with buffing and spray cleaning speed is more important. With concentrated-weight machines the total weight of the machine is borne on the brushes and pads, whereas with distributed/divided-weight machines some of the weight is carried on the wheels.

The machine can be fitted with all or some of the following depending on the type of work to be carried out and the choice of the individual:

- Brushes — buffing/polishing, shampooing, scrubbing, scarifying.
- Drive plates fitted with foam rubber, nylon, lambswool or mesh.
- Pads.
- Tanks for cleaning solution, polish solution.
- Sprays for emulsion/solvent-based detergents.

The disposition of the brushes or pads is a matter of great importance for the general efficiency of the operation. There are currently three different methods of disposition and they are classified as single- , double- , and three-brush machines.

Single-brush machines have a central shaft, either gear- or belt-driven. A brush or drive plate and pad is fitted directly to the shaft. They are available in a variety of sizes from 30 cm to 75 cm (12 in to 30 in), normal speed or high speed.

Advantages
- Relatively easy to connect brush or pad to machine.
- Weight of motor is directly over centre of machine — producing more concentrated weight.
- Usually fitted with dead man's handle for safety in operation.

Disadvantages
- Tendency for machine to swing around because of motor torque.
- Could be more difficult to operate.

Two-brush machines have two brushes or pads which rotate counter to each other so that the torque is equalised.

Advantages
- Easier to operate than single-brush machines.

Disadvantages
- May be more expensive to purchase.
- Machine has 'dead' space down the centre between brushes or pads and requires more overlapping of machine paths to cover floor thoroughly.

Three-brush machines contain three brushes or pads driven by friction.

Advantages
- Relatively easy to operate.

Disadvantages
- More costly to purchase.
- It may be more time-consuming to attach pads or brushes.

Job Instruction Cards for Floor Polishing Machines

An example of a job instruction card for a floor polishing machine is given overleaf.

Instructions for 40 cm (16 in) high-speed machine

1. Select the correct type of pad or brush for the machine.
2. Attach drive plate and pad or brush to the machine.
3. Secure handle in the right position depending on type of machine.
4. Plug in machine at the mains.
5. Keep the flex behind you.
6. Switch on machine — place both hands on machine.
7. Make sure machine is under control.
8. Slightly raise handle to move machine to the right.
9. Slightly lower handle to move machine to the left.
10. Walk with machine across floor area from left to right, allowing machine to do the work.
11. Then walk with machine from right to left across floor area — half covering first movement.
12. When work is completed, switch off machine; remove pad or brush; clean as required; wind up the flex and store machine away correctly.

SCARIFYING MACHINES

These are used to remove heavy grease, mud, wet sawdust, and other thick deposits from the floor surface. The conventional scrubbing polisher will only skim over the surface. For this purpose a much heavier machine is used and it is fitted with special wire brushes.

Care and Maintenance

- Clean all equipment each day after use.
- Empty the tanks, clean, rinse and store them.
- Remove the brushes, clean them appropriately and store them with the bristles uppermost.
- Remove the pads — wash, rinse and dry them.
- Remove the drive plates and store them correctly.
- Wind up the flex before storing the machine.
- Report any faults immediately, to the housekeeper.
- Make sure the machines are regularly serviced and maintained by a contractor or engineering staff.

AUTOMATIC FLOOR MACHINES

These are also known as 'auto-scrubbers'. There are a number of different types on the market. Each machine has a brush or brushes fitted at the front and a wet suction squeegee at the rear. It can be used for dry vacuuming, wet scrubbing and picking up excess water or slurry cleaning. Machines are available as single- , double- or multiple-brush machines, powered by electricity, petrol or battery, and can be used both indoors and outdoors. They are not suitable for heavily or moderately obstructed areas but need open spaces. Greater efficiency can be obtained if a second worker helps the operator (i.e. removes obstructions, prepares the solution, and does spot cleaning, etc.) so that the machine works uninterrupted. Machines must be cleaned and maintained regularly and stored correctly.

A detailed list of terms associated with mechanical equipment is given opposite.

Automatic floor machines

TYPE	ADVANTAGES	DISADVANTAGES
Belt drive	Quiet — belt centres automatically on crowned pulley wheels	Belt slips
Gear drive	Positive drive	Noisy, particularly with age. Wear on gears
Friction drive	Mainly for domestic use — cheaper to produce	Low-powered — time consuming. Wear on friction surfaces
Rotary drive	Cheaper to produce	Uneven wear on brushes or pads
Reversible drive (contra-rotating)	More even wear on brushes — provides longer life	More expensive to produce
One-brush head — (rotating, oscillating)	Cheap to produce. Can act as a vacuum	Tendency of pull on machine. More difficult to operate
Two-brush head	Easier for operator to handle	Amount of dead space — not as much contact with floor surface
Three-brush head	Easier for operator to handle	Amount of dead space — not as much contact with floor surface
Mains-operated	Can be used indoors or outdoors where there is a ready supply of electricity	Trailing flex. Cannot be used during power cuts if there is no private generator
Battery-operated	No need for electrical supply on site — no trailing flexes	Batteries may be heavy to carry, also need to be recharged frequently
Petrol-operated	No need for electrical supply on site — no trailing flexes	Can only be used for outside work
High-speed machine	Ideal for buffing or spray cleaning	Not suitable for scrubbing, tends to scatter water around
Low-speed machine	Ideal for scrubbing	Requires longer use for buffing or spray cleaning, to give good results
Combined scrubbing/ polishing/drying machine	Cost. Two or more jobs can be carried out by one operator	Size, may be heavy to use. Can only be used in one area at a time

SUCTION DRYERS

These are machines which remove dirty solutions or water from the floor surface. The water, etc., is scooped up by a squeegee through a nozzle into a tank. When using these machines they should be restricted to long wide aisles and open spaces. They are usually used in a forward-and-backward movement. Some machines can also be converted to a dry vacuum with the addition of extra tools.

Care and Maintenance

- Clean the dryer after use.
- Remove and empty the tank; clean, rinse and dry it out.
- Rinse the squeegee blade and clean.
- Wind up the flex and store carefully.
- Report any faults immediately, to the housekeeper.
- Periodically have the machine serviced and overhauled, approximately every 6 months depending on use.

CARPET AND UPHOLSTERY EQUIPMENT

There is a variety of machines on the market for cleaning carpets and upholstery:

Liquid foam machines. (a) Purpose-built machines use a rotating brush and tank. A shampoo is added to the tank and the machine is moved backwards and forwards over the surface. Only attempt to clean a small surface at a time; spot clean before using the machine and use a more concentrated solution to remove stubborn marks. (b) An alternative to a purpose-built machine is a normal-speed scrubbing polisher with a shampoo brush. A liquid solution is then added to the tank. The machine should be used to clean a small area at a time; spot clean as above.

With both types of machine the degree of carpet wetting is dependent on the following:
- Type and size of machine.
- Amount of solution applied to the surface.
- Amount of heating and ventilation in the room. Leave surface to dry for 2-4 hours and vacuum the surface using a conventional vacuum cleaner.

A special tool can be attached to a wet/dry pick-up machine to remove excess foam before allowing surface to dry. Vacuum when the surface is completely dry.

Dry foam machines   are special carpet cleaning machines which have a tank incorporated. A shampoo is added with a very small amount of water. The shampoo is worked into the surface by a revolving brush. When cleaning a very heavily soiled surface at least two runs may be necessary. Some machines on the market will lay a solution on to the carpet and pick up the foam and dirt immediately. After shampooing leave to dry for 2–4 hours and finish with a vacuum cleaner.

High-pressure spray and soil extraction.   Controlled jets of hot water and a cleaning chemical penetrate the pile or fabric and the pressure loosens dirt, oil, grease, etc. This is then extracted by suction into a sludge tank, leaving the surface clean and dry.

Care and Maintenance
- Empty the solution from the tank, rinse and dry.
- Clean the machine and brushes, etc., and leave them to dry.
- Wind up the flex and store away.
- Periodically have the machine serviced, approximately every 6 months, depending on use.

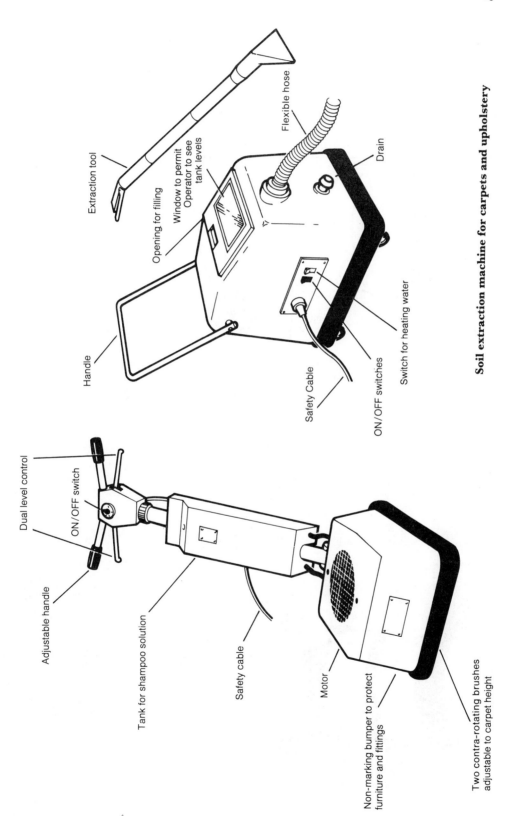

Extraction tool

Window to permit
Operator to see
tank levels

Opening for filling

Flexible hose

Handle

Drain

Safety Cable

ON/OFF switches

Switch for heating water

Soil extraction machine for carpets and upholstery

Dual level control

ON/OFF switch

Adjustable handle

Tank for shampoo solution

Safety cable

Motor

Non-marking bumper to protect
furniture and fittings

Two contra-rotating brushes
adjustable to carpet height

Carpet shampoo machine

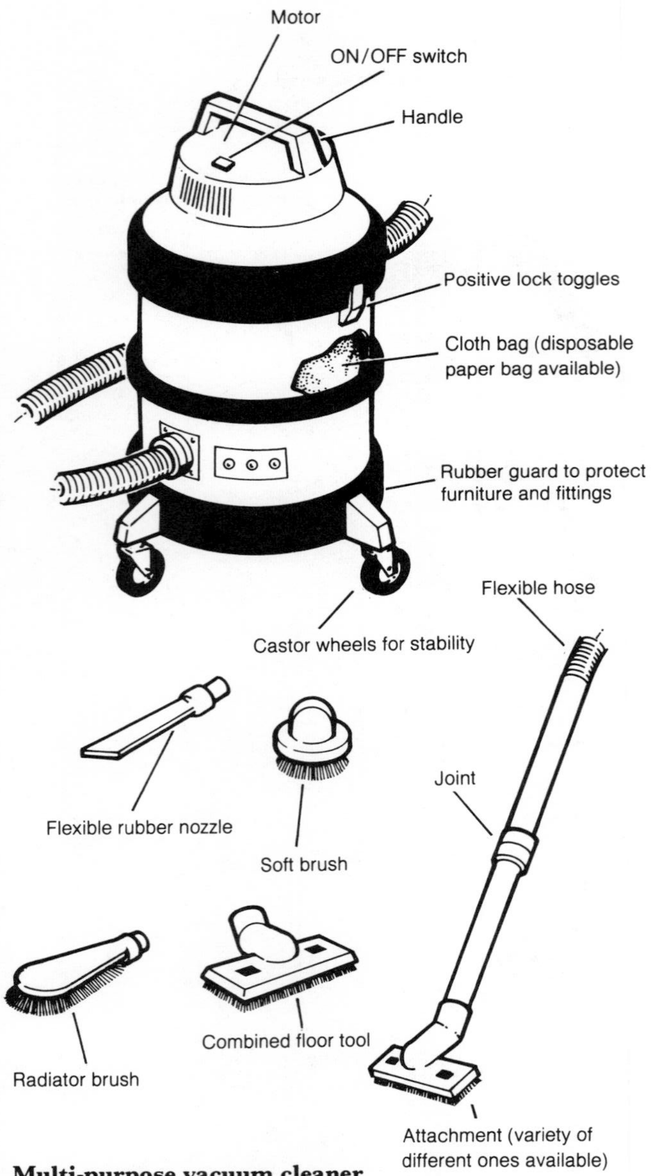

Motor

Tank

Flexible hose

Squeege blade
(Lower when in use
Raise during storage)

Flex

Clips to secure lid

Handles
(used to remove tank
for emptying)

Suction cleaner wet and dry pick up

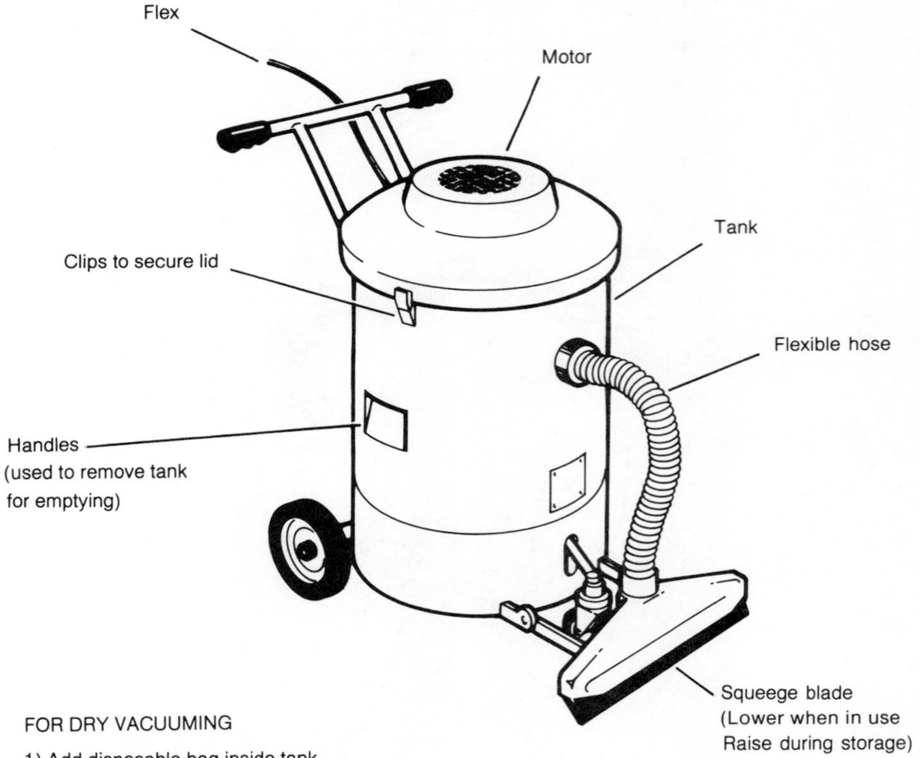

FOR DRY VACUUMING

1) Add disposable bag inside tank

2) Remove flexible hose and squeege blade —
add separate hose and attachments

Motor

ON/OFF switch

Handle

Positive lock toggles

Cloth bag (disposable
paper bag available)

Rubber guard to protect
furniture and fittings

Flexible hose

Castor wheels for stability

Joint

Attachment (variety of
different ones available)

Soft brush

Flexible rubber nozzle

Combined floor tool

Radiator brush

Multi-purpose vacuum cleaner

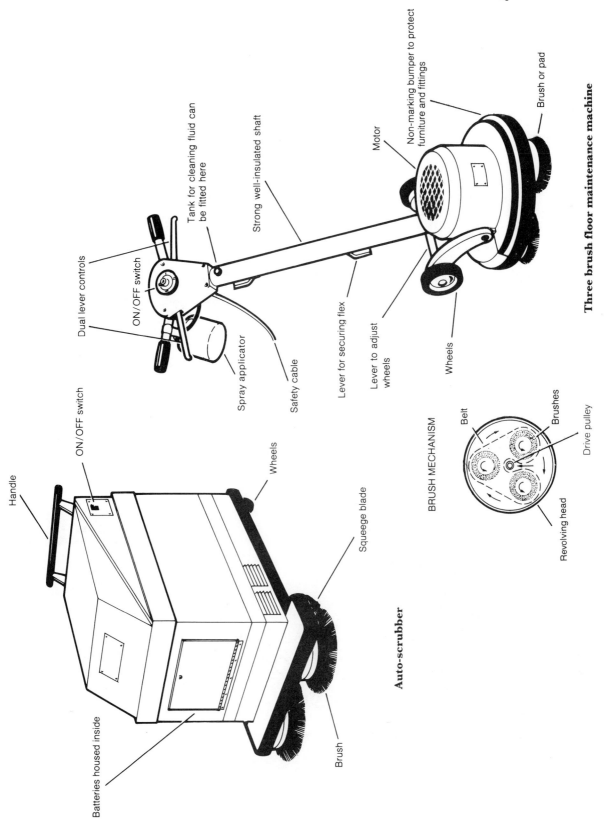

Handle

ON/OFF switch

Wheels

Squeege blade

Batteries housed inside

Brush

Auto-scrubber

Dual lever controls

ON/OFF switch

Tank for cleaning fluid can be fitted here

Strong well-insulated shaft

Spray applicator

Safety cable

Lever for securing flex

Lever to adjust wheels

Motor

Non-marking bumper to protect furniture and fittings

Brush or pad

Wheels

Three brush floor maintenance machine

BRUSH MECHANISM

Belt

Brushes

Drive pulley

Revolving head

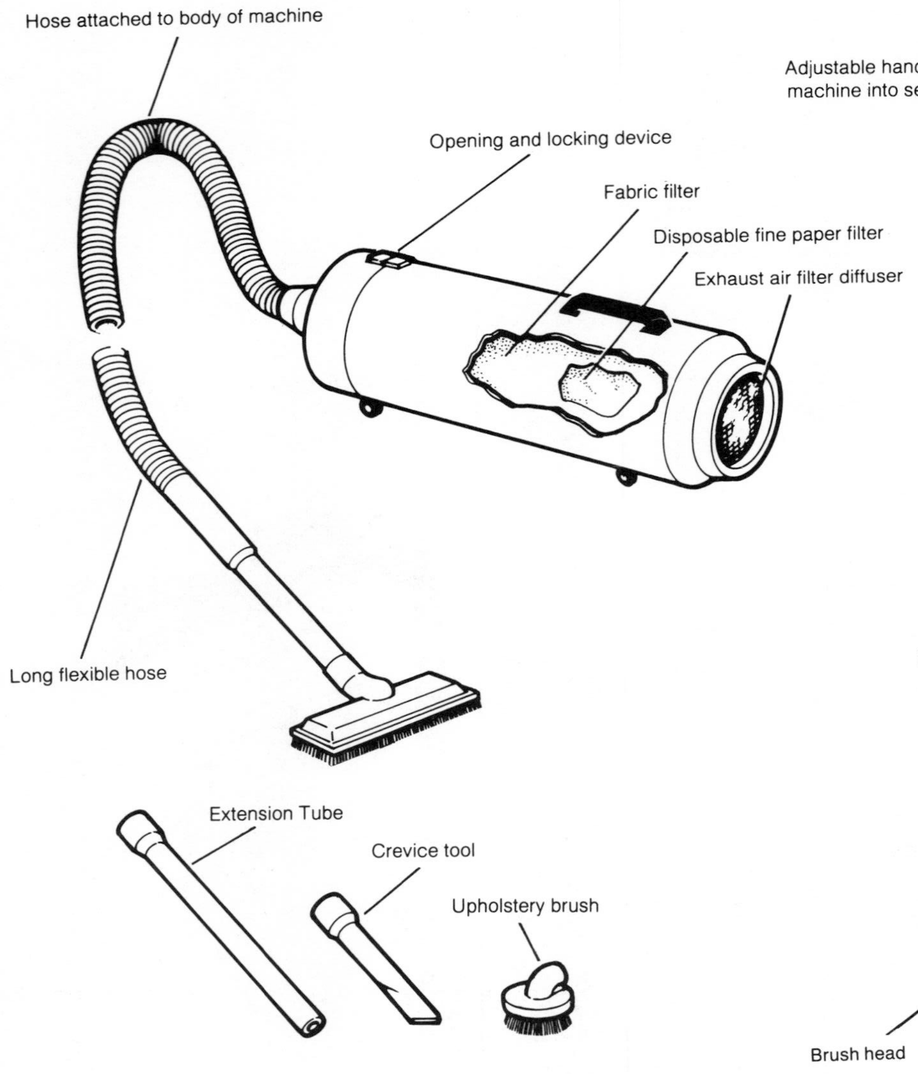

Safety device in handle prevents machine being started when handle is in upright position

Strong — well-insulated shaft

Safety cable

Tank for cleaning fluid or shampooing fluid

Non-marking bumper to protect furniture and fittings

Dual lever controls

Fluid feed to brush or pad

Adjustable handle automatically locks machine into selected height

Motor

Brush head

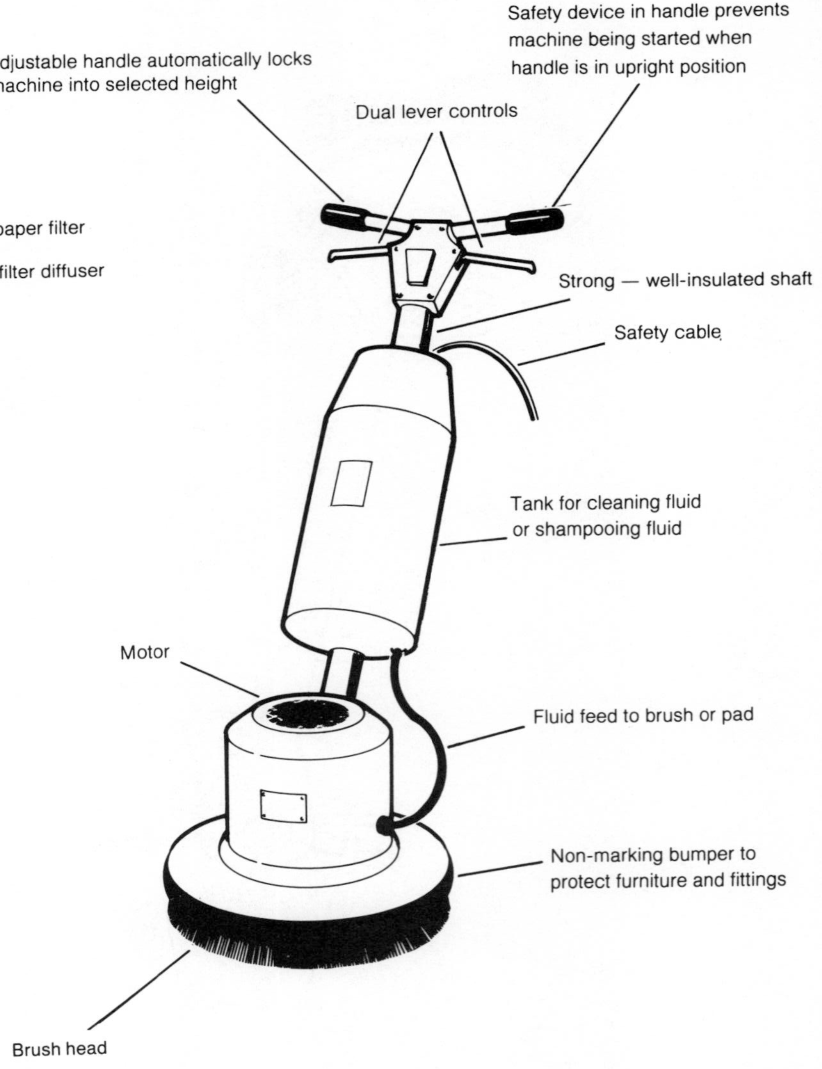

Floor maintenance machine (scrubbing, buffing, spray cleaning, carpet shampooing)

Disposable fine paper filter

Exhaust air filter diffuser

Fabric filter

Opening and locking device

Hose attached to body of machine

Upholstery brush

Crevice tool

Extension Tube

Long flexible hose

Cylindrical type vacuum cleaner

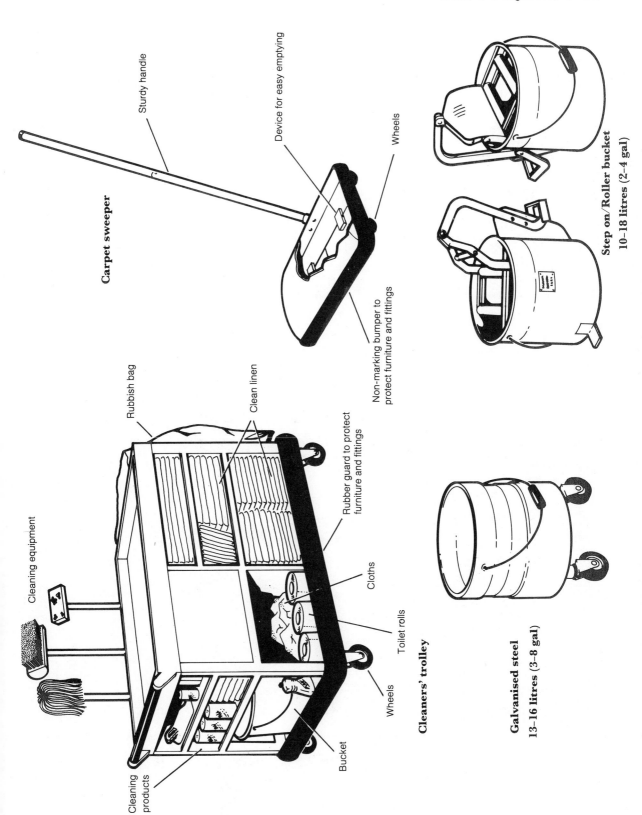

Carpet sweeper

Sturdy handle

Device for easy emptying

Wheels

Non-marking bumper to protect furniture and fittings

Step on/Roller bucket
10–18 litres (2–4 gal)

Cleaning equipment

Rubbish bag

Clean linen

Rubber guard to protect furniture and fittings

Cloths

Toilet rolls

Cleaners' trolley

Cleaning products

Bucket

Wheels

Galvanised steel
13–16 litres (3–8 gal)

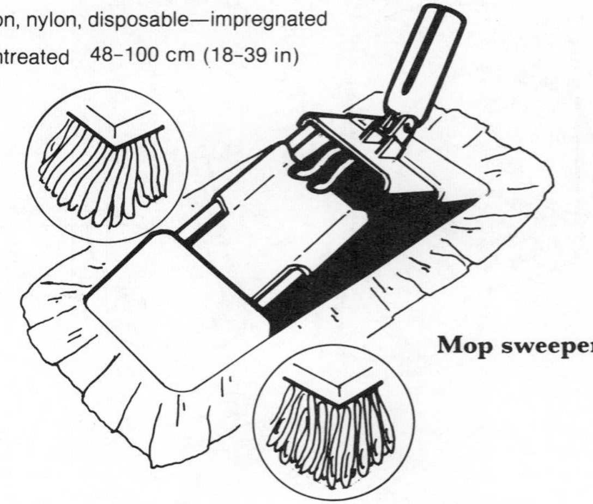

Mop sweeper

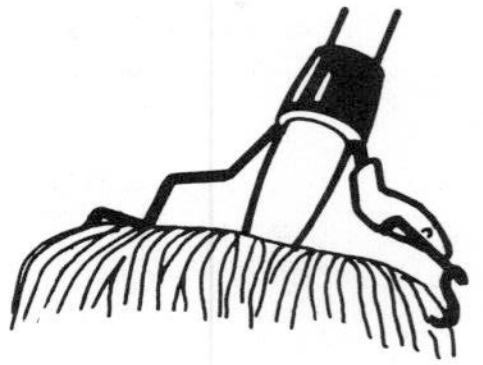

Cotton, nylon, disposable—impregnated or untreated 48–100 cm (18–39 in)

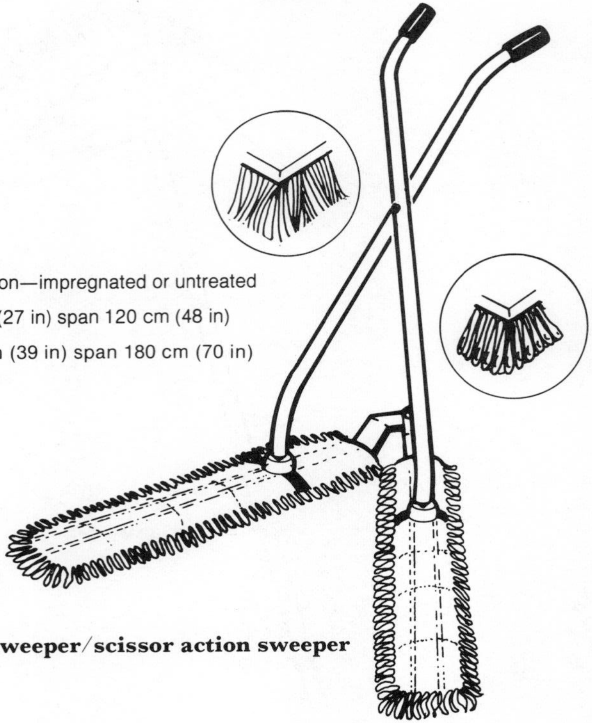

'V' sweeper/scissor action sweeper

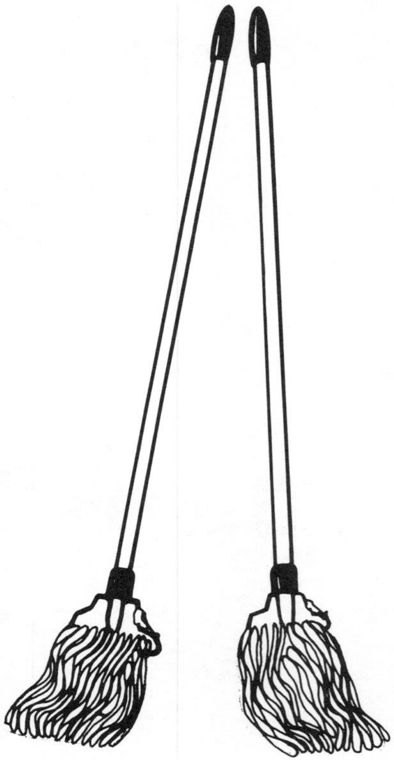

Cotton, nylon—impregnated or untreated
2 × 68 cm (27 in) span 120 cm (48 in)
2 × 100 cm (39 in) span 180 cm (70 in)

Kentucky mops

Cotton or cotton mixture
340–900 g (12–32 oz)

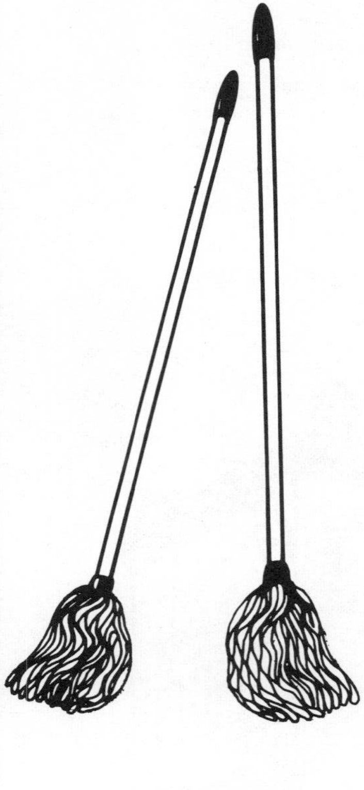

Treble life mops

Cotton or cotton mixture
340–900 g (12–32 oz)

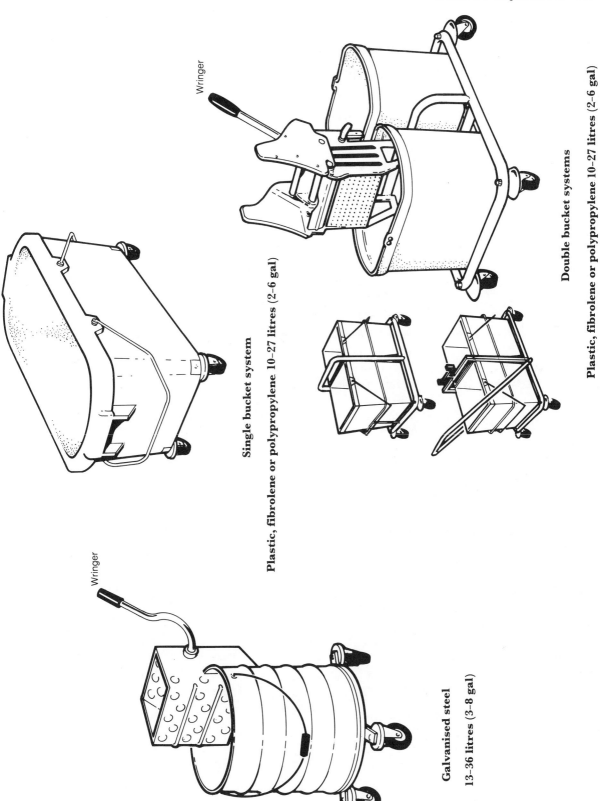

Wringer

Double bucket systems

Plastic, fibrolene or polypropylene 10–27 litres (2–6 gal)

Single bucket system

Plastic, fibrolene or polypropylene 10–27 litres (2–6 gal)

Wringer

Galvanised steel
13–36 litres (3–8 gal)

QUESTIONS

1. Discuss the main points to be considered when selecting cleaning equipment.

2. What is the purpose of a card index system?

3. Prepare a job instruction card for an upright vacuum cleaner.

4. Define the following:
   (a) dead man's handle,
   (b) concentrated weight,
   (c) divided weight,
   (d) contra-rotating brushes.

5. Indicate what colour pad should be used for:
   (a) scrubbing,
   (b) spray-cleaning,
   (c) buffing.
   Briefly explain how the life expectancy of pads can be prolonged.

6. Mechanical cleaning equipment is one of the modern aids to cleaning. As a domestic supervisor how would you ensure that the equipment is properly used and maintained to achieve total efficiency in operation.

7. You have been asked to examine different types of damp-mopping equipment available on the market today.
   (a) Outline the different types of equipment available.
   (b) Summarise their merits.
   (c) Write a report to be presented to your supervisor with your recommendations.
   (d) Select one system and prepare a job instruction card to be given to a new domestic assistant during a training session.

13 Floor Surfaces

INTRODUCTION

Floor surfaces cover a large area of a building and can be subjected to a great deal of wear and tear. In older buildings there may be as many as twelve to sixteen different surfaces, and they may all require different types of cleaning. In modern complexes, by contrast, the surfaces have often been standardised in order to be more cost effective. The standard of floor finish often reflects the standard of cleanliness and hygiene in the rest of the building. Approximately 50% of the cleaning and maintenance budget is spent on floors, so it is essential that care is taken over the choice and maintenance of floor surfaces. Initially it is often difficult to choose between floor coverings because of the different sizes, colours and finishes available.

Sub-floor. This is the part of the floor which is built into the construction of the building. In older buildings the sub-floor may be made of wood, whereas in modern buildings concrete is more likely to have been used. It is essential that a good level sub-floor is laid with a suitable damp-proof course; otherwise this will affect the life expectancy and maintenance of the floor finish.

POINTS TO BE CONSIDERED WHEN SELECTING FLOOR SURFACES

Cost. The cost of a floor surface varies from one type to another. Cheap floors are uneconomical. Consideration must be given to the initial purchase cost, cost of laying, maintenance costs and the life expectancy of the surface. Using the wrong treatments on the surface could increase the cost of maintenance and cause irreparable damage.

Type of sub-floor. Is it level, dry, porous or non-porous? Can the floor surface be laid directly on the sub-floor or does a sand and concrete screed need to be laid first?

Durability and quality. Consider the type and amount of 'traffic' especially where it is very heavy (e.g. in the reception foyer, corridors and other public areas). Floor surfaces can be damaged by grit and spillages of water, grease and food, so it is important to make the correct choice. Different types of floor surface are available for different circumstances. Consider the use of a drugget or matting in key areas, to prevent or minimise the entry of dirt or damage to the surface.

Appearance. This should be in keeping with the purpose of the area. Consider the colour, pattern and texture in relation to the decor, furniture, furnishings and fittings. Normally the floor surface is chosen first because of its size and cost and because it will not be changed as frequently as the decor and furniture. However, the policy in some establishments may be to select cheaper-grade surfaces and replace these more frequently to provide a fresh appearance and to be in keeping with the change in decor.

Safety.   Floor surfaces should have non-slip qualities when both wet and dry to help prevent accidents and falls. Correct cleaning and maintenance must also be done to improve safety.

Comfort.   The comfort of the floor surface is important for the staff and the 'customer'. If the floor surface is noisy, it could disturb people and if hard to walk on, it could be uncomfortable. Instead, it should be warm, soft and quiet and provide good heat and sound insulation.

As yet there is no ideal floor surface for all areas, so it is important to be careful and not buy on impulse.

CLASSIFICATION OF FLOOR SURFACES

Floor surfaces can be classified or grouped together in a number of different ways as follows:

By Degree of Porosity

GROUP 1	GROUP 2	GROUP 3
Porous	*Semi-porous*	*Non-porous*
Wood	Thermoplastic	Terrazzo
Cork	Vinyl	Quarry tiles
Concrete	Linoleum	Ceramic tiles
Chipboard	Rubber	Stone/slate
Asphalt		Marble
Pitchmastic		
Granolithic		
Magnesite		
Carpets		

By Origin of Materials Used

GROUP 1	GROUP 2	GROUP 3
Vegetable	*Plastic*	*Stone*
Wood	Thermoplastic	Terrazzo
Cork	Vinyl	Marble
Cork carpet	Pitchmastic	Concrete
Magnesite	Rubber	Granolithic
Chipboard		Quarry tiles
Linoleum		Stone/slate

The table on pp. 121–7 looks at these surfaces and their uses in more detail.
The table on pp. 128-32 looks at details of maintenance.

FLOOR SURFACES

TYPE	COMPOSITION	SIZE	COLOUR	USES	SPECIAL POINTS
(1) *Wood*					
(a) Board floor	Usually softwood, e.g. pine, spruce or deal. Occasionally hardwood is used, e.g. oak, beech, elm, birch	Width over 100 mm (4 in) in various lengths	Depends on type of wood used, grain, amount of wear and treatment given	Recreation rooms, gymnasium, library, ballroom, etc.	Often covered by linoleum, PVC sheet or carpets, etc. Usually treated and left uncovered as a decorative flooring
(b) Strip wood	Hard- or softwood used (as above)	Width up to 100 mm (4 in) in various lengths	As above	As above	Surface may be covered by linoleum, PVC sheet, carpets, etc., or treated and left uncovered, depending on use
(c) Wood block	Hard- or softwood used and laid in herring bone, basket pattern, etc. — tongue and grooved	Width up to 89 mm (3½ in); length from 150 mm (6 in), 300 mm (12 in); thickness from 25 mm (1 in), 38 mm (1½ in)	As above	Boardrooms, libraries, offices, etc.	Usually treated and left uncovered as a decorative flooring
(d) Parquet	Decorative hardwoods, e.g. oak, teak, mahogany — laid individually or in panels in herring-bone or basket pattern	Width: 50 mm (2 in), 75 mm (3 in); Thickness: 6 mm (¼ in), 10 mm (³⁄₈ in)	As above	Boardrooms, prestige areas, etc.	As above
(e) Mosaic	Very similar to parquet. Decorative hardwoods used and laid in panels or blocks — smaller blocks than parquet	Width: 113 × 25 mm (4½ × 1 in); Thickness: 10 mm (³⁄₈ in)	As above	Boardrooms and prestige areas	As above

TYPE	COMPOSITION	SIZE	COLOUR	USES	SPECIAL POINTS
(1) *Cont.*					
(f) End-grain block paving	Softwood blocks — end grain is vertical — impregnated with creosote. Hardwood blocks (decorative)	Width: 75 × 225 mm (3 × 9 in); Thickness: 63 mm (2½ in), 113 mm (4½ in)	As above	Heavy traffic areas, e.g. workshops, factories. Prestige areas, public buildings	Usually treated and left uncovered
(g) Wood composition or chipboard	Wood chips, resins, colourings and linseed oil — subjected to heat and pressure. Available as boards or panels	As wood block	Light brown	Factory floors, bedrooms, corridors, etc.	Can be covered with PVC, lino, carpets, etc., or treated and left uncovered as a decorative flooring
(h) Granwood/ wood cement	Portland cement, aggregate limestone or silica sand and sawdust (wood flour) laid either herring-bone or basket pattern	As wood block	Light brown, dark brown and green	Heavy traffic areas, workshops, factories, corridors, etc.	Usually treated and left uncovered
(2) *Cork*					
(a) Cork tiles	Cork granules, natural and synthetic resins and gum — compressed and baked	Tiles — 100 mm (4 in) squares up to 900 mm (3 ft) × 300 mm (1 ft); Thickness: 3 × 14 mm (⅛ × 9/16 in)	Light and dark brown or pigments may be added, e.g. green	Libraries, offices, art galleries, light traffic areas	Usually treated and left uncovered — or used instead of carpet squares, mats, etc.
(b) Cork carpet	Coarsely granulated cork mixed with pigments, gum and hot linseed oil applied to jute backing	Sheet form up to 1800 mm (6 ft) wide; Thickness: 3 mm (⅛ in), 10 mm (⅜ in)	As cork, depending on pigments used	Libraries, halls, offices, hospitals, etc. Light traffic areas	As above

TYPE	COMPOSITION	SIZE	COLOUR	USES	SPECIAL POINTS
(3) *Linoleum*	Ground cork or cork granules, resins, linseed oil, gum, wood flour and pigments — compressed onto a woven jute backing — available in sheet or tile form in different grades	Sheet form up to 1800 mm (6 ft) wide; Thickness: 6.70 mm (¼ in). Tiles — width: 225 mm (9 in), 300 mm (12 in); Thickness: up to 6.70 mm (¼ in)	A wide range of colours available in different patterns, e.g. marble, plain, jasper, etc.	Offices, domestic use, corridors, bedroom, ward areas, reception, etc.	Can be either treated and left uncovered or covered with carpets, carpet squares or mats
(4) *Magnesite*	Magnesium oxychloride, fine sawdust and silica dust. Similar to cork in appearance, laid *in situ* — not used a great deal in new buildings	One coat: 13 mm (½ in), up to 25 mm or 38 mm for 2–3 coats	Red or brown	Linen rooms, industrial, commercial purposes	Usually treated and left uncovered
(5) *Asphalt and Pitchmastic*	Asphalt, bitumen/coal tar and powdered limestone grit or powdered granite laid *in situ* in a hot state — coved skirting to facilitate cleaning	16 mm (⅝ in)	Black, red, brown, green or grey	Often used as a waterproof sub-floor. Industrial and commercial uses (offices and factories)	Can be treated and left uncovered
(6) *Thermoplastic*	Two types: (a) Asphalt, asbestos fibres, pigments and mineral fillers. (b) Synthetic resins, pigments, asbestos fibres and mineral fillers	Tiles: 225 × 225 mm (9 × 9 in); Thickness: 3 mm (⅛ in), 5 mm (³⁄₁₆ in)	Various colours and patterns depending on pigments added	Hospitals, schools, canteens, shops, offices, corridors, etc.	Hard and noisy but often PVC is added to give flexibility. Can be treated and left uncovered or treated and covered with carpets, mats, etc.

TYPE	COMPOSITION	SIZE	COLOUR	USES	SPECIAL POINTS
(7) *PVC — polyvinyl chloride*	(a) Vinyl asbestos — PVC fibres, fillers, pigments and plasticisers. (b) Flexible PVC similar to above but no asbestos fibres and more plasticisers. May have felt or sponge rubber backing to give more resilience	Sheet: 900 mm (3 ft), 1800 mm (6 ft); Tiles: 225 mm (9 in), 300 mm (12 in); Thickness: 5 mm (1/16 in), 3 mm (1/8 in);	Various colours and patterns — usually lighter and brighter colours than thermoplastic floorings	(a) As above (b) As above — also libraries where extra quietness is required	Usually treated and left uncovered
(8) *Rubber*	Natural or synthetic rubber, fillers, e.g. china clay and pigments — very resilient and quiet underfoot. May have a sponge backing incorporated for extra resilience	Sheet: 900 mm (3 ft), 1800 mm (6 ft); Tiles: 225 mm (9 in), 450 mm (18 in); Thickness: 3 mm (1/8 in), 13 mm (1/2 in);	Various, depending on pigments added	Hotels, hospitals, libraries, etc. May have a ribbed effect to provide extra non-slip properties — also made into link mats	Usually treated and left uncovered
(9) *Marble*	Naturally occurring stone. Natural limestone in calcium carbonate crystallised form. Very expensive but very good life expectancy	Slabs or tiles: 305 × 102 mm (12 × 4 in), 305 × 305 mm (12 × 12 in); Thickness: 19 mm (3/4 in), 25 mm (1 in)	Various, depending on type of marble used, e.g. white, blue, green, black, etc.	Entrance halls and corridors of public buildings	Very hard and noisy and cold — very durable and easy to maintain
(10) *Terrazzo*	Marble chippings set in fine cement — coved skirting incorporated to facilitate cleaning	Laid *in situ:* Panels of 1.2 m² (12 ft²). Tiles: 305 mm² (12 in²);	Various, depending on type of marble used (as above)	Entrance halls, corridors, hospital operating theatres, toilet areas, main traffic areas in department stores	Hard, noisy, cold, very durable. Easy to maintain and can be treated or left untreated

TYPE	COMPOSITION	SIZE	COLOUR	USES	SPECIAL POINTS
(10) *Cont.*		Thickness *in situ*: 9 mm (³/₈ in), 15 mm (⁵/₈ in); Tiles: 19 mm (³/₄ in), 38 mm (1¹/₂ in)			As above
(11) *Stone*	Natural stone, e.g. granite, sandstone, slate, quartzite and limestone	Slabs: 600 mm² (2 ft²), 900 × 600 mm (3 × 2 ft), 900 mm² (3 ft²)	Various, depending on type of stone used	Public buildings, churches, dairies, farmhouses, markets, etc.	Noisy, hard, cold surface, very durable. Easy to maintain
(12) *Quarry tiles*	Baked clay, coved skirting incorporated to facilitate cleaning. Precast slabs fitted above service pipes, gullies, etc.	Tiles: 100 mm² (4 in²), 150 mm² (6 in²), 225 mm² (9 in²) precast slabs	Usually red, buff, or blue	Kitchens, corridors, toilet areas, food factories, breweries, dairies, etc.	As above
(13) *Ceramic tiles*	Made from fine quality baked clay — usually have a glazed appearance	As above	Various colours and patterns available	Canteens, kitchens and cloakrooms	As above
(14) *Concrete*	Sand, cement and aggregates of chippings	Laid *in situ* — one or two courses up to 200 mm (8 in) or slab form	Natural but pigments can be added to give variety	Factories, stores, corridors, sub-floors, laundries, stairs, cloakrooms	Very porous, hard, noisy and tends to 'dust' — usually treated with a seal (often pigmented)
(15) *Granolithic*	Graded granite chippings set in fine cement. Coved skirting to facilitate cleaning	Laid *in situ* or precast slabs (as above)	Natural or pigments added to give a range of colours	Factories, stores, cloakrooms, corridors, laundries, stairs — very heavy duty surfaces	As above
(16) *Iron and steel*	Mild steel, stainless steel or iron	Tiles: 300 mm² (12 in²). Sheet form: thickness depends on requirements	Natural	Heavy engineering, shops, raised platform fire escapes	Very hard, noisy and cold — easy to maintain

TYPE	COMPOSITION	SIZE	COLOUR	USES	SPECIAL POINTS
(17) *Plastic — seamless* (paved floors, floors for cars, floor toppings, etc.)	Synthetic resins, e.g. polyester, polyurethane and epoxy	3 mm ($1/8$ in), 50 mm (2 in)	Various, depending on pigments used	Industrial wear or decorative wear in corridors, etc.	Easy to maintain in use — use treated or leave untreated
(18) *Antistatic (Conductive)*	Manufactured to eliminate the hazards of fire or explosions. Terrazzo, magnesite (laid *in situ*). Linoleum, rubber and PVC (laid in sheet form), PVC (tile form). Copper salts, carbon black or wire mesh added to give antistatic properties (skill required in laying)	Various, depending on type	Various, depending on type used	Operating theatres, factories, X-ray rooms, delivery rooms in hospitals, anaesthetic rooms, computer rooms, flour mills and some light engineering factories	Correct maintenance is essential so as not to destroy antistatic properties. Frequent cleaning with minimum water and neutral detergents. Care should also be taken of adjacent floorings to make sure treatments are not transferred to antistatic floorings — surface must be tested regularly to check properties
(19) *Carpets* (a) Pile carpets, e.g. Wilton, Brussels and Tapestry	Natural fibres, e.g. wool, hair, cotton or linen — wool most widely used. Synthetic fibres e.g. nylon, acrylic, rayon, Terylene, polypropylene, etc., or a combination of natural and man-made fibres	Light domestic use. *Body or strip carpet* 68 cm (27 in), 90 cm (36 in)	Various, depending on type and method of manufacture	Reception areas, lounges, day rooms, corridors, bedrooms, restaurants, offices, schools, etc.	Do not vacuum a new carpet for a few weeks — leave it to bed down. Spot clean. Shampoo when required using one of the recognised methods. Carpets should be laid by experts who will use one of the following: (a) Tackless grippers. (b) Turn and tack. (c) Suckers. (d) Press studs, ring and peg, etc. (for ease of lifting)
(b) Tufted carpets, e.g. Axminster, Persian, Indian and Turkish		Light medium domestic use. *Stair carpet* 45 cm (18 in), 68 cm (27 in), 90 cm (36 in)			

TYPE	COMPOSITION	SIZE	COLOUR	USES	SPECIAL POINTS
(19) *Cont.*					
(c) Ingrained carpets woven but no pile, e.g. cord		Medium domestic (light contact) *Broadloom* 180 cm (6 ft), 540 cm (18 ft)			*Underlays* Used to extend life expectancy and help provide more insulation. Types: felt, sponge rubber, etc.
(d) Adhesively bonded carpets		Heavy domestic (medium contact). *Thickness* Depends on type and quality			Static electricity is more prone to build-up in a synthetic carpet than a natural one
(e) Heuga tiles (pig hair)	*Backings used:* Hessian or jute, PVC, foam, etc.	Luxury domestic (heavy contact) *Carpet tiles* 305 mm^2 (12 in^2)			*Cost of maintenance* The cost of maintaining carpets is approximately 50% of hard floors

FLOOR MAINTENANCE

Wood and wood composition (e.g. granwood or chipboard)

If the floor has been treated with a permanent seal, treat as for cork and vinyl.

FREQUENCY	PROCESS	CLEANING AGENTS	EQUIPMENT	REMARKS
Daily	As vinyl (1)			
Weekly (or 2–3 times per week)	Buff	Desirable	Floor machine/pad. Polishing brush — beige or red	To improve appearance
Monthly (or 1–4 times per month)	Apply polish	Essential for appearance and condition of wood	Solvent-based wax, emulsion or paste	Floor machine. Polishing brush	
Periodic (very variable, according to site, etc.)	Remove dirty wax	(a) Essential to prevent darkening of the wood and obscuring of the grain	Solvent-based wax	Floor machine. Green pads. Buff pads or polishing brush	Paste is applied generously to a small area of floor. Then the floor is 'scrubbed' with a green pad. Pads need to be changed frequently as they rapidly become filled with the dirty wax. When whole area is completed, buff as normal.
		(b) In extreme cases or on badly neglected floors	Solvent stripper. Solvent-based detergent wax remover	Floor machine. Scrubbing brush/pad	Follow instructions supplied with solvent stripper. Follow with fresh applications of solvent-based wax.

Vinyl floors (including all types of 'plastic' floors, e.g. PVC, thermoplastic)

FREQUENCY	PROCESS	CLEANING AGENTS	EQUIPMENT	REMARKS
Daily	(1) Mop or sweep	Essential		Mop sweeper or 'V' sweeper, preferably impregnated	To remove dust, litter, etc.
	(2) Spot mop and/or damp mop	Desirable	Neutral detergent and warm water	Sponge mop and plastic pail, or string mop and wringer bucket	To remove spillages and foot marks

FREQUENCY		PROCESS	CLEANING AGENTS	EQUIPMENT	REMARKS
Daily (Cont.)	(3)	Remove stains, e.g. carbon black	As necessary	Neutral detergent	Green scouring pad	Use gentle friction only in order to retain polished surface
	(4)	Wet mop (surface maintenance)	Essential in areas with heavy traffic	Wash-and-wax product	As (2)	To remove soilage and protect surface finish
Weekly (or 2–3 times per week)	(5)	As (4)	Frequency depends on amount and type of soilage	As (4)	As (2)	As (4)
	(6)	Spray clean	Alternative process to (5), used only in restricted areas	Water and emulsion, floor wax solution	Hand spray or aerosol can, floor machine with blue or green pads	Specialised treatment — expensive. Always use clean pads; wash pads after use
	(7)	Light scrub	Desirable in dirty areas	Neutral detergent	Floor machine, green pad/ scrubbing brush, string mop and wringer bucket	Can be followed by a dilute coat of top dressing. *NB* Care must be taken to avoid a 'build-up'
	(8)	Buff	Optional, frequency depends on amount of traffic		Floor machine. Buffing brush or beige or red coloured pad	To improve appearance and increase durability of wash-and-wax treatment
Periodic (1–4 times per year)	(9)	Resurfacing or preparation of a new floor	Essential. *NB* Procedure (a) must be followed by (c); (b) is optional			
	(a)	Stripping (of floor dressing)	Essential — frequency depends on the amount of traffic	(1) To strip non-metallised top dressing: alkaline detergent (2) To strip metallised top dressing: use alkaline or fortified alkaline detergent. Rinse, then neutralise using a small amount of vinegar in water	Floor machine (preferably fitted with a water tank). Black stripping pad, edging tool, rubber gloves, hand pads (e.g. green scouring pads, or pieces of discarded black pads). Two string mops Two wringer buckets	After scrubbing, floor should be well rinsed with plenty of *clean* cold water, then neutralised with a solution of vinegar and water. Rinse again with clean cold water, then test with indicator paper to ensure neutrality of floor surface before base coat is applied

FREQUENCY		PROCESS	CLEANING AGENTS	EQUIPMENT	REMARKS
Periodic (Cont.)	(b)	Applying water-based seal if required	Desirable — especially on old or porous floors. Prevents floors from soaking up top dressing	Water-based seal	Clean string mop and wringer (kept especially for the purpose)	1–2 coats, depending on type and porosity of floor
	(c)	Applying top dressing	Essential	Water-based wax	As above or polish applicator and trough	1–3 coats, depending on type of floor and area (preferable to buff between coats to 'harden' polish)

Rubber (sheet and tile) Follow the same procedures as for vinyl, except: when using alkaline detergents for stripping (as in 9a):

(a) Remove the solution as quickly as possible, then immediately neutralise, using vinegar and water. Rubber deteriorates rapidly in contact with an alkali.

(b) When cleaning a *red* floor, rinse until the water is clear. This is to avoid a cloudy effect on the top dressing as the red dye 'bleeds' very freely in the presence of alkali.

Linoleum (sheet and tile) Follow the same procedures as for vinyl, but: *avoid* excess water which will damage the linoleum if it seeps below the surface.

Cork should be treated with a permanent seal applied by the firm laying the floor to render the floor non-porous, then the same procedures as for vinyl should be followed. But, if the seal becomes damaged (e.g. in traffic lanes) 'repair' must be done promptly by:

(a) painting the worn area with permanent seal — a temporary measure, or

(b) complete the resurfacing procedure, using sanding machine (not stripping agent) to remove permanent seal, etc. — a costly operation by a professional firm only.

Quarry tiles

FREQUENCY	PROCESS	CLEANING AGENTS	EQUIPMENT	REMARKS
Daily	Sweep or mop sweep	Essential		Mop sweeper or brush	
	Wet mopping	Frequency depends on situation	Neutral detergent and hot water	String mop and wringer bucket, or squeegee or wet pick-up	Only in kitchens with floor drainage
Weekly (or daily)	Scrubbing followed by rinsing	As above	As above	Floor machine. Scrubbing brush/green pad. String mop and wringer bucket, or squeegee or wet pick-up	Remove stubborn marks using fine steel wool and fine scouring powder

Terrazzo (tiles and laid *in situ*)

FREQUENCY	PROCESS	CLEANING AGENTS	EQUIPMENT	REMARKS
	As quarry tiles			Avoid use of acids and strong alkali as these can cause yellowing

Concrete

FREQUENCY	PROCESS	CLEANING AGENTS	EQUIPMENT	REMARKS
	As quarry tiles			Should be sealed with either: (a) rubberised sealing paint (semi-permanent) or (b) colourless concrete sealer (permanent)

Natural stone (e.g. slate, granite)

FREQUENCY	PROCESS	CLEANING AGENTS	EQUIPMENT	REMARKS
	As quarry tiles			

Antistatic floor (e.g. terrazzo, magnesite, linoleum, rubber, flexible PVC)

FREQUENCY	PROCESS	CLEANING AGENTS	EQUIPMENT	REMARKS
Daily	Mop sweep or vacuum	Essential		Mop sweeper or vacuum cleaner	(1) Only use floor dressings recommended for antistatic floors
	Damp mop	Essential	Neutral detergent	String mop and wringer bucket	(2) Only synthetic detergents must be used — *not* soap, as this can leave a thin film on the floor

FREQUENCY		PROCESS	CLEANING AGENTS	EQUIPMENT	REMARKS
Daily (Cont.)	Light scrub	Especially in hospital operating theatres	Neutral detergent or disinfectant solution as directed by hospital authorities	Floor machine. Scrubbing brush/pad. String mop and wringer bucket, or squeegee or wet pick-up	(3) Avoid the possibility of floor dressings (especially solvent waxes) being carried on the soles of shoes from adjacent areas on to the antistatic floor. *NB* Points (1), (2) and (3) are *very* important. If disregarded, the antistatic property of the floor will be destroyed and the whole surface will have to be relaid with new flooring

QUESTIONS

1. Discuss the main points to be considered when selecting a floor surface.

2. What is the composition of the following:
   (a) magnesite,
   (b) terrazzo,
   (c) granolithic,
   (d) cork?

3. Suggest the most suitable types of floor surface for the following areas and give reasons for your choice in each case:
   (a) Hospital ward area.
   (b) Public library.
   (c) Sports hall suitable for a variety of sporting activities.
   (d) Reception areas in a large central hotel.
   (e) A works canteen.
   (f) College refectory.

4. Prepare a daily and periodic maintenance programme for the following floor surfaces:
   (a) Cork tiles in college library.
   (b) Flexible PVC in hospital corridors.
   (c) Quarry tiles in central kitchen.
   (d) Terrazzo in public toilets.
   (e) Heuga tiles in restaurant.
   (f) Wood block in lecture room.

5. (a) Explain the terms 'antistatic' and 'conductive' floorings.
   (b) Indicate six different types of antistatic floor coverings.
   (c) What materials are added to provide these properties?
   (d) Explain why the care and maintenance of antistatic floorings is critical.

6. (a) Describe the main types of carpet available on the market today.
   (b) Indicate the different methods of securing carpets.
   (c) Prepare a cleaning schedule for the maintenance of carpets.

14 Fibres, Fabrics and Soft Furnishings

INTRODUCTION

Fabrics are manufactured from fibres, which may be woven, knitted or bonded together. Fibres may be natural, synthetic or a mixture of both. It is often difficult to identify a particular fabric just by looking at it, because some synthetic fibres look very much like natural fibres. Not only may they be a mixture (e.g. Terylene and cotton, Acrilan and wool, nylon and wool, etc.) but special treatments are sometimes given during manufacture, e.g. the fabric may be teased, crimped, kinked, bulked or brushed.

To ascertain the particular type of fibre(s) used (where no label is available), take a sample of the fabric and examine:
- the effect of heat and flame,
- the effect of certain chemicals, e.g. acids, alkalis and solvents,
- the appearance, feel, weight, weave and finish,
- the appearance under a miscroscope,
- the effect of laundering, dry-cleaning, colourfastness, shrinkage rate, etc.

TYPES AND CLASSIFICATION OF FIBRES

Each fibre, whether it is natural or synthetic, has its own characteristics (e.g. strength, lustre, elasticity, softness, resistance to wear). Sometimes confusion arises as to whether the name is associated with the fibre, fabric or trade name of the manufacturer.

The chart below shows a classification of fibres:

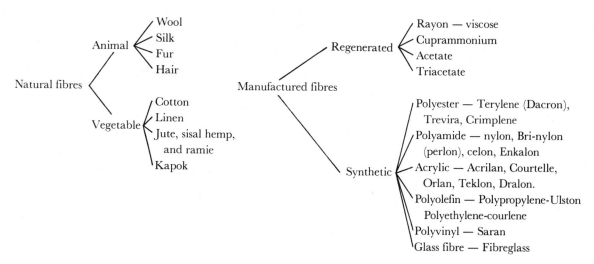

The following table outlines the qualities and uses of the fibres in more detail.

TYPE OF FIBRE	COMPOSITION	QUALITIES	USES
(1) *Natural — Animal*			
(a) Wool	Fibres from the fleece of live or dead sheep (also fibres from goats, llamas, camels, and horses)	Fibres are not smooth but have overlapping scales. Scales can interlock with careless laundering, etc., and cause felting and shrinking. Length of fibres 5–40 cm (2–10 in). Can be attacked by moths — but fabric can be moth-proofed. Harmed by alkalis and bleaches but fairly resistant to acids	Carpets, blankets, baize to cover boardroom tables, store silver, etc. Tailored uniforms, upholstery, curtains, etc.
(b) Silk	Manufactured from filaments spun by the cultivated silkworm	Fibres are smooth and tube-like with a lustre. Silk is elastic and resilient and does not crush easily — disintegrates in sunlight and is weaker when wet than dry. Length of filament — 274–456 m (300–500 yds). Harmed by alkalis and bleaches but fairly resistant to bleaches	Curtains, wall coverings, bed linen, etc., in luxury establishments
(2) *Natural — Vegetable*			
(a) Cotton	Manufactured from the seed of the cotton plant	Fibres are flat and ribbon-like and have a natural twist. Good conductors of heat and have a slight airiness. Not harmed by alkalis but affected by acids; easily creased. Length of fibre 1.25–5 cm ($\frac{1}{2}$–2 in)	Bed linen, soft furnishings, uniforms and carpets
(b) Linen	Manufactured from the stem of the flax plant	Fibres are straight, smooth and almost solid. Very good dirt- and abrasion-resistant qualities. has little resilience and creases badly. Not harmed by alkalis but affected by acids. Length of fibre, 0.5 m–1 m (20–40 in)	Bed linen, soft furnishings, glass cloths, upholstery and table linen
(c) Jute	Manufactured from stem of the jute plant	Very strong and durable	Manufacture of carpets, backings for linoleum, etc., and for upholstery
(d) Ramie	Manufactured from stems of the ramie plant	As jute	As jute
(e) Hemp	Manufactured from stems of the hemp plant	As jute	As jute
(f) Sisal	Manufactured from leaves of the sisal plant	As jute	As jute
(g) Kapok	Manufactured from the seed of the kapok tree	Fibres are very light, smooth and soft	As a filling for pillows and cushions in upholstery, but largely superseded by foam or Terylene

TYPE OF FIBRE	COMPOSITION	QUALITIES	USES
(3) *Manufactured — Regenerated*			
(a) Rayon (i) Viscose	Manufactured from pure regenerated cellulose — wood pulp or cotton linters — can be modified to improve its quality, e.g. Evlan, Vincel, Durafil, Sarille	Has smooth filaments with a lustre. Has little resilience, flattens easily and creases badly. Harmed by bleaches and other chemicals. Decomposes without melting at 185–222 °C	Furnishing fabrics, blankets, soft furnishings, etc., (often blended with other stronger fibres)
(ii) Cuprammonium	Manufactured from regenerated cellulose dissolved in a solution called cuprammonia	Fibre is soft, silk-like, lustrous and it drapes well. Harmed by bleaches and other chemicals	As above
(iii) Acetate	Manufactured from pure cellulose but final filament is a chemical derivative of cellulose known as an ester	Not as absorbent as viscose rayon. Softens at 180 °C and melts at 230 °C. Harmed by acids and alkalis and soluble in some solvents	Curtains, furnishings, linings (often blended with other stronger fibres). Blended with wool for uniforms
(iv) Triacetate	Very similar to acetate	Low moisture absorbency, melting point 260 °C — not easily harmed by alkalis	In the manufacture of candlewick fabrics or bulked and used as fillings
(4) *Manufactured — Synthetic*			
(a) Polyester — Terylene	Manufactured from petroleum products	Polyester has a low moisture absorption and very good resistance to abrasion and sunlight. Melts at 243 °C	As fillings for duvets, sleeping bags, pillows, etc. Bed linen, furnishing fabrics, uniforms, etc., where it is often blended with cotton
(b) Polymide — nylon	Originally manufactured from coal-tar products — nowadays petroleum chemicals are used	Attracts dirt easily but very easy to launder and dry because of its low moisture absorption. It is very durable, elastic and abrasion-resistant. Produced in various forms, can be brushed or bulked and melts between 185 °C and 250 °C	Bed linen, funishing fabrics, uniforms, etc., carpets
(c) Acrylic (i) Acrilan	Manufactured from petroleum chemicals or natural gas	Has a fluffy, warm and soft feel and closely resembles wool. Very low moisture absorbency and good resistant to sunlight and chemicals. Melts at 246 °C	Furnishing and upholstery fabrics, blankets, carpets
(ii) Courtelle	As above	Very similar in appearance to Acrilan but does not melt	Furnishing and upholstery fabrics
(iii) Orlon	As above	Very similar in appearance to Acrilan but has very good resistance to sunlight	As above
(iv) Dralon	As above	As above	As above
(d) Teklon	Modified acrylic fibre	Very similar properties to Acrilan but is also flameproof	Furnishing fabrics, industrial overalls, rugs
(e) Polyolefin (i) Polypropylene	Manufactured from petroleum chemicals	Very good abrasion resistance and very light in weight. Moisture absorption nil	Twine, carpets

TYPE OF FIBRE	COMPOSITION	QUALITIES	USES
(4) *Cont.* (ii) Polyethylene	As (i)	Highly resistant to acids and alkalis, non-absorbent and a very low melting point —softens at 95 °C and melts at 120 °C	Upholstery fabrics, deckchairs and plastic floor mats
(f) Polyvinyl	Derived from coke and lime	Softens and shrinks at low temperatures — is non-flammable and non-absorbent	Upholstery fabrics, deckchairs
(g) Glass fibre	Manufactured from molten glass	Highly resistant to chemicals, and strong sunlight. Non-absorbent and fireproof. Very poor resistance to abrasion	Lightweight curtains and shower curtains. Reinforced to provide panels, baths, basins, etc.

POINTS TO BE CONSIDERED WHEN SELECTING FABRICS

- Cost — initial purchase cost and cost of cleaning.
- Consider hiring/leasing rather than purchasing.
- Buy the best quality for money available — consider seconds.
- Type of establishment, use within the establishment (e.g. bedrooms, lounges, dining areas, wards, corridors, etc.).
- Amount required and frequency of purchasing.
- Durability and reliability — life expectancy.
- Type of cleaning required — laundering or dry-cleaning.
- Appearance, texture, colour, pattern, type and size of repeat.
- Colourfastness — resistance to fading by sunlight and abrasion.
- Resistance to attacks by moths, mildew, chemicals, etc.
- Flame-resistance.
- Water-repellence, crease resistance and shrink resistance.
- Thermal properties — warm or cool.

WOVEN FABRICS

Fabrics are manufactured by weaving together two or more threads or yarns. Similar or totally different types may be woven together to produce the final fabric. During the weaving process the vertical thread (or yarn) is known as the *warp* and the horizontal thread (or yarn) is known as the *weft*. As the weft finally turns at the edges of the fabric this forms a *selvedge*, i.e. a firm edge.

Types of Weave

The main types of weave are as follows:

Plain weave.   The weft is woven over and under alternate warps as in darning. This is the weave most frequently used to produce a variety of fabrics. The fabrics are usually smooth in appearance but this depends on what types of thread are used, and the firmness of the fabric depends on the number of wefts and warps to the centimetre (or inch). The closer the weave, the stronger the fabric will be, but it does tend to tear easily. The following fabrics are produced from a plain weave: lawn, sheeting, scrim, poplin, flannel, taffeta, repp, cretonne and chintz.

Twill weave.   A series of diagonal lines is produced by the wefts crossing over the warps at different stages in different rows, and this provides a very durable and firm fabric. The following fabrics are produced from a twill weave: serge, gaberdine, denim, flannel, whipcord and twill sheeting.

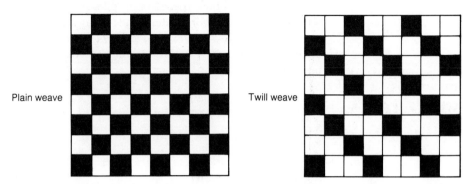

Plain weave

Twill weave

Satin weave.   The warp 'floats' over a specified number of wefts (e.g. three or four) at regular intervals and then under one weft. The fabric is said to be 'warp-faced'. It is smooth and generally has a lustrous appearance. Unfortunately it does have a tendency to become pulled and snagged. The following fabrics are produced from satin weave: silk satin, cotton and linen satin, and satin drill. A sateen weave has wefts which 'float' and is very similar to satin weave. The fabric is said to be 'weft-faced'.

Figured weaves.   During the weaving process a pattern is introduced either by combining two of the previous weaves or by introducing coloured threads as well as the foundation cloth. The finish, weight and appearance will depend on the type and closeness of the threads used as well as the type of weaves used. The following fabrics are produced from a figured weave: damask, huckaback, brocade, tapestry.

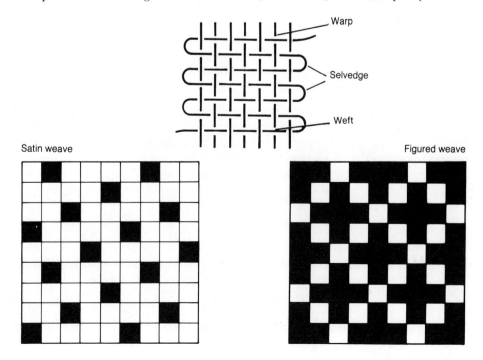

Satin weave

Figured weave

Pile weave. During the weaving process extra warps or wefts are woven at right angles through the base cloth. These extra threads form the pile and may be left looped (uncut) or cut. In some fabrics a pattern can be introduced by inserting both uncut and cut pile. The denseness or thickness of the fabric will be determined by the type of fibres used, the closeness of the pile, and whether the pile is cut or uncut. This type of weave does unfortunately tend to snag and collect dust. The following fabrics are produced from a figured weave: velvet — warp pile, cut loops; terry towelling — uncut or loop pile; velveteen and corduroy — weft pile, cut; moquette — cut or uncut pile fabric.

Widths of Fabrics

There are four fabric widths:
- 1 m (36 in)
- 1.3 m (48 in)
- 1.5 m (54 in)
- 1.6 m (60 in)

1.3 m and 1.5 m are the most common widths for soft furnishings.

SOFT FURNISHINGS

Soft furnishings are used to provide privacy, to introduce colour, texture and pattern into a room and generally to improve the overall appearance. In addition, they may provide extra warmth and comfort to the user. They include curtains, bedspreads, loose covers and cushions, and can either be purchased, hired or leased from a supplier. The most suitable type of fabric should be used to meet the needs of the establishment as well as the customer.

CURTAINS

Curtains are used for many purposes: to provide privacy, especially if the building is overlooked; to exclude draughts; to help soundproof a room; to reduce the amount of sunlight entering a room; to make the windows appear larger or smaller; and to bring colour and pattern into a room. They can also be used as room dividers, especially in sleeping areas.

Curtains may be subjected to much wear and tear. They should drape or hang well and preferably be lined. Curtains can either be laundered or dry-cleaned, and the frequency depends on the following:
- Type of fabric and weave.
- Amount of soiling and pollution.
- Type of establishment.
- Policy of the establishment.
- Amount of wear.

Suitable Materials

Prestige areas (e.g. public rooms, suites, high-class restaurants, etc.). Use brocades, tapestries, velvet, velveteen, Courtelle, satins, heavy cottons, etc.

Bedrooms. Use rayons, printed cottons, Terylene and cotton, repp, chintz, etc.

Bathrooms. Use net, Terylene or nylon, glass fibre, printed cottons and terry towelling.

Common rooms. Use printed cottons, Courtelle, Terylene and cotton, repp, etc.

Corridors. Use printed cottons, Terylene and cotton, net, etc.

Curtain Linings   Ideally curtains should be lined to make them drape well, to provide more insulation and privacy, to give added protection against wear, and to provide uniform appearance. Linings can be fixed at the top and sides or made separately and attached by the holes and tapes at the top with an occasional tacking stitch at the sides. There are advantages and disadvantages to both methods, especially if the curtains are very full and heavy and difficult to launder or if the curtains and linings shrink at different rates. The linings are often made of cream or beige sateen or a colour which matches the background of the curtains. With some curtains, small weights are often sewn into the hem to make them drape well.

Amount of Material Required

Width of curtains.   The minimum allowance is $1\frac{1}{2}$ times the width of the track, depending on the type of headings used.

For turnings.   An allowance of 15–30 cm (6–12 in) is made, depending on the type of fabric used and the shrinkage rate.

Pattern match.   Extra material should be allowed so that the pattern will match exactly across the curtains. The larger the pattern, the more material required.

Full-length curtains.   The finished length should be 1.25–2.5 cm ($\frac{1}{2}$–1 in) above the floor to prevent dirt and excess friction wear.

Short-length curtains.   The finished length should be approximately 15 cm (6 in) below the windowsill.

CURTAIN FIXTURES

Curtain rails should be at least the full width of the window frame, or extend either side, especially if the window is very small or narrow. This will make the window appear larger, allow more light into the room and help prevent fading occurring in the folds of the curtains. The rails are made of metal, wood or plastic — plastic is preferable because it is easier to maintain and lighter in weight. In some cases wooden rods can be used. The curtains are fixed to the rails by hooks or rings, depending on the type of heading used. On average allow one hook to every 7.5 cm (3 in) of curtain. Some curtains just meet in the centre, or there may be an overlap in the rail to help prevent draughts. There are different types of tape available for attaching curtains to the rails, such as narrow or wide tape which provide pleats and stiffen the top of the curtains, hide the rails and avoid the need for pelmets. Curtains can be drawn across by hand, or by the use of manually or electrically operated pull cords. The pull cords will help to prolong the life of the curtains and prevent extra wear and abrasion.

Pelmets, Valances and Swags

These are decorative headings which are fixed over the top of the curtains to hide the rail and tapes, but consideration must be given to their use, cost and maintenance.

Pelmets are made of wood or hardboard which may be painted, sealed or covered with a stiffened fabric to match the curtain.

Valances are made of pleated or frilled fabric and fixed to the rail.

Swags are made of material which is draped to hide the curtain heading, rail and sides.

Blinds

Venetian blinds consist of horizontal or vertical slats made of light alloys or coloured plastics. They are used to provide privacy, reduce and prevent excessive sunlight and heat entering a room, and protect furniture, furnishings and carpets. They can be fitted internally or externally to a window. Venetian blinds tend to attract dust and dirt and require constant cleaning and care. They can be cleaned regularly *in situ* using a damp cloth, sponge or specially designed tool. More thorough cleaning can be done by a contractor.

Roller blinds are made of fabric which may or may not match the curtains or room decor. They are used for the same purpose as venetian blinds. They are easy to clean and maintain and should be dusted and wiped over occasionally.

BEDSPREADS

There are two main types of bedspread, namely fitted and 'throw-over'. Both should preferably have rounded corners so that they do not trail on the floor, collect dirt and dust or cause accidents. They are used to cover the bed during the day and should be either removed and folded up neatly at night or left on the bed, depending on the policy of the establishment.

A bedspread should:
- be easily laundered,
- be crease- and snag-resistant,
- have colour and pattern in keeping with the rest of the decor in the room,
- be made of suitable fabric, e.g. Terylene and cotton, candlewick, folkweave, rayon, heavy cotton, tapestry, etc.,
- be hardwearing because of the amount of wear they may have,
- look attractive and be the right size.

LOOSE COVERS

Loose covers are used for the following reasons:
- To protect the original covering.
- To change the appearance of the room.
- To give a clean, fresh appearance to the room.
- To cover a shabby appearance.
- To provide uniformity to a room where there is a selection of different types of furniture, e.g. chairs or sofas, etc.

Careful consideration should be given to their use because they may be expensive. It may be cheaper to have the furniture completely re-upholstered with a surface that wipes clean or buy new furniture. It is essential that the covers fit well and can be tailored and fixed or pleated at the bottom. The type of fabric used is also very important and may be the same or similar as the curtains (e.g. repp, tweed, linen, chintz or cretonne). It should be hard-wearing, crease-resistant and shrink-resistant.

Consideration should also be given to the greatest wear areas (e.g. arms, backs and front edges of the seats). Additional protection can be given by fitting extra shields to these areas. Nylon stretch covers are easy to launder, remove and replace, and do not shrink, but they may not be suitable for the style of furniture in the establishment.

Amount of Material Required

Easy chair
- 5.5 m (6 yd) of 1.2 m (48in) wide material — plain fitted style
- 6.5 m (7 yd) — frilled or box-pleated

Sofa
- 9.2 m (10 yd) — plain fitted style
- 11 m (12 yd) — frilled or box pleated

Fitted cushion 1 m (1 yd)

Three-piece suite 19.3 m (21 yd)

CUSHIONS

Fitted, scattered or conventional cushions may be provided to bring extra colour, pattern or texture into a room, provide extra comfort and prevent wear areas. They may be filled with down, feather, Terylene, foam or kapok and covered with a suitable fabric (e.g. tapestry, velvet, Terylene and cotton, Dralon or heavy cotton). Shake and tidy frequently, remove covers, and wash or dry-clean as required.

DISPOSABLES

Disposables have been with us for some time, and today there is a wide range of different types on the market. In some establishments they are used extensively, but in others they may be used only in an emergency. With the constant increase in the costs of cleaning and maintenance, it is essential to look closely to see where savings can be made. Analyse very carefully the possibility of introducing disposables into the work situation. Some disposables can be reused, but study carefully the hygiene risks and costs involved in cleaning and reusing disposable items.

Advantages

- Convenience
- Light in weight.
- Savings in cost.
- Quiet to use.
- Compact.
- Some can be reused.

Disadvantages

- May be unacceptable to the user.
- Increase in cost due to wastage.
- Possible fire hazard.
- If used extensively may require a lot of storage space because of the amount used.
- May create problems of disposal.

The Main Types of Disposables

- Tableware — tablecloths, slip cloths, napkins, place mats, banqueting rolls, etc., available in one- two- or three-ply in a variety of patterns, sizes and colours; cutlery, plates, dishes, cups and holders, tumblers, trays, containers, serving dishes, etc.
- Bedding — sheets, pillowcases, covers in a variety of sizes, patterns and colours.
- Towels — individual hand towels or a perforated roll.
- Bathmats, toilet-seat covers, tissues.

- Uniforms, aprons, gloves.
- Mop-heads, dusters, swabs, etc.

The materials most commonly used in the manufacture of disposables are polypropylene, PVC, polystyrene, moulded wood pulp, paper, aluminium foil and cling film.

Points to be Considered before Introducing Disposables

- Cost — amount of capital tied up.
- Type of establishment — are disposables suitable? Are they reliable? Are they acceptable to the user and staff?
- Storage space available — keep disposables away from direct heat, damp and sources of dust and dirt.
- Requirements — type, size, shape, colour and finish.
- Hygiene aspect concerned with reusing disposables.
- Security — need for quality control, check on usage rate and pilfering.
- Means of disposing of disposables (e.g. chutes, incinerators, dustbins, compacters).
- Safety and fire prevention.
- Staff — will additional training be required? Will there be a reduction in hours or redundancies or redeployment?
- General problems involved when introducing a change into the work situation.
- Carry out a trial period — look carefully at findings and conclusions. Always shop around for the best supply source, delivery and price.

QUESTIONS

1. Briefly outline the main types and classifications of fibres. Give examples.

2. Discuss the advantages of blending fibres.

3. What points must be considered when selecting fabrics for soft furnishings?

4. Discuss the use of loose covers in hotels, student hostels and hospital day rooms.

5. Suggest suitable fabrics for curtains in the following establishments:
   (a) a four-star hotel — all areas,
   (b) a study bedroom in a hall of residence,
   (c) a hospital ward,
   (d) a conference centre — all areas.

6. As a supervisor you have been asked to look at the possibility of introducing disposables into your establishment. Outline the investigations you would carry out.

7. Discuss the different methods for disposing of disposables.

15 Furniture and Fittings

CHOOSING FURNITURE

Since the 1960s the design of commercial furniture has changed dramatically. Previously, it tended to be either very utilitarian or expensive. Today, however, there is a vast choice of design to cover every situation and budget. Furniture is not cheap, and it is vital that the purchaser understands what is required and recognises quality and good design.

When buying furniture the purchaser must be aware of the difference between commercial or industrial furniture and furniture produced for the domestic market. Normally when furniture is bought for hotels, hospitals or residential establishments, the choice is made from specialist manufacturers, or wholesalers.

When selecting furniture the following points must be considered:

Frequency of use. Furniture must be durable, versatile and easy to store, especially for reception areas, work areas, etc. It must be able to withstand any knocks and also possible misuse.

Design and comfort. Furniture should be pleasant to look at and should blend in with the area in which it is situated. Comfort is paramount, especially with beds and chairs. The type of use should always be considered.

Repair and replacement. Most commercial furniture manufacturers give a good 'back-up' service for repairs and replacements.

Ease of cleaning and maintenance. As far as possible, the design of furniture should be simple for ease of cleaning. Carvings, crevices, ledges, etc. can be dust traps which have to be cleaned regularly. A piece of furniture should have a gap of at least 255 mm from the floor to the base in order that the underneath may be cleaned.

Castors can facilitate the moving of heavier furniture (e.g. beds, sideboards and sofas). Many chairs now have removable, washable covers which can cut down on cleaning bills. Consider wipe-easy, self-shine protective coatings for surfaces of furniture.

When selecting furniture check the joints to see if they fit well, making sure that glue and tacks are not the only items used to bond the pieces together. The method of construction of a piece of furniture will determine its durability and comfort. Joints on furniture should be smooth fitting. See the diagram below for various types of joint used in furniture construction.

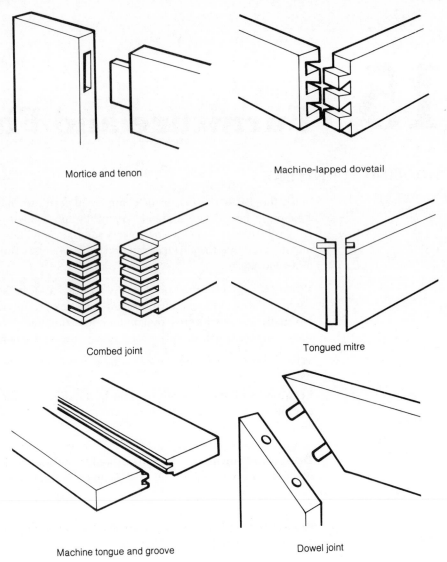

Mortice and tenon

Machine-lapped dovetail

Combed joint

Tongued mitre

Machine tongue and groove

Dowel joint

Various types of joint used in furniture construction

Free-standing furniture should stand easily and not rock. Drawers should run freely and be well constructed. (It may be advisable for the inside of drawers to be plastic coated for ease of cleaning.) Any locks on drawers should function and duplicate keys should be available. Handles on doors and drawers should be firm and smooth. Check free-standing wardrobes with mirrors to see if they remain stable if opened when empty.

TYPES OF FURNITURE

There are three types of furniture.

Free-standing — chairs, beds, tables, etc. This type of furniture can easily be moved or rearranged when necessary. It is normally not so expensive as built-in or fitted furniture because it is not custom-made. Free-standing furniture accumulates dust and dirt, behind, above and beneath it.

Built-in — wardrobes, kitchen fitments, etc. Usually the cost is incorporated into the initial building cost. If required to be installed in established premises, this type of furniture can be expensive. There should be no gaps underneath the furniture, therefore cleaning is minimised. Once built in, the item cannot be removed, so the piece remains permanently fixed and this may sometimes be a disadvantage, e.g. in long-stay hostels where guests often like to rearrange furniture to their own individual tastes.

Fitted — shelves, headboards. This type of furniture makes use of recesses and alcoves, thereby saving valuable space. The room may appear neater and more streamlined (as in the case of headboard units instead of bedside cabinets). In older premises fitted furniture may not be suitable because of the unevenness or unsuitability of the walls. Many housekeepers and manufacturers interchange the words 'built-in' and 'fitted' to mean the same type of furniture.

MATERIALS USED BY FURNITURE MANUFACTURERS

Wood. Solid wood furniture is expensive and may be costly to maintain. It needs constant attention. It is absorbent (unless treated) and stains easily. The bulk of furniture on the market is made from plywood or laminated wood with either a wood or special plastic veneer.

Plywood is built up from odd (3, 5, 9) numbers of layers or slices of wood (veneers) that run at right angles to each other. Therefore plywood is extremely strong because it takes the strain in many directions. The advantages of plywood are that it can be bent easily into shapes, and it does not need much glue or many tacks to hold the shaped parts together. It is also lighter than solid wood and can be made waterproof.

Laminated wood is also built up in layers, but unlike plywood the grain of the veneer runs in the same direction. It is not so strong as plywood, but one piece can be moulded into curved shapes by steaming, so no glue or nails are required to keep the shape in position.

Chipboard is made from wood chippings moulded and pressed together with steam and glue. Usually the finished chipboard has a surface of plastic or wood veneer. Plastic veneers are hygienic and decorative, and are usually rendered water-, scratch- and vermin-proof by sealing the finished edge of the chipboard.

Veneers are cut from the barks of trees either by thinly slicing a continuous piece from the bark as the log is turned on the machine, or by slicing through the bark vertically. The veneer is usually stuck to the plywood or laminated wood by glue and then gives the appearance of solid wood.

Plastics. It is unusual to see a chair of 100% plastic. Normally plastic is used for upright chairs, especially for dining or work room areas. The seat and back are made of plastic and attached to a metal frame. Plastic chairs are very easy to clean and maintain. They are very durable and light to move and stack.

TABLES

The first point to consider when choosing a table is what will be its primary use — is it for eating or working, for a lounge or reception area? Each area requires tables of different heights, materials and specifications.

- Is the surface heat- and stain-proof? Resurfacing a table is costly.
- Can the surface be easily cleaned and maintained within the daily routine?
- If required, can the table be taken down and stored easily (for functions, conferences, etc.)?
- Domestic tables should be avoided if possible, as many have a centre panel, and food, dirt, etc. can become lodged inside.
- Will existing chairs fit underneath the table if required to do so? Most tables are approximately 770 mm high; is this sufficient?
- Is the table steady in use?
- Floor space and design ideas dictate whether a round or square table is suitable. Round tables are often used in dining and reception areas as they allow guests to sit around in a more informal manner.
- Glass-topped tables should be avoided in commercial premises. They are difficult to clean and maintain and may be dangerous.
- For dining and conference areas it is possible to obtain leg frames. These allow various shapes and sizes of tops to be used because they are interchangeable.
- Coffee tables are approximately 360–510 mm high and bedside tables tend to be 200 mm higher than the made-up bed. Dining tables should seat the maximum number of persons in the minimum space. Allow on average 580 mm overall space per person for eating; slightly more space is needed on circular tables.

CHAIRS

Ideally each chair should be individually made for maximum comfort and support, but this is obviously not realistic, so when purchasing chairs, average body dimensions are used. There are special situations (e.g. in hospitals and children's homes) where it would be advisable to seek advice from a specialist furniture manufacturer regarding chair sizes and shapes. In general, upright chairs should be approximately 420 mm from the seat to the ground, and the seat depth (i.e. from front to back) 480 mm, although the seat depth for easy chairs could increase up to 520 mm. If there are arms on the chair they should not protrude more than 25 mm further than the front of the chair. With bulk purchases, it is normal trade practice for the manufacturers or wholesalers to lend a chair for the purchaser to test. The test would be for durability, comfort, ease of cleaning and stacking, etc. Upright chairs are usually made from plywood, plastic, or metal, with a combination of a padded seat and back of vinyl, cloth or plastic. When purchasing upright chairs for use with tables, check the dimensions carefully; it is usual to have at least a 300 mm gap between the table and chair for ease of sitting. If upright chairs are to be used for conferences or lectures, it may be useful to have clips fitted on to the legs of the chairs or on to the backs to enable the chairs to fit together for easy assembling in rows.

Upholstered Easy Chairs

It can be difficult to evaluate the quality of an upholstered chair as much of the work is covered by the outside fabric. Test the chair for comfort and design, ease of cleaning and durability. The most important point to consider when purchasing an upholstered chair or sofa is the material used inside it. Since June 1981 there have been strict fire laws regarding the sale of furniture containing foam to commercial premises. Always check the label and ask if in any doubt. The fabric used to cover easy chairs can be Dralon, moquette, brocade, damask, etc. These fabrics nearly always dictate the final price of the chair. They must be hard-wearing, non-slip and easy to clean. The main areas of wear are the arm rests, the head area and the seat. The seat supports should be strong and easy to replace if necessary. The larger types of chair may have castors fitted to allow for easier movement.

WARDROBES

Wardrobes, whether free-standing, built-in or fitted, all have the same internal dimensions. These are approximately 1850 mm high, 500 mm deep. The width of the wardrobe required depends on the type of establishment (e.g. whether it is a short-stay hotel or a resident hostel). It is usual for hotels to provide space for at least six garments to hang easily. Before purchasing wardrobes it is advisable to consider the following points:

- The type of user — short-stay, long-term, residential, children, handicapped, etc.
- If the wardrobe is to be free-standing, is it stable when empty, and can the top be cleaned easily? It may be advisable to fit 'cups' underneath the legs of the free-standing wardrobe to protect the carpet.
- Is there enough space in the wardrobe (whatever type) to allow air to circulate around the clothes?
- Can the bottom or sides of the wardrobe be used for storing hats, shoes, etc?
- Could built-in wardrobes be cheaper and easier to clean than free-standing ones? Compare the costs.
- A light inside the wardrobe is often appreciated.

Note: The dimensions for wardrobe and shelf and drawer units are minimum internal clear dimensions
(All measurements in millimeters)

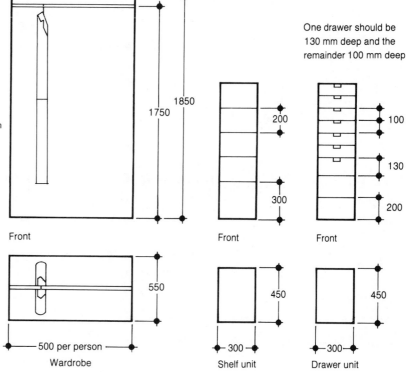

One drawer should be 130 mm deep and the remainder 100 mm deep

Diagram showing dimensions for wardrobe, shelf and drawer unit

CHESTS OF DRAWERS, DRESSING TABLES AND DESKS, LUGGAGE RACKS

Modern residential premises usually have a combination of chests of drawers and desks, or dressing tables and mirrors. In the more modern hotels there is often a simplified version of the above, with a long chest of drawers plus mirror; this is used for writing, dressing, etc. It is usually a fitment attached to the wall and makes cleaning easier as there is only one continuous surface. A newer idea is to replace the free-standing chest of drawers with shelves built into a wardrobe. This also makes cleaning easier, and streamlines the room.

Where there are guests or residents staying overnight or for long periods there should be at least one lockable drawer provided. It should be emphasized, however, that all valuable items are best kept in the supervisor's or manager's office.

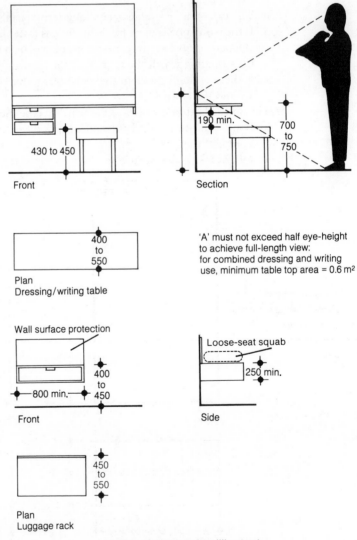

Front

Section

Plan
Dressing/writing table

'A' must not exceed half eye-height
to achieve full-length view:
for combined dressing and writing
use, minimum table top area = 0.6 m²

Wall surface protection

Front

Side

Plan
Luggage rack

(All measurements in millimetres)

Diagram showing dimensions for a dressing/writing area and luggage rack

Buying a bed for a non-domestic situation can be difficult as guests or residents do not always come in average shapes and weights!

When choosing a base and mattress look at all the types available. Check sizes, working heights, comfort and suitability for the given area, and if possible consult a specialist bed manufacturer who will have commercial beds made with heavier-gauge wire.

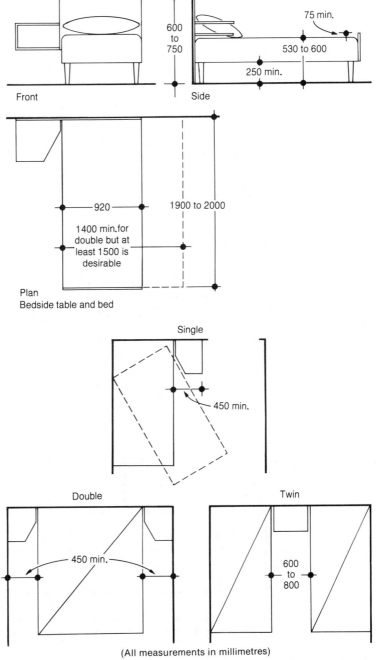

(All measurements in millimetres)

Diagram showing space requirements for various items of hotel bedroom furniture

Bed Sizes

- Standard double 150 × 200 cm (approximately 5 x 6½ft).
- Small double 135 × 190 cm (approximately 4½ × 6¼ ft).
- Standard single 1 × 2 m (approximately 3¼ × 6½ ft).
- Small single 0.9 × 1.9 m (approximately 3 × 6¼ ft).

Many manufacturers will make other sizes on request. Remove the protective polythene cover from beds before making them up.

Living spaces

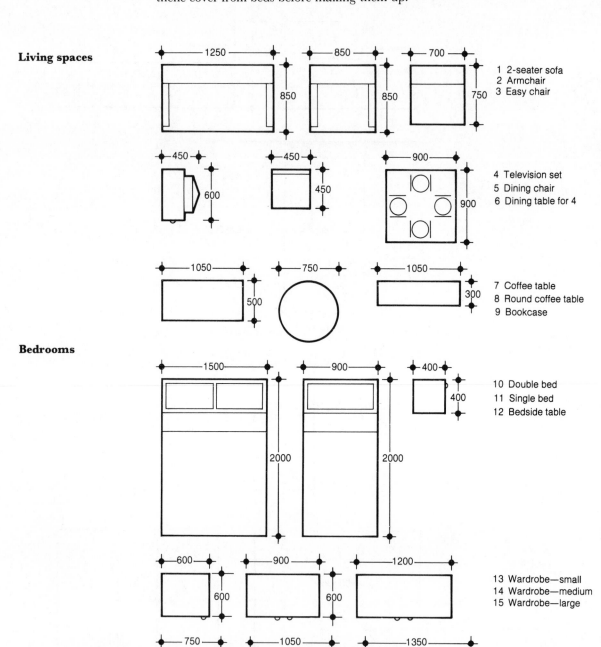

1 2-seater sofa
2 Armchair
3 Easy chair

4 Television set
5 Dining chair
6 Dining table for 4

7 Coffee table
8 Round coffee table
9 Bookcase

Bedrooms

10 Double bed
11 Single bed
12 Bedside table

13 Wardrobe—small
14 Wardrobe—medium
15 Wardrobe—large

16 Chest of drawers — small
17 Chest of drawers — large
18 Dressing table

(All measurements in millimeters)

Bed Bases

The firm-edge divan has a wooden-sided base with rows of springs set within the frame. The springs are covered with stretched, interlaced webbing and a strong synthetic material or a steel wire and cord sheet. Between this and the surface lies the soft filling material. Firm edge divans do not 'give' on the sides. They are suitable for hotel bedrooms or student accommodation where the bed may also be used as a seat.

The spring-edge or soft-edge divan has a wooden base, usually about 100 mm in depth, with an open coil spring unit on top which is similar to that used in a mattress. Because the edges 'give', the sleeper can lie equally as comfortably at the edge as in the centre. This type of base tends to be more expensive but luxurious.

The slatted base consists of a wooden frame with wooden slats running across the width. Some are manufactured with rubber fixings for the slats to allow a limited 'give'.

In older establishments there may still be wire nest bases. These are difficult to clean and maintain. For long-stay residential establishments it is possible to provide bed bases that contain drawers for storage. These, however, can make the bed difficult to move when full.

The different bed bases are illustrated below.

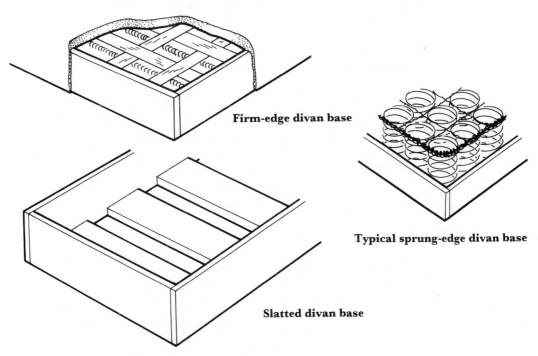

Firm-edge divan base

Typical sprung-edge divan base

Slatted divan base

Mattresses

There are two main types of mattress: spring interior and foam.

Spring interior. There are two types: open coil and pocketed.

The most common is the 'Bonnel' *open coil*, which consists of rows of waisted springs held together by vertically opposed spiral wires, and a perimeter rod. Continuous springing, a variation on open coil, consists of a single length of formed spring wire, running the length of the mattress held together by vertically offset spiral wires with a perimeter frame.

The *pocketed* spring interior has a series of individual springs, each enclosed in a calico or synthetic fabric pocket. There are two types: barrel shaped springs held together by twine at the waist, and cylindrical springs, joined at the top and bottom by metal clips or twine. The pocketed spring mattress is the most expensive type, but it gives extra comfort and durability.

Both types should be turned regularly to even out the wear and both should always be stored flat.

Spring interior mattresses are illustrated below. Ventilation holes in the sides of mattresses help to keep the interior well aired.

Filling materials tend to vary from one manufacturer to another. They include: coir fibre (coconut fibre), woollen mixture felt, pure cotton felt and fleece wool.

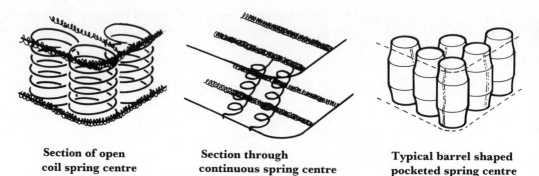

Section of open coil spring centre   **Section through continuous spring centre**   **Typical barrel shaped pocketed spring centre**

For details of individual mattresses consult the manufacturer's handbook.

The surface of the mattress can be either deep stitch-quilted, multi-quilted, tufted or, on a cheaper mattress, a cover can be stretched over the filling. All methods of finishing stop the fillings from moving and parting under stress. Tufting secures the top and bottom of the mattresses by buttons and ties, which penetrate right through, keeping the springs under compression. See the diagram below.

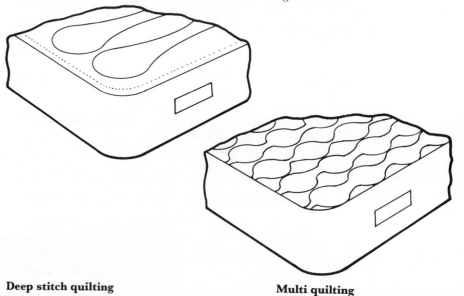

Deep stitch quilting   **Multi quilting**

Foam mattress.   This type of mattress is constructed from either latex foam or polyether foam, or from a combination of the two.

They are best made to a density of between 27 and 29.5 kg/m³, ideally with a combination of densities and minimum hardness to give optimum support.

Foam mattresses tend to be cheaper than the interior spring ones because of the lack of springs. They are ideal for guests or residents with allergies or hay fever. They are not attacked by moths. Very cheap foam mattresses should be avoided; often they are only pieces of foam encased in material and they give no support.

Better quality layered foam mattresses usually consist of a layer of soft polyether foam on top of latex. The two layers are combined with a firm polyether foam on the bottom. Layered foam mattresses usually have a quilted-top surface for extra comfort. Less expensive foam mattresses are usually made from polyether. As with other mattress types, foam should be used with bases designed for them; wooden slat bases are particularly good.

There is also a combination of foam and spring interior mattresses, where individual springs are recessed in foam to form the mattress core.

Foam mattresses are self-ventilating through the cell structure; the movement of the sleeper effectively pumps air through the foam.

Three types of foam mattress are shown below.

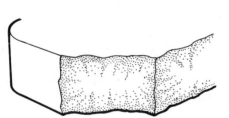
Section of a polyether foam mattress

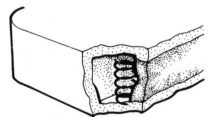
Individual springs recessed in foam

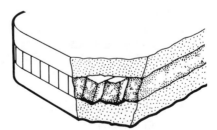
Section of a layered or structured foam mattress

Cleaning bases and mattresses.   Every 3 or 4 months it will be necessary to inspect and clean bases and mattresses. Use a soft brush or upholstery nozzle on a vacuum cleaner. If the mattress has buttons (tufting), use a crevice tool to remove dust, crumbs, etc. Avoid excess use of suction when cleaning as it may dislodge the filling under the cover of an interior sprung mattress.

Stain removal.   If an accident occurs, act quickly to stop water or a stain getting into the upholstery filling where it could cause real problems: dried stains can be difficult to remove. Strip off the bedclothes and stand the mattress on its side. Seepage is slower on a vertical surface. Blot off as much liquid as possible with an absorbent cloth, old towel or plain paper towels. Immediate sponging with cold water clears many liquid stains. Do not worry about leaving a small water mark; it will not show when the bed is made. It is more important to get rid of any smell. Avoid over-wetting by blotting as you work. If necessary, treat further, as recommended, and dry by one of the methods given below.

Leaking hot water bottle or flood damage.   Use an electric hair-dryer or, for large areas, protect the floor and support the mattress safely (lengthwise, on its edge) in front of a carefully positioned fan heater. Inspect frequently.

Tea, coffee, milk-based drinks.   Sponge first with warm borax solution (1 dsp) laundry borax to 250 ml ($\frac{1}{2}$ pt) water and then with clear water. When dry, an aerosol grease solvent should clear any grease but use it sparingly on a foam mattress. Brush the cover lightly but thoroughly to clear any deposits.

LEASING FURNITURE

There has been a vast increase in the leasing of furniture within the last 10 years. The idea of spending large amounts of capital on furniture and fittings is changing. Leasing has many advantages over the traditional methods of acquiring furniture. Used carefully it allows businesses to change and expand for different needs and situations, without using their capital. The leasing costs can be set against income for tax purposes. The furniture is owned by the leasing company, but is leased on a contract for approximately 3–5 years. At the end of this period there may be an option to buy the furniture at a reduced rate from the leasing company or to carry on the agreement at a much reduced rate. At the end of the leasing contract most items need replacing because of wear and tear, or a new design or colour is required, so the contract will be renewed. It is essential that when contracts are replaced or renewed the terms are carefully studied. A fixed rate of payment should operate over the set period of the agreement.

QUESTIONS

1. Why is it advisable that chair arms do not protrude more than 25 mm over the front of a chair?

2. State in your own words the BSI specification for furniture.

3. What type of chair would you recommend for:
   (a) a dining area in an industrial canteen,
   (b) a reception area in a hospital?
   Give details of materials used and sizes, etc. Also give a cleaning work card for each chair.

4. Write down the missing dimensions:

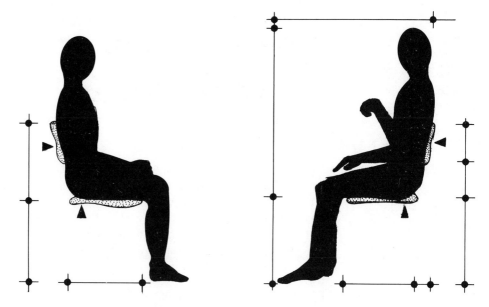

5. List the disadvantages of leasing furniture.

6. Discuss the factors to be considered when selecting beds and mattresses for a residential conference centre. Outline a programme for the care, cleaning, and maintenance of the above.

16 Pest Control and Timber Decay

THE IMPORTANCE OF SURVEYS

Regular surveys, external and internal, almost always detect timber decay and signs of pests and infestation. If members of staff are not capable of carrying out surveys, it is possible to hire specialised contractors to do the work. It is important to recognise active infestation and timber decay and to know how to eradicate and treat the affected areas. Insect and fungal infestations are living organisms and require food (untreated timber) and moisture to survive. By removing one or both, eradication is easier.

BEETLES

There are four common types of insect that attack timber in Britain. They are the common furniture beetle, deathwatch beetle, the lyctus or powder post beetle, and the house long-horned beetle. Grouped together they tend to be called 'woodworm'.

The Life Cycle of Insects

Life cycle of insects

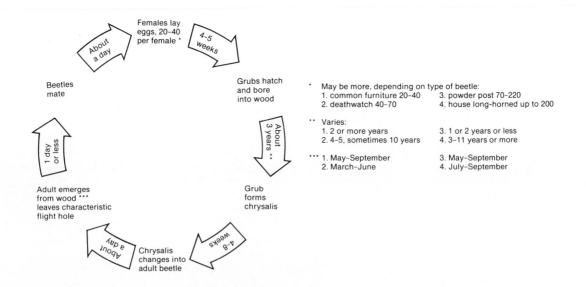

Beetles mate — About a day — Females lay eggs, 20–40 per female * — 4–5 weeks — Grubs hatch and bore into wood — About 3 years ** — Grub forms chrysalis — 4–8 weeks — Chrysalis changes into adult beetle — About a day — Adult emerges from wood *** leaves characteristic flight hole — 1 day or less — Beetles mate

* May be more, depending on type of beetle:
1. common furniture 20–40   3. powder post 70–220
2. deathwatch 40–70   4. house long-horned up to 200

** Varies:
1. 2 or more years   3. 1 or 2 years or less
2. 4–5, sometimes 10 years   4. 3–11 years or more

*** 1. May–September   3. May–September
2. March–June   4. July–September

156

The life cycle of insects is illustrated on the previous page. Eggs are laid in cracks, crevices and old exit holes on the surface of the wood by the female adult beetle, after mating. The eggs, as many as 80, hatch into larvae or grubs which burrow into the wood. These larve eventually pupate, approximately 3 years later (depending on the species of beetle) and emerge through new exit holes as adult beetles. The life cycle then begins again. The adult beetle can fly, so it may lay eggs on another piece of timber thereby spreading the infestation.

Common Furniture Beetle

This beetle attacks most woods and plywoods. Round exit holes appear on the surface of the wood approximately 1.5 mm wide. The adult beetles usually emerge in May through to September. Bore dust (or frass) is fine, granular and loosely packed, so that it drops out of the exit holes like very fine sand. Piles of fresh frass and newly made exit holes are signs of active attack.

Treatment

- Where attack is severe it may be necessary to replace the infected wood with new preserved timber.
- Furniture and small articles can usually be treated by fumigation, but this should only be carried out by professionals.
- The most convenient way of treating woodworm in infected furniture and timber is by applying insecticide solution to all infected parts and surrounding areas. Attention must be paid to undersides of drawers, tables, unpolished ends of legs and backs of cabinets.
  The insects cannot lay eggs on a polished or painted surface, but may use old exit holes, so use of a wax polish could be helpful.
- The most effective time to apply insecticides is from early spring to the late summer. Two applications are advisable, and then treat again the following year.

Deathwatch Beetle

This beetle normally attacks hardwoods (e.g. oak, teak, mahogany) in which there is already some fungal decay. It can attack softwoods (e.g. pitch pine, red cedar) if they are near hardwoods.

Deathwatch beetle is common in damp old buildings. Flight holes are approximately 3 mm in diameter. Frass contains bun-shaped pellets which distinguishes deathwatch attack from other wood-boring insects. The life cycle is approximately 4–5 years. The adult emerges between April and June. Attack by deathwatch beetle and furniture beetle in timber is common.

Treatment
- Make a specialised inspection between April and June.
- Remove infected areas and replace with treated new timber.
- Collect all debris and frass from area before treating with insecticides.
- Two applications of insecticide are advised during April to June. Yearly application for four consecutive years is recommended.

Powder Post Beetle

Wood over 15 years old is unlikely to suffer attack from this beetle. It only attacks the sapwood of certain hardwoods (oak, ash, walnut) for a few years after felling.

Exit holes are approximately 1.5 mm in diameter and the frass is very fine, similar to talcum powder. The life cycle is approximately 1–2 years, but in hot atmospheres it could be shorter. The adult beetle emerges from May to September.

Treatment
The treatment is similar to that for deathwatch beetle, but the time to apply insecticide is between May and September.

The House Long-horned Beetle

This is a larger beetle than the other three. It attacks only certain areas of the United Kingdom, namely Surrey and the surrounding counties. In these areas the use of wood preservative on new timber is required by the building regulations. It only attacks the sapwood of softwoods, and is usually found in attics and roof spaces. The grubs and larvae destroy the wood completely, so new wood is needed. It is difficult to detect this beetle because, unlike the other three, it does not emerge from circular exit holes. The exit holes are narrow slits and are often filled with fine frass. The life cycle is 5–11 years. Adults emerge from July to September and the adult female can lay up to 200 eggs. Infestation has to be reported to the Forest Products Research Laboratory.

Treatment
Use a pressure application of preservatives into the bore holes.

Using Wood Preservatives

Preservatives can be applied by:
- brushing,
- spraying,
- steeping in cold preservative,
- hot and cold steeping in open tanks,
- pressure impregnation,
- Boucherie process (replacement of copper sulphate in the cells of the sap).

Once dry, treated wood is no more flammable than untreated wood. If treating timber without expert help, follow instructions for use carefully.

Points to remember
- Watch out for exit holes, fresh exit holes, or small piles of frass which are signs of active attack.
- Check timber in damp, dark and out-of-the-way places; check the back and undersides of furniture.
- Deal quickly with any attack.
- Consult specialist if not sure of signs.
- Report suspected house long-horned beetle to The Forest Products Research Laboratory.

DAMPNESS

Dampness entering a building must be treated quickly, otherwise it causes deterioration of materials and shortens the life expectancy of the building, as well as making it unpleasant to work and live in. The three main causes of dampness are:

- poor design or deficiencies in construction,
- structural deterioration,
- condensation.

Dampness can cause deterioration by:
- stains left by moulds and condensation,
- wet and dry rot growing from fungus,
- rusting iron and steel,
- making the adhesion of paints and plasters difficult.

Dampness nearly always produces an unpleasant smell and can produce a damp atmosphere.

The causes of dampness are illustrated below.

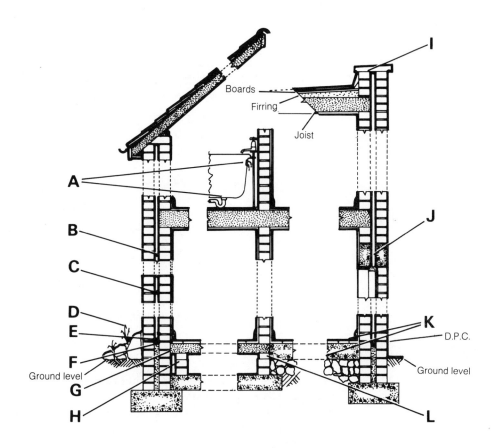

CAUSES OF DAMPNESS

A Slightly leaky joints behind bath panels keep floor damp.

B Moisture runs down wall tie that tilts downwards.

C Cavity bridged by mortar droppings.

D Earth for rockery built up over damp-proof course and airbrick.

E Damp-proof course bridged by mortar droppings.

F Damp-proof course punctured by stone in mortar.

G End of joist touching wall.

H No damp-proof course under wallplate.

I No damp-proof course here — water can soak into wall, and thence into joist.

J No damp-proof course between lintels — moisture can reach inner leaf of wall and joist above, and head of window frame.

K No horizontal damp-proof course in sub-floor, and tile floor bridges damp-proof course in wall.

L No through ventilation.

Rising Damp

Rising damp comes from the ground into the walls and spreads rapidly; it must be treated quickly and thoroughly. Most walls (except in older property) that come into contact with the ground have a damp-proof course (DPC).

Damp-proof courses are made from sheet metal, lead, copper, bituminised felt (with or without a thin core of lead), polythene, asphalt, slates and engineering blocks.

The damp-proof course at the base of a wall should be at least 150 mm above ground level, so that any earth that builds up against the base cannot pass moisture into the walls.

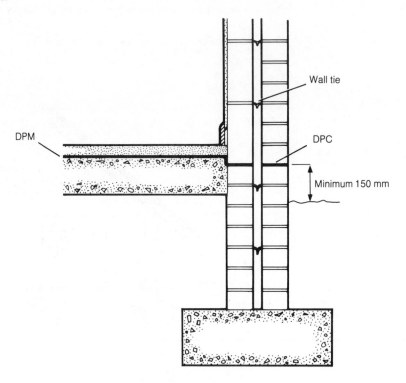

DPM

Wall tie

DPC

Minimum 150 mm

A damp-proof course

Other Causes of Dampness

Damaged, or leaf-choked guttering and rainwater pipes   must be cleared and repaired or replaced at once. Ideally all external gutterings and pipes should be checked in autumn and spring. If water cannot run away quickly, dampness could occur internally through water seepage through bricks, mortar, etc. The back of rainwater pipes should be protected from the wall by brackets so that in the event of a leak the water is not drawn in internally.

Damaged pointing.   All external walls should be examined for loose or missing mortar as well as damaged bricks. If allowed to go unrepaired, these damaged areas will cause dampness and spoil decorations.

Rotten doors and window frames   let in water. Doors and window frames must fit correctly and they should be painted and maintained to avoid damp patches and buckling.

Defective roofing.   On pitched roofs the usual cause of dampness is missing tiles or slates. With flat roofs the damp problem can be more severe (see section on roofs p. 34). Occasionally sunshine on flat roofs causes the final roof fabric to blister and crack, thereby offering dampness a channel.

Condensation

Condensation usually occurs in moist, damp conditions. It is at its worst when the surfaces of the area are cold and non-absorbent, and the surroundings are badly ventilated. The risk of condensation is high when the relative humidity (percentage of water vapour) is above 60% and the temperature of the air is 20°C. The temperature at which water vapour in the air changes to liquid is known as the 'dew point'.

Common Areas of Dampness Caused by Condensation

- Walls, damp all over but normally worse at ceiling height.
- Window-sills.
- Points where ceilings and walls join a flat roof.
- Areas in kitchens and bathrooms near pipes, sinks and radiators.

Remedies for Condensation

Condensation can nearly always be cured by taking the following steps:
- Improve the ventilation and overall temperature.
- Extract steam quickly.
- Provide warm, absorbent surfaces (e.g. timber floors, polystyrene on the walls).
- Use specialist paints containing fine particles of cork, pearlite, etc.
- Clad walls with wood panelling or cork.

Deliquescent salts.   These are water-soluble salts which are sometimes present in the plaster or brickwork. They have the property of attracting moisture so if the air is humid a damp patch occurs. This damp patch disappears when the air is dry again. The only way to treat these patches of dampness is to remove the affected plaster and replace with fresh correctly mixed plaster.

DRY ROT

When a fungus appears externally in wood it has already caused extensive internal damage. True dry rot is extremely difficult to eradicate because it spreads so quickly and the fungus mycelium prepares the path for itself by adjusting the water content of the wood to a maximum for its water-conducting strands. The conducting strands allow the fungus to spread to outside material (e.g. bricks). If the fungus is not destroyed from the walls, which in itself is difficult, it can lie dormant and then become active again when conditions are right. The name 'dry rot' results from the appearance of the affected timber. The fungus requires a high moisture content in the wood to flourish (higher than 20%).

All cases of dry rot are caused by an initial source of dampness; before any treatment and restoration commences the source must be found.

How to Recognise Dry Rot

- The fungus appears on wood or other surfaces — although types of fungus other than dry rot can grow on wallpaper and damp areas. The fungus appears as a fluffy white area with yellow patches or a matted grey patch with staining of yellow, lilac or thin grey strands.

- Dry rot has a characteristic moulding smell, like toadstools.
- Mycelial growth sends out fruiting bodies which may be found in areas other than the main decay region. These fruiting bodies are flat and plate-like with white edges and bright red centres. Mycelium and the fruiting bodies can sometimes be seen on walls as well as on wood. Water stains on brickwork and plaster are an indication of water seepage through the structure, creating suitable conditions for fungal growth.
- The affected wood appears dry and crumbly and can be cracked especially across the grain.

Treatment
- On finding dry rot examine the surrounding timber and walls.
- Treat the source of dampness.
- Cut away all infected timber. Cut out not less than 1 m beyond the obvious rot. Plaster showing signs of infection must also be cut, at least to 0.5 m beyond the infected area. Brickwork with fungus or fruiting bodies should be scraped clean and sterilised with a blow lamp and treated with fungicide. All debris, including dust or any contaminated insulation material, must be destroyed. Burn infected wood at once.
- All replacement timber must be treated with preservative and any sound timber remaining in the area should also be treated. Some plastics used in buildings are attacked by some preservatives. Seek advice before using them near electric cables, plastic drains or water pipes.

The treatment for dry rot is usually carried out by professional contractors.

WET ROT

This is also sometimes called 'cellar rot'. Wet rot only occurs in wet conditions, and is easier to cure than dry rot. The essential remedy is to air the source of dampness, and dry and treat the timber. Wet rot requires conditions of around 30% moisture in the wood in order to grow, but unlike dry rot it will not spread beyond the immediate wet areas and does not spread into walls. Wet rot occurs internally and externally.

How to Recognise Wet Rot

Wet rot is harder to recognise than dry rot because of the lack of external signs. There may be a lightening of the wood, which crushes easily when tapped. If unsure, seek expert advice.

How to Treat Wet Rot

- Treat the cause of dampness.
- Cut away the infected timber.
- Check that ventilation is allowing the timber to remain dry and that the damp-proof course is still effective.
- All new timber must be treated with preservative.
- Preventing wet rot is easier than curing it; regular maintenance and painting of external woodwork is essential.

CONTROL OF OTHER PESTS

Rodents (rats and mice)

Rats and mice can be a problem, but with a planned maintenance programme, staff training and co-operation, infestation need not occur.

Rodents are prolific breeders, and if they are not exterminated they can cause great damage. Rodents spread disease and rats can bite through cables and plaster.

Common areas of infestation are: kitchens, boiler houses and lift shafts. Signs of rodent presence are droppings, gnawed food and grease marks along skirting boards.

In most infestation cases it is advisable to contact the local department of health. They give free expert advice. There are many specialist companies who deal with infestation. When poison or traps are laid it is vital that staff are informed.

Cockroaches

Cockroaches usually appear at night. They eat almost anything including paper, certain fabrics and animal or human food. They live in warm places (behind radiators, under sinks, etc.) and hate light. They can be difficult to control. Insecticide powder and spray can be effective but care is needed in food areas. Closing cracks and crevices in plaster, brickwork and tiles can help. Keep all areas clean and ensure that no food is left uncovered (cockroaches leave excreta on food).

Flies

Flies spread disease rapidly in food areas. It can be relatively easy to prevent the entry of flies by taking a few cheap precautionary measures. Dustbins should be kept covered, emptied regularly and periodically sterilised. Most establishments now use paper or plastic refuse sacks, which make handling of rubbish easier and more hygienic. Waste disposal units in kitchens help to dispose of food waste quickly. Fine mesh screens can be incorporated into the design of kitchen windows, allowing the window to be open but denying access to flies. Insect-ray machines are helpful and kill flies on contact. The use of aerosol sprays should be avoided, particularly in kitchen and dining areas.

Paint containing particles of insecticides could be helpful for a limited time.

Ants

There are two types of ant: Pharaoh's (small, light yellow) and black garden ants. Both types like high humid temperatures, so kitchen or bathroom areas are usually where ants are found. They tend to live behind pipes, radiators, etc. and they weave a trail of infection on floors and surfaces. If ants are found in food areas, suspect food should be destroyed. Insecticide in powder or spray form should be placed into or near the affected area.

Bed bugs

Bed bugs are normally only detected when a guest complains of bites. They cannot fly like most insects; they are transferred from one infected area to another either by luggage or books, or they can move along pipes. Spraying with insecticide may solve the problem. This is usually done by the Public Health Department, and it involves the fumigation of mattresses and blankets.

QUESTIONS

1. Try to find out how you would recognise moth attack in a wool carpet. Could it be repaired?

2. During which months are wood-boring insects most lively?

3. Would it be possible to treat timber joists that had woodworm?

4. List the safety precautions that should be observed when placing rat or mouse poison.

5. What are the signs of mice infestation?

6. Name the laws that govern the control of infestation in kitchens.

7. What are the causes and effects of rising damp?

17 Buying Techniques, Stores and Stock Control

THE IMPORTANCE OF BUYING

Buying is one of the main functions of management and a great deal of success in any establishment depends upon careful and intelligent buying whether it be cleaning materials, equipment, furniture or fabrics. The responsibility for buying varies according to the type and size of the establishment and the particular type of items required. It is often taken out of the hands of the supervisor/user and carried out by the supplies/purchasing officer or the manager or storekeeper. Whoever in the department is responsible for buying should not simply reorder on the basis of past experience but should take into account the current requirements and prices.

AIMS OF GOOD BUYING

It is essential to do the following:
- Buy the best value for money available.
- Keep up to date with current market trends, and prices.
- Know the shelf-life of products.
- Be able to assess quality in relation to costs.
- Make sure goods are bought from a reputable firm.
- Make sure goods are ordered in good time and the correct details are given to the supplier.
- Maintain optimum stock levels.
- Ensure a continual source of supply and find substitutes where necessary.
- Arrange for goods to be delivered punctually — organisation and flow of work can be disrupted if goods do not arrive on time.
- Check all goods on arrival for quantity and quality against the official order form and delivery note. Note and follow up any discrepancies immediately. It is essential that substitute goods are received or a credit note is issued by the supplier.

METHODS OF BUYING

There is a number of different methods of buying available and the following points must be considered prior to selection being made:
- Type and quantity of products required.
- Amount of capital available.
- Amount of storage space available.
- Shelf-life of the products.
- Policy of the establishment or group.

- Whether standardisation of products is required or not.
- Whether the number of suppliers needs to be restricted.
- Method and frequency of issuing stores.

METHOD A: WHOLESALE BUYING

Goods are purchased from a supplier who deals direct with the manufacturer or distributor.

Advantages	*Disadvantages*
• Competitive prices for goods. • A ready supply of cash is not necessary because invoices can be paid at the end of the month — depending on the agreement. • Regular delivery can be made, thereby helping to eliminate unnecessary stockpiling. • Discounts are available for quantity and prompt payment.	• Range of goods available may be limited. • It may be impossible to purchase half loads or half cases. • Containers may be very heavy and require special racking. • Storage space may be limited and prevent ordering in large quantities.

METHOD B: BUYING DIRECT FROM THE MANUFACTURER

By buying goods and services direct from the manufacturer the 'middle man' will be cut out completely and prices will be very competitive. Goods can also be supplied according to the establishment's own size and specification. Bulk orders can be made, accounts settled and delivery dates staged so as not to use up valuable storage space. The advantages and disadvantages of this method are very similar to those for wholesale buying.

Both methods A and B are suitable for buying on a contract, either for the individual establishment or group of establishments. With some products (e.g. equipment, detergents and bed linen) these may be bought on an area, regional or national contract. Suppliers will be invited to put in tenders for particular goods and services. After receiving these tenders the buyer will then compare at least three of them with particular reference to quality, cost and delivery arrangements. After careful consideration, a contract will be drawn up with the supplier for a specified period of time (e.g. 6, 12 or 24 months) depending on the type of goods and services required. A price will be fixed unless conditions change considerably. Often the establishment is not free to buy elsewhere during the contract period. On completion of the specified period of time the buyer is free to negotiate a further contract with the supplier or invite new tenders and start the process all over again.

METHOD C: RETAIL BUYING

With this method of buying the establishment usually buys from a local supplier, who in turn has bought goods from a wholesaler or direct from the manufacturer.

Advantages
- Quick turnover of goods.
- Wide range of products available.
- Quick, efficient service offered.
- Value for money.
- If order is large, discounts may be favourable.
- More suitable for smaller establishments.
- Useful method in an emergency.

Disadvantages
- Cost of goods may be higher than method A or B, but this may be balanced by the reliability of back-up service.
- Bulk size containers may not be available, only domestic sizes.

METHOD D: CASH-AND-CARRY BUYING

This is usually done at a warehouse where goods can be selected, paid for in cash or by cheque, and then transported by the buyer to the particular establishment. Often a card of introduction is necessary and the establishment may be required to spend a minimum amount of cash over a specified period of time.

Advantages
- Competitive prices.
- Wide range of products available depending on type and size of cash-and-carry.
- Can be used in an emergency if goods do not arrive from normal supplier.

Disadvantages
- Ready cash or cheque required in payment — no credit available.
- Range of products may be limited.
- Own transport required.
- Selection should be made carefully — costs may be higher than local retailer.

METHOD E: BULK BUYING

This method of buying is available from a wide range of suppliers but advantages and disadvantages must be considered before buying in bulk containers.

Advantages
- Cost — more competitive prices available.
- Wider choice of products.
- Standardisation of products, equipment, materials, etc.
- If storage space is available, large orders can be placed to give special discounts for quantity.
- Issuing may be easier to control, larger quantities less frequently.

Disadvantages
- Cost — a lot of capital may be tied up in stock.
- Products may deteriorate because turnover of stock is not quick enough.
- Storage space may be limited.
- Issuing may be more difficult because materials may have to be transferred to smaller containers and labelled with contents, hazards, dilution rates, etc.
- Careless use may lead to undue waste.
- Stocktaking — it may be difficult to gauge accurately amounts left.
- More staff may be required to control delivery, issuing, etc.

THE STOREKEEPER

The storekeeper plays a very important role in the control of stock and the smooth running of the establishment. It is essential that the storekeeper has an efficient and effective system of stock control and ensures that the goods are available in the right quantity and condition at the right time. He or she may be responsible for a large central stores, general stores within a unit or a cleaning and equipment stores in a particular establishment. A great deal of money may be tied up in stock for immediate or long-term use, so it is important that the storekeeper has the following technical and personal qualities to carry out the particular job:

- Good technical knowledge of the products — especially the shelf-life of products.
- Ability to make good personal relationships with suppliers, staff, cleaning personnel and other departments.
- Ability to handle figures, measure accurately and keep up-to-date records on costs and stock levels.
- Knowledge of up-to-date legislation — e.g. Health and Safety, and Fire Prevention.
- Absolute honesty and trustworthiness in all dealings.
- Ability to set an example to others in general approach to work, though storekeepers are not required to be leaders of men or women.

STORES AND STOCK CONTROL

Ordering

Each establishment or group of establishments will initiate its own system of ordering from a particular supplier by:

- telephoning,
- telephoning and completing an official order form as a back-up,
- sending an official order form to the supplier,
- using 'Tele sales' whereby the supplier telephones the establishment at a predetermined time for the particular order. This system reduces the amount of paperwork involved but care should be taken not to order something just because the supplier is at the other end of the telephone.

The person placing the order should be aware of the best buying rates and make sure orders are placed with the supplier in good time.

Delivery of Goods

On arrival all goods must be checked for quantity and quality by checking the official order to the supplier against the delivery note or invoice. Too often goods are delivered and not checked by the receiver because it is felt that this is too time-consuming on the part of the storekeeper. Control is essential for quality and quantity in order to reduce wastage and ensure cost effectiveness.

Storage

The stores area should be well positioned to provide ease of access for delivery of goods, to minimise handling problems and possible damage to products or equipment, as well as to aid issuing to the various departments. It should be large enough to cope with the necessary stock of items but not so large as to encourage overstocking. The stores should have a controlled access, within the sight of the storekeeper's office, so that goods can be checked into the stores and also control kept over the issuing to the departments. This should then provide security over the goods and help to prevent pilfering and poor stock control. The stores should be well laid out with adequate shelving so that the storekeeper can see at a glance what is in stock. It also helps to provide a good system of stock rotation — to ensure that goods are stored in ideal conditions, and to that old stock is used before new stock so that goods do not deteriorate. As a guideline, items which are used frequently should be placed within easy access. Goods less frequently used should be placed elsewhere.

Stock Records

An essential part of the storage function is the maintenance of clerical records to record all stock movements accurately in and out of the stores. The system used will depend upon the type and size of the establishment. On arrival at the stores all goods must be recorded and added to the original stock.

'Goods received' books give the details shown in the diagram below.

DATE	SUPPLIER	DETAILS	UNIT COST	TOTAL COST	OFFICE USE
	Clean Co Chemicals Ltd	4 × 5 litres Detergent D 25	£X	£X	
	,, ,,	4 × 5 litres PL 50 Emulsion Floor polish	£X	£X	

Bin cards are records of all receipts and issues of a particular item and are either attached to the particular bin or kept in a file. An example is shown below.

Item D 25 Detergent	Price	£X per 5 litres
Unit 5 litres	Supplier	Clean Company Chemicals Ltd
	Maximum stock	16 × 5 litres
	Minimum stock	2 × 5 litres

DATE	RECEIVED	ISSUE	BALANCE
	—	—	6 × 5 litres
	—	2 × 5 litres	4 × 5 litres
	12 × 5 litres	4 × 5 litres	12 × 5 litres

Monthly consumption sheets.   To find out the total of items used over a period of time or to compare usage rate, this information can be taken from the monthly consumption sheet. A typical page is shown below.

ITEM	UNIT	JAN	FEB	MARCH	ETC	TOTAL
Detergent	5 litres	2	3	2		7
Polish						
Emulsion	5 litres	1	2	1		4

STOCKTAKING

Stocktaking may be done monthly, quarterly or yearly, depending on the policy of the establishment. It is an essential process to prove the accuracy of the stock records and should be carried out by departmental heads or external auditors. In order to carry out stocktaking it is necessary to suspend all movements of goods during the count and to make sure that all goods are checked and accounted for. For example, a count of bed linen and single sheets involves checking and counting:

- sheets on all beds,
- dirty sheets awaiting laundry,
- single sheets sent to the laundry,
- sheets in stock for use,
- new sheets in store.

Any discrepancies should be noted and investigated and where necessary deleted from the stock sheets.

ISSUING

The system of issuing goods from the stores to the various departments will vary, but a tight system of control should be in operation. All issues should be made against a requisition or specification form for ease of control. On the requisition form the items may be listed alphabetically, number coded, or each item may be handwritten as a list. On receipt of the requisition form, items should be checked and weighed accurately before the order is made ready for despatch or collection. In some establishments stores may be issued:

- daily,
- weekly,
- monthly,
- by a topping-up system on the cleaners'/chambermaids' trolley — to meet a required basic stock,
- by a topping-up system in the cleaners'/chambermaids' cupboard to meet a required basic stock,
- new for old, or full for empty.

Whichever system is used spot checks should be made by the supervisor to check usage rate, and prevent wastage and pilfering. Staff should be discouraged from ordering more than is required, and issues should be permitted only on the stated day or time unless there is an emergency.

When items are issued from bulk containers the following procedures should be adhered to:

- Try to standardise containers in size and colour.
- Make sure containers are labelled giving contents, dilution rates, hazards concerning use (e.g. poison).
- Measure out requirements very carefully to prevent spillage and wastage.
- Make sure containers used are made of the correct materials (e.g. do not put solvents in plastic containers).

After all the orders have been completed by the storekeeper they should be despatched to the various departments and then the appropriate records brought up to date.

PRODUCT SAMPLING

It is important that the supervisor and storekeeper keep up to date with new products and equipment on the market so that the most suitable product is used for a particular job. They can do this by using a testing panel over a period of time and analysing the results. These results can then be compared with those from the products previously used.

QUESTIONS

1. Briefly indicate the qualities you would look for when appointing a storekeeper.

2. Define the following methods of buying:
   (a) wholesale,
   (b) retail,
   (c) cash-and-carry.

3. Discuss the advantages and disadvantages of bulk buying cleaning materials.

4. Define the following:
   (a) stock rotation,
   (b) stocktaking,
   (c) the topping-up system.

5. Outline an efficient system for keeping records in the stores.

6. Prepare a stock-control system for use in:
   (a) a large central stores,
   (b) cleaning stores in a residential college for 500 students.

18 Maintenance

All too often the maintenance of buildings and equipment is on the bottom rung of the priorities ladder. Initial costs are discussed carefully, but future maintenance and aftercare are often forgotten. Loss of an area or equipment due to faults, breakdowns or damage is expensive, wasteful of resources, and inconvenient. Every item, every surface, and even the fabric of the building have to be replaced or renewed at certain times because they are worn, damaged, disused, difficult to clean, expensive to maintain or obsolete.

REPAIR OR REPLACE?

Before a decision is made the following questions should be asked:
- Will the allocated budget cover the cost of replacement?
- Can the existing item be remodelled or repaired to meet new needs, especially safety?
- Would a newer item save fuel, staff and maintenance costs?
- How long is left in the life cycle of the old item?
- Is there a replacement item already in stock?

TYPES OF MAINTENANCE

There are three areas of maintenance: planned, preventive, and emergency.

Planned Maintenance

Planned maintenance is a more detailed look at all plant on a regular basis. The time factor for each check is determined by the use, age and appearance of the area; legal and safety factors must also be considered. Planned maintenance is normally carried out in quiet periods, at the end of the season, vacation time or even during the night, by highly trained staff.

The type of work done during a scheduled planned maintenance check can be:
- cleaning, servicing, oiling, adjusting of equipment, and *in situ* repairs,
- periodic 'deep' cleaning of surfaces, fabrics, furnishings, and fittings,
- redecoration of internal and external surfaces,
- checking for minor and major faults, and safety and legal requirements.

Planned maintenance needs to be well organised to work efficiently. It is often possible to combine many operations in one area — periodic cleaning with redecoration and replacement of plant, for example.

Planned maintenance will often be contracted out to specialist firms. This provides expert service, allows permanent staff to carry on routine duties, and can be allowed for in the yearly budget.

If an area or item is leased or hired, then the maintenance costs should be taken into account in the terms of the contract.

When the establishment is large it may have its own team of plumbers, electricians, engineers and decorators. Group hotels or hospitals have skilled staff within, thereby providing a bigger back-up team of specialists.

Detailed records of all planned maintenance are necessary. Each piece of equipment, new or old, internal or external, should have a card or file giving details of:

- date of purchase,
- area of use,
- guarantee expiry date,
- methods of cleaning and servicing.

It is customary for the housekeeper or supervisor to inform all departments of any planned maintenance that requires sealing off rooms or areas.

Preventive Maintenance

Preventive maintenance is usually incorporated in the daily check carried out by the housekeeper or supervisor. It usually takes place after an area has been cleaned. Oiling, belt replacement, regular cleaning and checking should prevent breakdowns in machinery. A check of faults, misuse and damage should be included. This check relies on the ability of the checker to see and report minor faults before they become major ones.

Good staff training is essential for daily cleaning and maintenance of surfaces and equipment; faults or damage quickly reported and corrected can save time and expense. Work cards are valuable for new and existing staff in explaining cleaning and maintenance procedures.

Emergency Maintenance

It is necessary to have allocated allowances for any unexpected breakdowns or faults, unless the equipment or premises are leased or hired. If the business is not large enough to have its own skilled work force, a list of specialists and emergency services should be drawn up to cope with any problems.

REPORTING MAINTENANCE

A daily checklist is carried by the housekeeper or supervisor. Faults, damage, missing items, etc. are noted down. These faults are then transferred to worksheets. One copy is sent to the relevant section (e.g. electricians, plumbing); the other copy is kept for future reference.

The worksheet should give exact details of:

- name of person reporting fault,
- date and time,
- area of fault,
- exact location of fault,
- date and time of repair and/or replacement,
- time taken to carry out repair,
- name of person who carried out the repair or replacement.

MAINTENANCE NEEDS FOR GIVEN AREAS

Details for different areas are given in the table below.

AREA	FREQUENCY OF CHECKS	PERIODIC CARE
Kitchen and dining room, equipment and linen	Check at least every month to keep standards high and maintain safety and hygiene levels. Gas and electrical equipment must be serviced at least once a year by specialists	Daily cleaning is often enough, except for gas and electrical equipment. Kitchen and dining room linen should be inspected for stains, tears and damage and sent immediately to the linen room for repair. Most equipment needs replacing every 5–8 years. Defrost refrigerators regularly
Fixtures and fittings	Most items are cleaned and maintained in the daily or weekly routine	Careful cleaning of upholstery and wood surfaces will help maintain condition longer. Fixtures and fittings are often changed in hotel guestrooms every 5 years; this will depend on amount of use, budget and appearance. Light bulbs and tubes are usually replaced as necessary, although it may be policy to replace all bulbs and tubes together. Inspection of furniture for insect holes will be necessary. Curtains should be cleaned
Ventilation systems	Should be checked at least once a year, more if conditions are dirty or greasy	Filters need frequent checking and cleaning if the area is in constant use. Motors and fans need to be inspected for faults and wear
Structure and fabric of building	Checked twice a year, autumn and spring. If possible, inspect on a wet day to see if water is entering the building	Roofs, windows, insulation and DPC all need careful inspection and repair or replacement as soon as possible
Electrical systems	Six-monthly checks by qualified electricians are necessary	Cables, sockets, flexes and light switches may need attention. Constantly blowing fuses may be an indication of a fault
Water, sanitation and drainage systems	Six-monthly checks by specialist companies are preferable	Before winter starts check and clear overflows, gullies, etc., to make sure water will run free. External pipes should be lagged. Tanks and cisterns must be in good condition and free from silt. Lift manholes to clean grease and silt traps

AREA	FREQUENCY OF CHECKS	PERIODIC CARE
Painting and decorating	Frequency depends on appearance and condition of the surface and on money allocated	Painted internal surfaces can be cleaned as required within the daily routine. Other internal surfaces, wallpaper, fabrics, etc., are difficult to maintain. These are usually replaced every 3–4 years, depending on the area and degree of damage. External surfaces are painted on average every 5–7 years, depending on conditions and budget allowances

QUESTIONS

1. What are the advantages of keeping individual maintenance records?

2. List the advantages and disadvantages of having maintenance contracts with specialist companies instead of using direct labour.

3. Try to find out the meaning of the word terotechnology.

4. How would you start to introduce a system of planned and preventive maintenance in a small private hospital, which previously had no system in operation?

5. What are the effects of poor maintenance on:
   (a) staff welfare and morale,
   (b) guests' comfort,
   (c) establishment's image and standards?

6. Prepare a six-monthly maintenance schedule for a restaurant seating 180 guests.

19 Colour, Design, Decor and Lighting

COLOUR

The appreciation and use of colour may be gained by learning and understanding a few basic guidelines. Colour scheming is an interesting mixture of art and science. Most people will, at some time, have to prepare a colour scheme for either business or home. Materials, labour and overheads are expensive, so it is important to be confident in the use of colour, texture and design.

Understanding Colour

White sunlight may be broken down into a band of different colours by passing it through a triangular prism. These colours are red, orange, yellow, green, blue, indigo and violet, and are known as the 'spectrum colours' or 'simple hues'. They are present in all white light. When white light falls on to a surface some of these colours are absorbed, others are reflected. Observation of colour depends on the amount of absorption and reflection. A white surface reflects all colours equally; a black area absorbs all colours equally. Coloured areas are ones that only reflect their particular colour, so red reflects red, green reflects green, etc. Red, yellow and blue are classed as 'primary hues', because they cannot be obtained by mixing any other colours together.

Secondary hues can be obtained by mixing two primary hues:
- Red and yellow form orange.
- Red and blue form purple.
- Yellow and blue form green.

Tertiary hues can be obtained by combining two secondary colours together:
- Orange and green form citrine.
- Green and purple form slate.
- Purple and orange form russet.

The diagrams opposite show a colour circle (with hues in their natural order) and the primary, secondary and tertiary colours.

Colour Scheming

There are other requirements needed to experience the sensation of colour. Apart from the source of light and the surface appearance, the perception of the viewer is of fundamental importance.

This perception gives us information on distance, scale, proportion, shape, colour, range and texture. However, our perception can be deceived, especially if the colour designer so wishes.

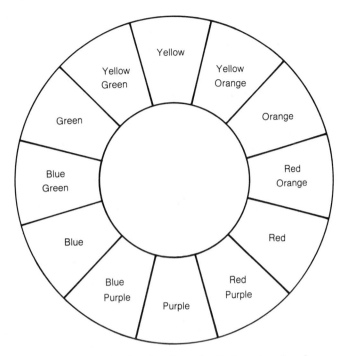

The colour circle showing hues in their natural order

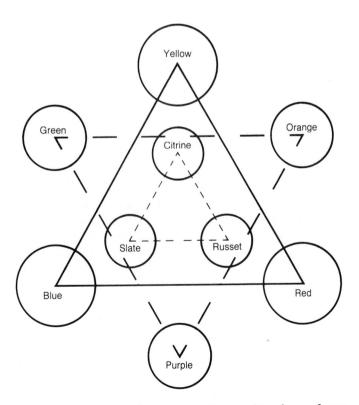

Diagram showing: primary, secondary and tertiary colours

There are also physiological reactions to colour. After closely watching a certain colour (e.g. red) the eye retains an 'after-image' for a few moments after turning away from it. It is necessary for the walls and ceilings of operating theatres to be painted pale green to provide a complementary or opposite colour to give the eyes a rest after working in an area with so much red. Factories mass-producing items of one or two colours need careful colour planning.

The appearance of any colour, fabric or wall-covering is influenced by the background colour next to it, and the amount and quality of light that falls upon it. A primary or secondary hue will appear richer and darker when placed on a white background rather than a grey one, and brighter and lighter on a very dark grey or black background. All types of artificial lighting change or alter colour:

- Incandescent light absorbs blue and green; colours look warmer than in natural daylight.
- Fluorescent light absorbs red and orange, so colours look colder.
- Sodium light absorbs red, blue and green, making most colours look either yellow or black.
- Mercury light absorbs red and yellow; other colours in this light can look bluish green.

Warm colours give a feeling of closeness or advancement. High ceilings or end walls of long corridors could be designed with warm colours. Cool colours create the opposite effect, giving the feeling of distance, space and calmness. For designs with cold colours in mind it is necessary to appreciate that these colours are best used in south, or south-west facing areas. Beige, greys and lilacs can also be considered 'cool' unless they contain an element of pink.

Colour can affect the apparent weight or size of an area or object: a chair painted pinky beige appears lighter than the same chair painted black. Ugly defects and features in an area can sometimes be disguised by the clever use of colour blending.

DESIGNING

Closely examine one area at a time and consider the following:
- What is the area used for? Who will use it?
- Is the area north- or south-facing? A good rule of thumb would be warm colours for north-facing areas, cool colours for south-facing areas.
- What is the size of the area? Warm colours advance, cold colours recede.
- Are there any bad features that need to be disguised by colour?
- Existing furnishings have to be taken into consideration. In most cases the colour scheme is worked from the floor upwards, where there is a floor covering already *in situ.*
- Ease of cleaning and maintenance. Colours and paint types used on lower walls, skirting and doors should be chosen with care.
- Existing lighting, real and artificial. The colours used must promote good visibility without causing glare, except in specific designated areas such as restaurants, pubs, etc. Check all colour schemes during both day and evening light.
- The overall temperature of the area is important. A cool blue or green would give a feeling of coolness to a steamy kitchen or laundry; a warm orange or yellow gives the feeling of warmth.

PREPARING A COLOUR SCHEME

Monochrome. This is a scheme of one colour, although many shades, tints and textures can be incorporated.

Complementary. This scheme uses colours from directly opposite parts of the colour wheel or slightly grey hues of these colours, e.g. red and blue, yellow and purple.

Analogous or related. This scheme uses colours that are side by side on the colour wheel. Care is needed if intending to use the blue and purples together.

WALL AND SURFACE COVERINGS

Wall Coverings

After the overall colour scheme has been decided upon the next area to examine is the type of fabric, wall coverings or paint to be used. There is a wide variety of coverings to choose from, ranging from traditional paint and wallpaper through to hessian and silk grasses. Each covering has to be judged by its characteristics, expected durability, suitability and price. All coverings can damage easily, especially around skirtings, staircases, light switches, etc. With extra thought at the design stage, many forms of protection against damage can be incorporated. A clear emulsion varnish can be used over paper in danger areas to help keep walls grease- and scuff-free. Perspex fitted behind luggage racks and light switches also helps.

Wall surfaces, once covered, should act as a background for furnishings. Too strong a colour or pattern can produce a hard effect. Broad vertical stripes make a wall seem taller, horizontal stripes give an impression of width. Try not to combine different patterns or textures in the same area unless you are really confident of the effect. The best mixes often combine opposites (e.g. small floral with bold geometrical designs).

How to Calculate the Amount of Paper Needed

Measure the height of the room from the skirting to the picture rail or ceiling and also the distance around the walls, including doors and windows. Check with one of the calculating charts on the next page to see how many rolls of wallpaper you need. If your measurement for the distance around the room falls between two measurements on the chart, use the larger figure. Basic measurements will be sufficient for plain or free match papers. Where you need to match the pattern you must allow for wastage at the foot of each length according to the depth of the repeat. Usually an extra roll for every five is enough, although you may need to allow extra if the repeat pattern is very deep.

Extra paper will also be needed if the room has recesses or projections since the pattern should be centred on these to give a balanced look.

Storage of Wallpaper

Always store rolls of wallpaper flat. Never stand them on end or you will damage the ends and make it difficult to obtain neat joins between lengths when hanging.

Number of Rolls required — Metric Chart

Distance in metres round walls incl. doors/windows	Height in metres from skirting							
	2 – 2.2	2.2 – 2.5	2.5 – 2.7	2.7 – 3	3 – 3.2	3.2 – 3.5	3.5 – 3.7	3.7 – 4
10	5	5	6	6	7	7	8	8
11	5	6	7	7	8	8	9	9
12	6	6	7	8	8	9	9	10
13	6	7	8	8	9	10	10	10
14	7	7	8	9	10	10	11	11
15	7	8	9	9	10	11	12	12
16	8	8	9	10	11	11	12	13
17	8	9	10	10	11	12	13	14
18	9	9	10	11	12	13	14	15
19	9	10	11	12	13	14	15	16
20	9	10	11	12	13	14	15	16
21	10	11	12	13	14	15	16	17
22	10	11	13	14	15	16	17	18
23	11	12	13	14	15	17	18	19
24	11	12	14	15	16	17	18	20
25	12	13	14	15	17	18	19	20
26	12	13	15	16	17	19	20	21
27	13	14	15	17	18	19	21	22
28	13	14	16	17	19	20	21	23
29	13	15	16	18	19	21	22	24
30	14	15	17	18	20	21	23	24

Number of Rolls required — Imperial Chart

Distance in feet round walls incl. doors/windows	Height in feet from skirting						
	7 – 7½	7½ – 8	8 – 8½	8½ – 9	9 – 9½	9½ – 10	10 – 10½
30	4	5	5	5	6	6	6
34	5	5	5	5	6	6	7
38	5	6	6	6	7	7	8
42	6	6	7	7	7	8	8
46	6	7	7	7	8	8	9
50	7	7	8	8	9	9	10
54	7	8	9	9	9	10	10
58	8	8	9	9	10	10	11
62	8	9	10	10	10	11	12
66	9	9	10	10	11	12	13
70	9	10	11	11	12	12	13
74	10	10	12	12	12	13	14
78	10	11	12	12	13	14	15
82	11	11	13	13	14	14	16
86	12	12	14	14	14	15	16
90	12	13	14	14	15	16	17
94	13	13	15	15	15	16	18
98	13	14	15	15	16	17	19

Wall Finishes

These are itemised in the table below.

TYPE OF FINISH	SIZE	CHARACTERISTICS AND USES
Embossed	530 mm × 10 m	Slightly heavier quality paper than pulp, which is cheaper and thinner. Can be coloured and patterned. *Use:* Lounges, bedrooms, reception areas
Woodchip	530 mm × 10 m	Woodchips are incorporated into paper to provide a textured surface. Has to be painted. Soils and tears easily. *Use:* Mainly domestic
Washable papers	530 mm × 10 m	Spongeable. Durable. Acrylic/resin based. *Use:* Bathrooms, corridors and toilets. Not suitable for industrial or commercial kitchens
Flock	530 mm × 10 m	Modern imitation of handmade 18th and 19th century papers. Large-scale designs. Expensive to purchase. Tends to hold dust and dirt. *Use:* Very limited, mainly dining areas and lounges
Anaglypta	530 mm × 10 m	Embossed to provide a raised or textured pattern. Initially cheap but must be painted after hanging. *Use:* Ceilings and walls
*Vinyl	530 mm × 10 m	Very durable. Useful for areas where a high resistance to water and abrasion is required. Must not be applied to new surfaces or where there is a history of dampness. *Use:* Corridors and dining rooms
*Laminated plastic sheets	Cut to required size	Comes in a wide range of designs. Bonded to blockboard or chipboard. Very durable even to cigarette burns. *Use:* Bathrooms, cloakrooms, corridors, toilets
*Wood	Panels cut to size	Initially expensive to purchase and install but needs minimum aftercare. *Use:* Panels in walls and ceilings
*Glass	Sold as tiles or sheets	Fixed as tiles or screens, clear or tinted. Useful for areas needing extra light. Easy to clean and maintain. *Use:* Halls, corridors, small rooms

TYPE OF FINISH	SIZE	CHARACTERISTICS AND USES
*Marble and ceramic tiles	Approximately 6 mm thick, 110 mm² or 152 mm²	Available in a wide range of colours and textures. Should be cemented professionally. Usually expensive. Extremely hard wearing. Use: Bathrooms and kitchens
*Hessian wool strands Suede		Usually used in luxury areas. Expensive but hard-wearing. Care is needed in cleaning and maintenance. Use: Reception areas, restaurants and bars

Note: Hand-printed, continental or special coverings may be supplied in non-standard sizes.

* Special adhesives and fixing methods are required for certain finishes; consult manufacturer.

PAINT

Paint can have many advantages over other wall finishes. It is usually the least expensive; it is readily available; it is suitable for most areas; colour schemes are easily changed; and it is easy to clean and maintain. All paints are basically a pigment mixed with a selected medium, and other additives.

Paint is used on surfaces to protect, to decorate, for information (i.e. for direction signs, colour coding for pipes carrying gas or electricity) and to make the surface washable.

Types of paint are shown in the table below.

Types of Paint

TYPE	CHARACTERISTICS
Emulsion paints 5 litres cover approximately 60–65 m² on smooth non-porous surfaces. Different qualities for interior or exterior use	Water-based paint, consists of particles of synthetic resin dispersed in water. Not as durable as oil-based paint. Moisture is able to pass through some types. Washable. Quick and easy to apply over a wide range of surfaces. Non-toxic. Little or no smell. Quick-drying. A full range of BS 4800 colours available
Eggshell finish Also known as satin or lustre finish. 5 litres cover 80 m² on smooth, non-porous surfaces	Usually an oil-based paint. The finished result has a slight sheen. Washable and stain-resistant. Takes approximately 12–16 hours to dry. Limited range of colours available
Alkyd gloss finishes 5 litres cover approximately 75–85 m²	Interior and exterior paint, made up from pigment mixed with a medium of oil and white spirit. Durable. Has a strong distinctive smell. Heat-resistant to 93 °C. Easy to apply, takes approximately 12–16 hours to dry. Available in a full range of colours

TYPE	CHARACTERISTICS
Multi-colour finish 5 litres cover approximately 14–20 m² depending on type — cellulose or vinyl resin medium	Not suitable for exterior use. Two types available. Decorative finish of 2, 3, or 4 specks, spots or streaks. Non-toxic. Washable. Durable. Provides good camouflage for uneven surfaces, unsightly pipes, etc. Hard wearing. Cellulose has strong unpleasant odour
Varnish	Clear, unpigmented finishes. Oil and water types available in one- or two-pack mixes. Finish is either high gloss, eggshell or matt. High gloss may be used internally or externally. Eggshell and matt internally only. Use where clear finish is required, e.g. to enhance the natural grain of the wood. Water varnishes may be used in certain circumstances to seal natural surfaces, internal brick and stone — also to make washable, patterned wallpapers

COSTING

For large contracts, the procedure is as follows:

> Architect or designer prepares a specification and scaled plans in consultation with the client.

> Quantity surveyor prepares the quantities needed to carry out the proposed scheme.

> The bill of quantities, specification and scaled plans are put out to tender.

> Decorating contractors, after studying the quantities, specification and scaled plans, submit their tenders to the architect for approval.

> One tender is accepted.

> The client pays the approved contractor at the completion of the job, provided everything is satisfactory.

For small contracts, there is another procedure:

> The prospective client approaches the decorating contractor direct.

> The contractor obtains details from the client or his agent after the site has been inspected and measured.

A specification is then given to the client listing the work to be carried out, cost, time, etc., for his approval.

If the estimate and specification is acceptable to the client or his agent, work can commence.

LIGHTING

Light is a form of energy that enables the eye to see. It can be natural (from the sun) or artificial (from lamps).

Measurement of Light

- The lumen is a unit of luminous flux (flow), i.e. the amount of light emitted per second in a cone of a certain size by a point source of known intensity.
- The lux is the unit of illumination, equal to one lumen per m^2.

A light meter is essential to architects, designers, etc., in assessing a building's lighting requirements.

Some materials — glass and certain plastics — absorb little light, and allow light to pass through. The thicker the glass, etc., the less light filters through.

There are situations where natural light is either not sufficient, non-existent or not needed. Artificial light can have many advantages: it is readily available, predictable, and reaches inner work areas, etc. Most buildings are designed to use both forms of illumination.

TYPES OF ARTIFICIAL LIGHTS

There are three types available: tungsten, discharge, and filament.

Tungsten bulb or filament lamp.   The filament is a tungsten wire encased in sealed glass. When electric current is passed through the bulb, the filament glows white hot and gives off light.

Lamps last approximately 1000 hours. Special long-life bulbs are more expensive but provide up to 2000 hours of light. Lamps may be labelled 25 W, 40 W, 60 W, 100 W, 150 W. W is an abbreviation for watts, the unit of power.

Tungsten bulb finishes are:
- clear — filament is visible, not suitable for all fittings,
- pearl — best for general use,
- silica-coated — silvery light, best for open lighting fittings.

Discharge lights   are sodium or mercury vapour-filled glass tubes, which have metal plates at each end of the tube to allow electric current to flow along. The type of gas used inside the tube dictates the colour of the lighted tube. Sodium glows yellow, mercury vapour produces a blue to white glow.

Fluorescent lamps   contain mercury vapour and work like discharge lamps. The inside of the tube is coated with a fluorescent powder, and when the electricity flows through the tube the mercury vapour hits the powder and gives off a glow. Fluorescent lamps are versatile in that different powders can be used inside the tube to obtain a wide range of colour glow, from white to 'de luxe' warm white.

The average life of a fluorescent lamp is 7500 hours, as compared with approximately 1000 hours for a filament lamp.

The properties and uses of artificial light are summarised in the following table. Some examples of bulb and lamp fittings are shown on p. 188.

Properties and uses of Artificial Light

TYPE	LUMENS PER WATT	MAIN USE	CHARACTERISTICS
Tungsten bulb or filament lamp	5–8	Domestic lighting	Cheap to install; yellowish light; inefficient
Fluorescent	25–80, depending on colour of tube	Wide use. Size ranges: 15–244 cm. Various wattages	Expensive to install; tends to be inefficient in high or low temperatures; cheap to run
Sodium discharge	120–175	Street lighting, car parks, loading bays	Cheap to run; changes surface colours
Mercury fluorescent	35–55	Commercial, industrial	Cheap to run; expensive to install; changes surface colours

EFFECTS OF ARTIFICIAL LIGHT ON COLOUR

Colours appear differently under artificial light compared with daylight. A comparison is shown in the following table.

COLOUR OF SURFACE IN DAYLIGHT	OUTSIDE LIGHTING SODIUM	MERCURY	DOMESTIC LIGHTING TUNGSTEN	FLOURESCENT
Red	Brown	Brown or black	Bright red	Dull red
Blue	Brown or blue	Deep violet	Dull green-blue	Bright blue
Green	Brown-yellow	Dark green	Yellow-green	Cool blue-green
Yellow	Yellow	Green-yellow	Intense yellow	Green-yellow
White	Light-yellow	Blue-white	Cream-off-white	White

Factors to Consider When Planning a Lighting System

- Decide on the amount of light needed for the area. Seek professional advice.
  Recommended values of illumination
  General laboratories 400 lux
  Library reading tables 600 lux
  Restaurant tables 100 lux
  Bars 50-70 lux
  Kitchens 200 lux
  Bedrooms 100 lux
  Hospital wards 50 lux
  Cash desk 400 lux
  Stairs and corridors 100 lux
- If artificially lighting an area, check heat gains. Tungsten lamps give off more heat than fluorescent. If heat gain is high, light fittings can be designed to extract the hot air and either reuse it or dispel it.
- Design and durability. Decide if the general lighting scheme is to be: *general* (for the whole room), *direct* (mainly for a particular surface) or *indirect* (lighting by reflection).

Lamps dispel light upwards, sideways and downwards. Most commercial fittings aim to provide some general, and some direct light. It is unwise to choose solely indirect lighting as a means of illumination as this usually means the ceiling is the brightest area. Light fittings are expensive. Will the shades and cases be easy to handle? If the light is to be hung from above, will the ceiling need to be reinforced?

All light fittings should carry the yellow and black safety tag of the British Electrical Approvals Board for Domestic Appliances.

- Ease of replacement especially if glass shades are used. Fluorescent tubes can be difficult to replace if fitted inside a diffuser or box.
- Cleaning. It has been estimated that as much as 50% of the illumination can be lost if lamps and reflectors are not cleaned regularly. Can the fittings be cleaned easily and replaced?
- Cost. Tungsten lamps are generally cheaper to install and operate except in large areas where artificial light is used for a large part of the day. Tungsten lamps are more economical for areas which require lighting at irregular times.
- Will the lighting scheme provide adequate illumination of the work surface?
- Any lighting scheme should allow for reflection, absorption of light and glare.

Light can be reflected by walls, furnishing fabrics, floors, etc. Artificial light in particular has a 'lightening' effect.

Fabrics, painted surfaces and building materials can absorb a percentage of light rays while reflecting the remainder. On a sunny day this gives the surface a much lighter appearance, but on a dull day the surface appears much darker because fewer rays have been reflected. Glare and reflected glare should be avoided; it increases eye strain and produces harsh, lighted areas for working.

Light Distribution from the Different Lamps

The ways in which light may radiate from a light source are illustrated in the diagram opposite.

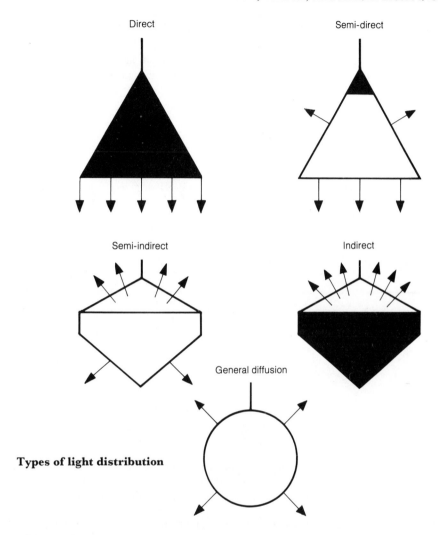

Types of light distribution

Types of Lighting and Light Fittings — a Summary

Directional lighting.   Spotlight beams can vary from wide, soft-edged beams to narrow, hard-edged beams. 'Framing' spots can highlight a painting, and a floodlamp can highlight a china cabinet.

Working light.   Direct, glare-free lighting to worktops, sinks and cookers is the first priority in the kitchen and for areas where sewing, studying and hobbies take place.

General lighting.   About 20 Watts per square metre of floor area should be adequate to light rooms with light-coloured decor.

Local lighting.   Rooms can look attractive when pools of light are focused on an item of furniture or aimed to illuminate a picture.

Emergency lighting.   There must be an extra form of lighting totally independent from the main supply to provide lights for corridors, exit signs, staircases, and public rooms in cases of emergency.

Ceiling fittings.   Opal glass bowl shades are best for toilets, bathrooms and kitchens; similar decorative glass or plastic shades for halls, landings and lounges. Be careful not to exceed the recommended wattage of filament lamps in enclosed fittings. Use fluorescent fittings for utility areas where a good working light is necessary.

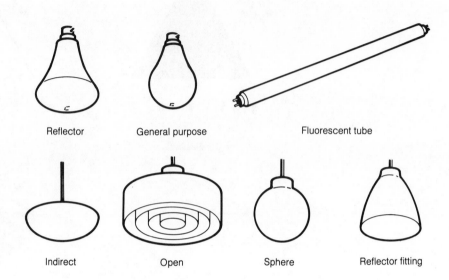

Reflector   General purpose   Fluorescent tube

Indirect   Open   Sphere   Reflector fitting

Examples of bulbs and electric light fittings

Lighting tracks.   Spotlights plugged into an aluminium channel, screwed to ceilings or walls and connected to a power point offer a greater degree of flexibility to lighting. Some tracks have independent circuits to permit individual switching.

Pendant fittings.   Diffusing shades provide more light but with harsher shadows. Unless coloured shades have white linings, light emitted at the top or base will also be coloured. Decorative reflectors concentrate light downwards, and rise-and-fall fittings over tables can create an intimate atmosphere at meal times.

Wall brackets.   Adjustable wall lights, with a wide soft beam, can be used to bounce light off the ceiling or can be directed downwards over furniture; 40–60 W lamps are usually adequate.

Portable lamps.   These can be traditional table or floor standing lamps or modern versions featuring one or more spotlamps directed at specific areas or objects. Dimmers can be plugged into lampholders and the lighting level varied.

Kitchen lighting.   Fit tungsten lamps or fluorescent tubes under the front edge of wall units so that the light falls directly where it is needed. Warm white de luxe or Softone fluorescent tubes are most suitable.

Down lights.   Cylindrical fittings mounted on or in the ceiling which use ordinary lamps or spots (up to 150 W) will light a restricted area beneath, so they must be sited carefully. Some will also throw light to one side to light walls only or illuminate pictures.

Top-up lighting. A small fluorescent fitting, up to 61 cm long, can be mounted behind a pelmet or under a wall-mounted cabinet to light up areas in shadow.

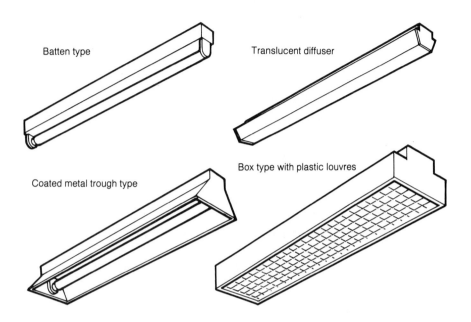

Examples of flourescent light fittings

QUESTIONS

1. Obtain a colour card and give five suitable colours for each of the following areas:
   (a) kitchens and bathrooms,
   (b) food preparation area,
   (c) restaurants, canteens and pubs,
   (d) schools, playrooms, circulation areas,
   (e) hospital wards, day and waiting rooms.

2. Give two examples of where an area is painted a specific colour to give 'eye rest', especially after perceiving the colour red for any length of time.

3. Obtain a colour chart and examine the colours and the relationships between the colours. Place the chart next to areas of light and then dark. Observe the difference. Alternatively, cut a 1 cm² hole in a piece of white, grey and black card, 6 cm². Place the cards over various colour squares in the chart and discuss the effect of each background.

4. List the advantages and disadvantages in general terms of wallpaper and paint.

5. How would you clean and maintain:
   (a) hessian,
   (b) wool strands on paper,
   (c) gloss paint.
   How would you remove grease stains from the above?

6. Using a colour chart give the names or numbers of three examples of colours forming each of the following schemes:

(a) analogous,

(b) monochromatic,

(c) complementary.

7. Prepare a colour scheme for a 24-bedroom hotel extension (all rooms are standardised in layout) facing south on the edge of a large city.

8. List the advantages and disadvantages of artificial and natural light.

9. Outline the lighting system you would choose for the following areas:

(a) bedroom,

(b) industrial kitchen,

(c) restaurant,

(d) bar,

(e) linen room,

(f) corridor,

(g) lift.

20 Fuels

ELECTRICITY Electricity is generated from four main sources: coal, oil, water power and nuclear energy. It is supplied from power stations and distributed by means of underground cables or overhead conductors to industry and domestic users. Electricity is initially distributed at 132 000 volts.

Transformers, placed strategically throughout the country, reduce the voltage to 11 000 for further distribution; local transformer stations reduce the voltage still further. This reduced supply is described as 'three-phase 415/240 volts, 50 cycles per second'.

In this supply, an electric current, whose voltage alternates from positive to negative 50 times each second, is distributed by three wires (phase wires) and a neutral wire which is earthed at the substation.

The voltage between any two wires is 415 volts; between any phase wire and neutral it is 240 volts. Small buildings, houses, shops, etc., are served by two wires; one phase plus the neutral. This is known as 'single-phase supply' and gives a voltage of 240 volts for the premises.

For larger premises it is usual to bring all four wires into the building; this is known as 'three-phase supply'.

Entry of Electricity into the Building

In towns, electrical cables are normally underneath the ground and are brought up into the building at ground level or into a basement. Rural areas often receive electricity from overhead cables. Once inside a building the cable passes through the main safety fuse and meters of the local electricity council and on to the consumer's main switch and distribution board.

Distribution Circuits

In most buildings, electricity is divided into three types of circuit: lighting, socket outlets and fixed apparatus.

Lighting. Each circuit has a cable with two conductors, live and neutral, which run between a number of ceiling roses or wall lights. Lighting is normally operated in circuits with 5 amp fuses, although for industrial areas or large buildings 15 amp is recommended. Several lamps can be controlled by one or more switches or several switches can operate one lamp. EEC regulations now require earthing of lighting systems. A lighting circuit is illustrated over the page.

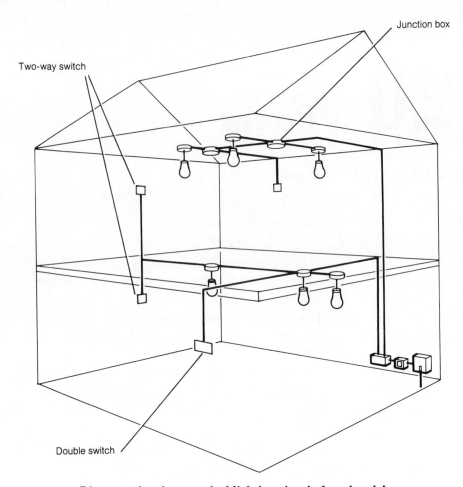

Junction box

Two-way switch

Double switch

Diagram showing a typical lighting circuit, loop in wiring

Socket outlets   enable portable electrical equipment to be used in a wide variety of areas . Modern buildings have 13 amp ring circuits. A cable carrying two conductors and an earth travel around part of the building to and from the distribution board where a 30 amp fuse serves the line conductor. Along this circuit are sockets which provide power for non-fixed electrical appliances. A plug is available that carries a 13 amp fuse; when a fault develops the fuse 'blows' and leaves the other sockets of the circuit intact.

The maximum number of 13 amp sockets on a ring circuit is 10, except for areas where there must be a separate ring for every 100 m² or part of 100 m².

Fixed apparatus.   Cookers and water heaters often have their own individual fuses and circuits. There should be a switch nearby to isolate the current so that repairs may be carried out in safety.

Earth Connections   All electrical supply must be well insulated. Standards of insulation vary with voltage. Conductors are covered with an insulating material, e.g. rubber, plastic, porcelain, ebonite or glass, or supported on insulators within an earthed casing, with a clear air gap round each conductor.

If insulation is damaged or wires are displaced, electrical wiring could become live and therefore highly dangerous. This is avoided by earthing the metal-work so that the fuse blows immediately the heavy current flows to earth. The neutral wire is earthed; but this earthing is not sufficient, so a separate set of conductors is designed for most electrical installations. The earth connection is situated in the building. Occasionally metal water pipes are used, or copper plates may be buried in the ground. In bathroom areas where special care is needed, no socket outlets are allowed. Light switches must be outside the area, or operated by a pull cord.

Fuse Boxes and Circuit Breakers

All electrical installations and circuits need to be protected by a fuse or by circuit breaker.

A fuse is designed to melt instantly and break the circuit if too much current goes through it. Fuses also 'blow' if an appliance develops a short-circuit. A circuit breaker will switch itself to the 'off' position if there is a problem with either overloading or short-circuiting. Once the problem has been rectified, switch the current to the 'on' position to restart. Sometimes the circuit breaker is a button that only needs pressing to reconnect the circuit.

Self-help

In most establishments staff are discouraged from tampering with the electrical supply or appliances. However, in small businesses or in an emergency it is necessary to know how to replace a fuse in a fuse box or plug, and how to change a plug.

First it is necessary to understand the connection to a fuse: current is carried from the power supply to the appliance through a plug and flexible cord. British and European regulations specify the same colour coding for all flexible cords supplying electrical appliances. Make sure the live lead (brown) is connected to the fused or live side of the plug. If connected to the unfused side the equipment is still live even if the fuse in the plug bows.

Replacing fuses. A ring main circuit has two types of fuse as protection against overloading — a small cartridge fuse in each plug and a main fuse in the consumer unit or fuse board. A lighting circuit is protected by a main fuse only.

Plug fuses. If an appliance stops working, switch off immediately (turn off the appliance itself and the socket outlet if both have switches). Remove the plug, unscrew the top and take out the fuse. Fit a substitute fuse or check the existing fuse as described below and replace if necessary. Also check connections for loose or disconnected wires. Refit the plug cover. If the appliance still fails to work, and the main fuse is intact, get the appliance checked by an approved electrician.

Main fuses. If a main fuse blows, first turn off the main switch. This may be on the consumer unit or on a separate switch box nearby. Remove and examine the fuses in turn. Check the cartridge fuses as described previously or try a substitute fuse. With rewirable fuses look for wire breaks or scorch marks on the fuse carrier.

Fit a new fuse wire as follows. Loosen the retaining screws and remove the old wire. Wind the new wire of the correct rating clockwise round one screw. Tighten the screw. Route the wire to the other screw and wind it round clockwise, leaving a little slack. Tighten the screw and cut off surplus wire.

Warning. If a fuse continues to blow, send for a qualified electrician — do not attempt to use a fuse of a higher rating.

Step-by-step guide to wiring a plug.   Adopt the following procedure:
- Uncrew the plug top. Remove the fuse (carefully lever it with a screwdriver if necessary). Loosen one flex-clamp retaining-screw; remove the other.
- Carefully cut away 50 mm (2 in) of the flex's outer sheath. Fasten the sheath firmly under the clamp. Cut the wires to reach approximately 13 mm ($\frac{1}{2}$ in) beyond each terminal.
- Carefully strip enough insulation to expose about 6 mm ($\frac{1}{4}$ in) of wire to pass underneath the clamp.
- Twist the strands of each wire and fit them into the holes or loop them clockwise round the terminals. Check that there are no stray 'whiskers' of bare wire. *Remember:* green/yellow wire to earth terminal (marked E $\frac{\perp}{}$); blue wire to neutral terminal (marked N); brown wire to live terminal (marked L). Note that if the flex has only two wires, the earth terminal in the plug is not used — the wires are connected to the live and neutral terminals only.
- Tighten the screws. Fit the correct fuse. Check that the wires are connected to the correct terminals. Make sure everything is secure. Refit the cover.

A correctly wired plug is shown in the diagram on p.000.

Basic Wiring Systems

Electrical wiring in buildings either runs on the surface or is built into the construction.

Sheathed wiring has two or more wires consisting of metal conductors and insulators in a PVC casing. This wiring can be used on the surface or concealed in timber floors or woodwork.

Conduit wiring can be used on the surface or concealed. It is made of steel, plastic or aluminium. If metal is used, no extra earthing is required. A tubing system is laid to the points where electricity is needed and insulated cables are drawn through them. The main advantage of this system is that the cables can be replaced easily. The British Standards Institution recommends that conduits carrying electrical services are painted orange for easier recognition in emergencies.

Diagram of an electric plug

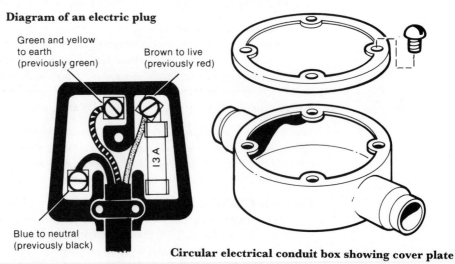

Green and yellow to earth (previously green)

Brown to live (previously red)

13 A

Blue to neutral (previously black)

Circular electrical conduit box showing cover plate

In addition to the wiring systems there are specially designed ducts that carry electrical wiring over and under rooms, around the skirting, etc. Any builder or registered electrician will give advice.

Technical Terms

Voltage. Electricity flows along wires similar to the way water flows through a pipe; it will, however, only flow if the circuit is intact. Voltage can be thought of as the 'pressure' at which the current flows along the wires. The unit of voltage is the volt (abbreviated to V). Electrical appliances should indicate the voltage needed.

Current. The rate of flow of electricity along a wire is called the 'current'. The unit of current is the ampere (abbreviated to amp or A).

Power. The power of an electrical appliance is the current passing through it multiplied by the voltage across it. The unit of power is the watt (abbreviated to W). In other words: 1 watt = 1 amp × 1 volt
Most equipment has the 'wattage' indicated on the outside (e.g. a 60 W bulb or a 3 kilowatt fire labelled 3 kW).

Amount of electricity. The amount of electricity used by an appliance is its power multiplied by the time it is in use. The unit is the kilowatt-hour, which is the amount of electricity used by a 1000 W appliance over one hour. The kilowatt-hour (abbreviated kWh) is the 'unit' referred to on electricity bills.

Electrical Safety

Electricity used carelessly can kill!
Faulty electrical wiring is one of the commonest causes of fire!
If at all unsure of electrical appliances or wiring, call for expert advice. Minor repairs, fuses, plugs, etc., can be changed if necessary with care by trained staff. Always disconnect electrical equipment from the power supply before inspecting for faults or maintenance. Here is a checklist:

- Check all flexes regularly and renew when frayed. *Never* staple flexes along skirting boards or allow carpets to cover them up.
- Place guards in front of all electric fires.
- Check that fuses are of the correct rating for the appliance.
- *Never* use a piece of equipment or machine for a purpose for which it is not designed.
- *Never* fix wires into sockets with matchsticks or pieces of wood.
- Do not tape joints; use junction boxes or connectors.
- Always report electrical defects or faults to the supervisor or housekeeper.
- Use the correct fuse in plugs:
  + 3 A (red) for appliances up to 700 W
  + 5 A (black) for appliances of 700-1000 W
  + 13 A (brown) for appliances of 1000-3000 W
- Do not overload circuits, especially by using adaptors. If necessary, provide an extra socket.
- All metal parts should be earthed. Check that equipment with three-core flex is properly earthed.
- Never touch electrical equipment with wet hands. If contact is made with earthed pipes or taps, the danger is greater.
- Check wires are wired to the correct terminal points. Make sure the earth wire is never connected to the L or N terminal.

- Service wiring systems and appliances regularly. Keep written details of date of service.
- Some equipment has no removable plug, so switch off current at the mains fuse box.

Double-insulated Equipment

The modern trend in design of electrical equipment is for double insulation. Appliances are constructed so that the metal body of the chassis of the machine is totally insulated from the external casing. There is then no need for earth wires. The symbol for double insulation is shown below.

Symbol showing machine is double insulated

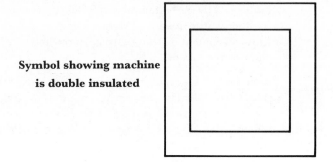

Main Fuses in main circuits

These are:
- 5 A for lighting circuits,
- 15–20 A for immersion heaters,
- 30 A for the ring main circuit and a domestic cooker,
- 45 A for an industrial cooker.

If a main fuse blows, first turn off the mains switch. This may be on the consumer unit or on a separate switch-box nearby. Remove and examine the fuses in turn. Check cartridge fuses by removing the base of a metal-cased torch and place one end of fuse on the bottom of the battery and the other end on the torch casing. If the bulb fails to light when the torch is switched on, the fuse has blown. It may be necessary to fit a new fuse. With rewirable fuses look for wire breaks or scorch marks on the fuse carrier.

Using Electricity Outdoors

Many establishments use electricity for floodlighting, providing power for pools and fountains, etc. Specialised help is needed for wiring and repairs.

GAS

Most of the gas used in the United Kingdom is natural gas or methane, taken from underneath the sea and distributed by a national system of pipes to the industrial and domestic consumer.

On arrival at an onshore terminal, water and impurities are removed, the gas is aired and measured, and the temperature is regulated.

Natural gas has no distinct smell, unlike the old town gas, so a 'gas smell' is added as a safety measure.

Gas is measured in cubic feet but is charged for by the Gas Board in therms. Each therm is 100 000 Btu. 1 kW = 3412 Btu. Therefore,

$$1 \text{ therm} = \frac{100\ 000 \text{ Btu}}{3412 \text{ Btu}} = 29.3 \text{ kW}.$$

One therm of gas can on average:
- heat enough water for 8 baths,
- boil 1 kg (2½ lb) of potatoes 40 times,
- work a small refrigerator for 10 days,
- run an average room heater, full on, for 6 hours,
- run a small background heater for 8 hours per day for 4 days.

Gas is always available. It does not have to be delivered or stored and is comparatively cheap.

Liquefied Gases

All known gases can be made liquid, provided they are made cold enough and/or put under pressure.

In a liquid state, gases take up much less space in transportation and storage. A liquid gas can expand approximately 250 times its volume on changing back into a gas. This happens when the pressure on the liquid gas is released by a valve. Liquid absorbs heat from the container and reverts to a gas. The most common forms of liquefied petroleum gas (LPG) are propane and butane. Both are flammable, have no smell, and are non-toxic. They are available in 0.45–36 kg (1–82 lb) cylinders.

Butane is used mainly for domestic consumers. Propane tends to be used by industry for heating and lighting.

The storage of liquid and compressed gas is governed by 'The Highly Flammable Liquids, And Liquid Petroleum Gases Regulations'. Permission for storage must be obtained from the District Inspector of Factories, when more than 50 litres of gases are stored.

BS 1710, 1975 recommends that all pipes containing liquid or gaseous gas be painted partially or wholly yellow ochre; butane cylinders should be painted blue, and propane cylinders, orange red. Gas levels are checked by weighing the cylinder and subtracting the tare weight. This is the weight of the empty cylinder, which is indicated on the outside of the vessel.

Ventilation

Gas appliances must 'breathe' inwards and outwards. While burning, air is needed so that combustion takes place safely and efficiently. Fresh air is provided by ventilators which are built into a wall, door or window. *Never* block a ventilator.

Many gas appliances need a chimney or flue to make sure the spent gases are removed and not returned to the fresh air in the room. Newer appliances will have built-in systems of ventilation and flueing which take care of the problem automatically. These are known as 'balanced' or 'room-sealed' appliances and they need to be fitted on outside walls. Older appliances connected to chimneys need maintenance more often to check that no blockage of the chimney has occurred. Signs of blockage are discoloration and staining of the wall, or on the appliance itself. If this happens, call the Gas Board immediately.

Safety Procedures   'The 1972 Gas Safety Regulations' lay down stringent laws to protect gas users. Under the regulations you must:

- not use, or let anyone else use, any appliance you know, or suspect, to be dangerous,
- have only competent people to install and service appliances,
- turn off the main gas supply if you suspect a gas leak, and inform the local gas service centre immediately if a leak continues after you have turned off the main supply,
- not turn on the gas supply or any appliance again until the leak or appliance has been repaired.

If you smell gas:

- Put out cigarettes; do not use matches or naked flames.
- Check for leaks by using soapy water.
- Do not operate electrical switches on or off.
- Open doors and windows to get rid of the gas.
- Check to see if a tap has been left on accidentally, or if a pilot light has gone out. Turn off the main gas supply at the meter. If you suspect a leak, call the gas service at once.
- Be alert on re-entering the room once the leak or fault has been repaired.

OIL

Oil is a liquid fuel, obtained from various parts of the world. The oil used in industry is petroleum or mineral oil. Oil as a liquid fuel was first used for heating buildings on the Pacific coast of the USA and became important around 1920.

It is the world's principal lubricant, and in industry the main provider of heat and power. Plastics, detergents, nylon, Terylene, fertilisers and weedkillers are all derivatives of oil.

The chief advantage of oil is that because it is liquid it can be easily and precisely controlled; it is clean and easy to store. At normal temperatures the fuel is non-flammable until it has been 'atomised' (i.e. made ready for combustion.)

Oil for Heating   Fuel for the heating system must be stored in tanks outside the building or underground. The fuel can be fed into the system automatically. Two types of boiler are available: pressure jet and vaporiser. Both use different grades of oil. Larger premises tend to use pressure jet boilers. Portable paraffin heaters can provide economical localised heating.

Safety Factors for Oil

- A service contract is essential. At set intervals arrange for the removal of sediment from the storage tanks.
- Warning notices, alarms and lights should be fixed in storage areas.
- BS 1710, 1975 recommends that pipes carrying oil should be painted either wholly or partially brown.

SOLID FUEL

With the introduction of the Clean Air Act in 1956, a whole range of smokeless fuels was introduced. Most commercial premises rely on central heating provided by oil, gas or solid fuel. Open fires are pleasant to look at, but are inefficient and need cleaning daily.

Solid fuel has disadvantages as a medium for heating systems. It is bulky to store and not so clean as gas, oil or electricity. Also it may require extra staff to operate and maintain plant areas. However, solid fuel does tend to be cheaper to buy than other fuels.

SOLAR ENERGY AND HEATING

The sun radiates energy across millions of miles every second of the day to give the earth life. Plants, animals and all living things use this energy to grow and flourish, but we have yet to realise the potential of its power.

If we sit out in bright sunshine for an hour or so we become sunburnt. Also, if we wear black or dark clothing in hot weather, the temperature becomes unbearable. To counteract this, we wear light colours. Heat can either be absorbed or reflected by dark or light materials. The idea of solar heating is based on these facts. The use of solar energy is becoming more popular around the world.

Solar heating panels usually consist of a matt black metallic surface with piping attached to them, covered with double or triple glazing (to prevent the re-radiation of the heat) and backed by an insulating material. The 'collector', as it is called, may consist of 8 m^2 of copper panel which is a pressurised, closed circuit, holding from 200–250 litres of water. This collector can be placed on the ground but is generally on the roof of a building and is angled to obtain maximum benefit of the sun's rays at midday, or it can be rotated to stay in line with the sun and produce a constant supply of heat all day.

Water is circulated through the system, which includes temperature controls, relief valves, expansion and header tanks. From the solar or collecting panel the water goes into a heat exchanger, which then supplies the hot water cylinder of the building. The closed circuit cuts down the risk of hard water deposits and oxidation in the system between the panel and the reservoir. Sometimes a pump is fitted and may be brought into use when necessary; also an immersion heater can be incorporated to 'top up' the temperature as required.

It is usual for the stored heat to be used for warming the water supply rather than providing energy for the heating system.

CONVERSION FACTORS

The conversion factor table below breaks down the amount of therms that each fuel produces per unit. It will be necessary to find out the current price of each fuel per unit before a cost comparison can be made.

Oil: 0.36 therms per litre (1.64 therms per gallon)

Anthracite: 315 therms per tonne (16 therms per cwt)

Smokeless fuel: 256 therms per tonne (14 therms per cwt)

LPG: 7.01 therms per 15 kg

Gas, 1 therm: 29.3 kWh of electricity

ENERGY CONSERVATION

Energy costs have risen sharply since the early 1970s. It is vital to look carefully at the way in which we use energy, especially for heating and lighting.

The general overall plan for saving energy is to:
- cut out waste,
- use energy to its maximum advantage,
- regularly check bills to see if energy could be saved,
- be prepared to check with professional bodies for new ideas, schemes and equipment. Is it possible to delegate the energy question to one or two members of staff? Try to get staff and guests to understand the problem.
- use insulation where possible. Seek expert advice.

Tips for Specific Areas

Kitchens. In many kitchens, particularly hotels, it may be the tradition for the first member of staff who arrives for work to switch on most of the appliances, especially gas ones. These appliances tend to be left on for much longer than needed. Here are some points to consider:
- Is it necessary to have heating and lighting on during staff breaks?
- Can standard lights be replaced by tungsten or mercury lamps? Remember to clean shades and reflectors periodically.
- Consider the use of microwaves and industrial pressure steamers to save space. It is rarely necessary to pre-heat an oven. Electric ovens could be turned off 20 minutes before the end of cooking time, except for delicate soufflés, etc.
- Instruct staff to close hotplate doors on both sides.
- Place lids on pans of steaming food; this cuts down on cooking time and condensation. Match the pan up with the burners.
- Service all equipment including fans, ducts, freezers, refrigerators regularly.

Restaurants and dining areas. Consider the following points:
- Could heating be turned down a few degrees from half an hour after the first sitting? Thermostats should regulate the heat locally, so if the restaurant is serviced by a central heating system it could be turned off during breaks.
- It saves time and energy if all dishes, crockery, etc., are washed at the same time.
- Radiators should not be blocked by tables or chairs. Is it possible to insulate the walls with special insulating wallpaper to reflect the heat inwards?

Public areas. Here are some ideas for saving energy:
- Thermostats and time switches can control heat: either to increase or reduce the temperature at certain times or at certain temperature levels. It is estimated that with controls it may be possible to save up to 50% of the energy wasted without controls.
- Dimmer switches on lights are a necessity in many areas during the night. Check that the level of light is sufficient for safety.
- Hot air rises rapidly through lifts or stair wells; it is safer and cuts down energy costs to have these areas boxed in.
- Keep doors closed as much as possible; check windows and doors for draughts which draw hot air outwards.

Bathrooms and bedrooms.   Electricity can often be saved, as follows:

- In hospitals or hostels lighting is often on a time switch. Basic and emergency lighting is then provided except in special areas where full light is provided.
- In many residential establishments low-wattage bedside lights are provided. These require less electricity and give a softer light.
- It is advisable that central heating be controlled locally for savings and comfort. Check the temperature of bathrooms and bedrooms regularly. An acceptable temperature would be 16°C for a bedroom, 20°C for a bathroom, except in hospitals or other special areas.
- Showers are more economical than baths. Spray-type taps also use less heated water.
- Chambermaids and domestics should be trained to turn off lights and any other electrical equipment as they move around the work area.

QUESTIONS

1. Which terminals would each wire be connected to, in the above diagram, considering a three-core wire with new colour coding (blue, brown and green/yellow)?

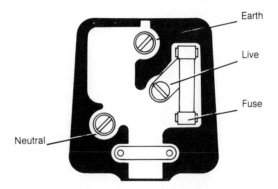

2. Draw up a comparison of fuels. Outline the advantages and disadvantages of each one.

3. Find out the up-to-date cost of 1 unit of electricity, 1 unit of gas and 1 tonne of smokeless fuel.

4. Design a leaflet to be given to:
   (a) chambermaids in a hotel,
   (b) staff on hospital wards,

   on ways of saving energy in those particular areas.

5. What energy saving devices could be fitted into a hotel bedroom to help the guest save fuel?

21 Water, Sanitation and Drainage

WATER SUPPLY Cold fresh pure water enters a building via a series of pumps and pipes connected by the local water authority to reservoirs. The water is filtered and sterilised, and in some areas fluoride and a softening agent is added. The 1965 Water Act covers the supply and distribution of water, and British Standard Code of Practice CP310: 1965 Water Supply, gives details of their requirements (see pp. 213–15).

There are two main sources of cold water supply:
- Main supply direct.
- Tank supply indirect.

Main Supply Direct

Water is supplied, under pressure, by means of a distributing main. This main runs underground and has water constantly flowing through it.

A communications pipe runs from the mains to the boundary of every building, whether commercial or domestic. A stopcock enables the water to be turned off, when necessary, outside the building. This stopcock is the responsibility of the water authority. From the boundary the communications pipe is the owner's responsibility. The total cold-water supply system of a building is shown opposite.

The pipe rises above ground level on entering the building and has a stop valve and drain-off valve for repairs and emergencies.

The pipe, now referred to as a rising main, runs upwards, on an internal wall towards the main water storage area, a cistern or tank, which is normally situated in the roofspace. It is always advisable that the rising main be situated along an internal wall because of the risk of frost damage. If this is not possible, the pipe must be well insulated, fixed on batons and inspected regularly, especially in the space between the floorboards and in the eaves.

Tank Supply Indirect

The water is discharged from the rising main into the cistern by a ball valve. Occasionally this ball valve fails, because of a worn washer, a wrongly fitted valve, or a puncturing of the ball or because the arm needs adjusting. An overflow pipe is fixed opposite just below the level of the inlet valve, to carry any surplus water through to an external wall should the level of the water rise too far.

Insulation is needed to stop the tank and pipes from freezing during bad weather; this is usually provided by a thermal material surrounding the sides and top of the tank.

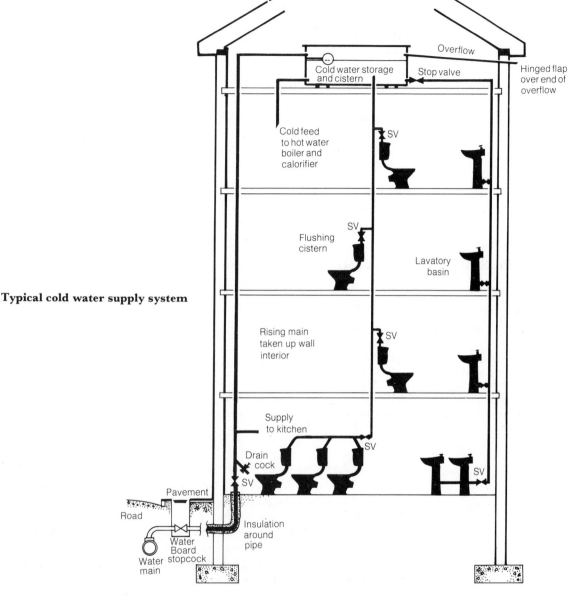

Typical cold water supply system

The bottom of the tank should not be insulated. The tank should have a close-fitting lid, though not completely airtight, to stop debris entering. The storage tank can be any size or shape, depending on individual requirements, amount of water consumed, and the local authority by-laws. Most tanks are now made from toughened plastic or glass fibre. Previously lead, galvanised iron and copper were used.

The advantages of storage tanks for a cold water supply   include the following points:

* Immediate reserve supply against failure of the water mains.
* Spread in the demand for water from the main, especially important where the supply is poor.
* Reduction of the pressure on the installation which in turn reduces noise and wastage.

The disadvantages   could include the following points:
- The storage space needed for tanks.
- An increase in strength of the building's structure could be needed to carry the weight of the tanks.
- If the tank is at ground level, pumps are needed to raise the water.
- Storage tanks can be a source of contamination.
- Large distribution pipes are required because of the reduced pressure, therefore more expense is incurred.
- Insulation is needed to prevent the water in the tanks and pipes from freezing during bad weather; this is usually provided by a thermal material surrounding the sides, and top of the tank.

Provision of storage to cover 24 hours' interruption of supply recommended: British Standard Code of Practice CP310: 1965 Water supply.

TYPE OF BUILDING	PERSON	LITRES	GALLONS
Hostels	Per resident	90	20
Hotels	Per resident	135	20
Offices without canteens	Per head	37	8
Offices with canteens	Per head	45	10
Restaurants	Per meal Per head	7	$1\frac{1}{2}$
Day schools	Per head	27	6
Boarding schools	Per resident	90	20
Nurses homes and medical quarters	Per resident	115	25

The inside of the cistern should be accessible for cleaning, maintenance and repairs. Most cisterns on commercial premises have a drip tray fitted below to catch moisture from condensation or leaks, protecting the property underneath. Cisterns should be positioned at the highest possible point to gain the greatest pressure in the internal distribution pipes. Tanks may be positioned on the roof as in special heated and ventilated cistern rooms. It may be necessary in certain areas, hospitals, residential homes, etc., to install a second connecting water cistern to avoid temporary loss of water due to repair or failure of the first tank.

The cistern may also supply cold water to a hot water supply system, but it is preferable to have a separate cistern, fed from the cold water supply (mains supply direct) for this purpose.

Cold water is distributed to various parts of the building for use as required. Each outlet pipe, except the overflow, from the cistern has a stop valve as has each pipe run. These are essential for allowing repair, maintenance and emergency work to be done.

COSTING

Cold water from the mains can be measured for costing purposes by meters, otherwise the cost is calculated as a proportion of the rateable value of the property, or a charge is made for each sanitary fitting.

Water Conservation

Water conservation is as vital as the economical use of energy. Manufacturers are now designing sanitary appliances which use smaller amounts of water in the cleansing process.

WCs can use as little as 9 litres (2 gal) of water if fitted correctly. Smaller washbasins are being installed in new buildings, and spray-type taps offer great savings in water and heat, as do press-down time-controlled taps.

Urinals can be a source of water-saving, if water is only used when the urinal is in use, rather than using a continuous flow of water flushing through.

Showers use less water than baths. On average a shower uses approximately a fifth of the amount of water needed for a bath.

HOT-WATER SUPPLIES

In most situations a tank has to be supplied for hot-water storage for use through the day and night. The size of the tank is dependent, like the cold-water storage system, on the type and number of residents, and use of the building. The types of system used are generally classified as local or central, and instantaneous.

Central systems.   In these systems the water is usually heated in the boiler room by the same fuel used for heating the rooms. The water is then carried via pipes to various parts of the building.

Local water-heater systems   are positioned near the appliances they serve; they use gas or electricity. Local systems save pipework because the water for heating is drawn off the cold-water supply. Also there is no heat loss through any distribution pipes. However, the system is expensive to operate unless only small amounts of water are needed.

Instantaneous water heaters   are similar to local heaters. They too are very expensive to operate, and are generally restricted to domestic situations as the flow of water is limited.

A typical hot water system is shown on the next page.

Recommended Temperatures For Hot Water

Bath 30–43°C   Sink 43-49°C
Shower 35–38°C   Washing-up by hand 60-82°C
Washbasin 38-43°C

DRAINAGE

Foul water, waste matter and other debris must be cleared from a building efficiently without fuss or inconvenience to staff or guests. Local authority by-laws and building regulations cover the removal of waste. The maintenance of sewers *inside* boundary lines is the occupier's responsibility; for *outside* boundary lines the local authority is responsible. Any plans for additions, alterations or repairs to drains or sewers must be submitted to the local authority for approval.

Drainage schemes are either: combined, separate or cesspools and septic tanks.

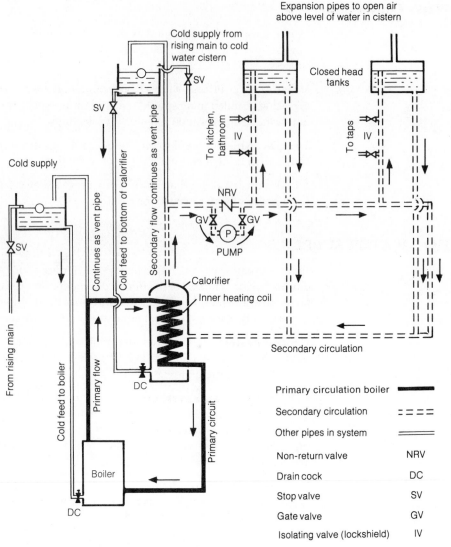

Expansion pipes to open air
above level of water in cistern

Cold supply from
rising main to cold
water cistern

Closed head
tanks

Cold supply

SV

SV

SV

Continues as vent pipe

Cold feed to bottom of calorifier

Secondary flow continues as vent pipe

To kitchen, bathroom

IV

To taps

IV

NRV

GV   GV

PUMP

Calorifier

Inner heating coil

Secondary circulation

From rising main

Cold feed to boiler

Primary flow

Primary circuit

DC

Boiler

DC

Primary circulation boiler	▬▬▬
Secondary circulation	= = = =
Other pipes in system	═══
Non-return valve	NRV
Drain cock	DC
Stop valve	SV
Gate valve	GV
Isolating valve (lockshield)	IV

Typical 'indirect' hot water system

Combined systems   have the rainwater carried to the mains sewers in the same pipes as the soil and waste, and it is treated along with all other waste at the sewage works. This process is expensive. Also if the rainfall has been heavy and the water level in the drain rises, there is a danger that infected water will leak into streams, rivers and the sea.

Separate systems have individual pipes: one for infected water and one for rainfall and surface water. Extra pipes are needed to disperse the fresh water into safe areas. In built-up areas it may not be possible to provide the extra pipe runs.

The use of cesspools and septic tanks is strictly governed by local authorities and the building regulations. They are not used in built-up areas but may have to be used in areas that are not serviced by mains sewers. There is usually a charge for emptying cesspools.

Gully traps are incorporated into the design of sewers and drains to help dispel the build-up of gases that may penetrate into the building, and to provide a barrier to rodents.

The traps are found at ground level; they open into the drain and have a water seal. There are many designs, but in all of them the down pipe or stack discharges at a level higher than water level. This makes sure that it is disconnected from the drain. Also a grate ensures that the area between the down pipe and water seal is ventilated. The construction underneath a manhole cover is shown below.

Where the drain joins a boundary or where the drain run changes direction there is an inspection chamber. This gives easy access to drains for clearing blockages.

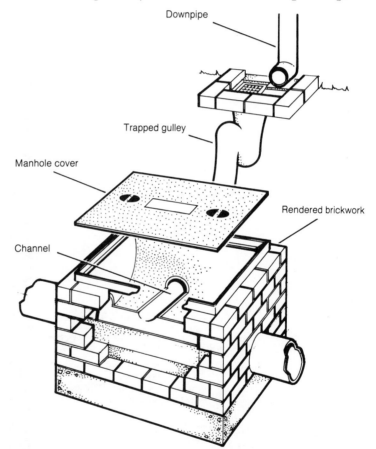

Downpipe

Trapped gulley

Manhole cover

Rendered brickwork

Channel

Diagram showing the construction underneath a manhole cover

Drainage Above Ground

Waste and soil systems have to carry infected water from sanitary appliances to the main drains and sewers without causing smell, blockages or leaks. Soil pipes carry flow from toilets, urinals and bidets. Waste pipes carry flows from sinks, baths, showers and washbasins.

One system of disposal is known as the 'two-pipe system'. This has two individual pipes: one carrying soil, the other waste. This system involves extra pipework which can be expensive.

'Single-pipe systems' have waste flows connected to soil stacks, which eliminate the need for extra pipes. However, these pipes must have anti-siphon pipes fitted, to prevent any risk of infected water flowing back into the building. Single-pipe systems are comparatively modern. The diameter, length and fall of the pipe are carefully designed, and the system can be used in buildings up to 20 floors high, subject to permission from the local authorities. Blockages are not as common in this system, and each sanitary appliance is fitted to the stack separately.

Building regulations sometimes change the siting of waste and soil pipes, so it is advisable to check for up-to-date information. Where soil and waste pipes run internally it may be possible to arrange them into central service ducts for ease of maintenance. This also reduces the risk of damage by vandals.

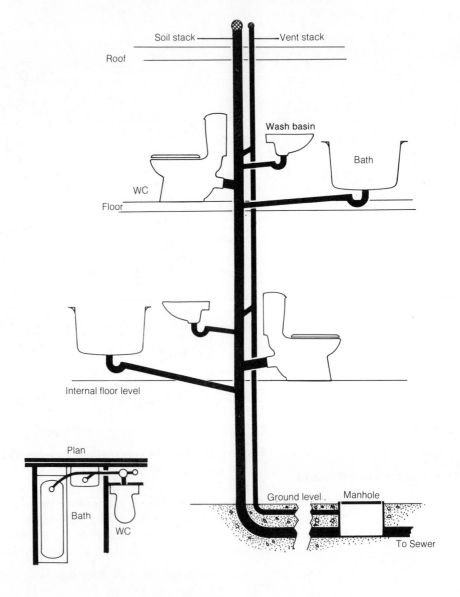

Typical vented or modified single pipe waste system

Internal Traps and Water Seals

In a WC the water seal is an integral part of the design; in other appliances a trap has to be fitted somewhere in the outflow. A water seal prevents foul air from the main drain entering the building. Traps are basically 'P- ', 'S- ' or bottle-shaped. Each appliance will have a trap fitted that is suited to its requirements. Traps, of whatever design, should be accessible and easy to clean and maintain. Bottle traps are perhaps the easiest to clean, and many are made in clear plastic, so that the build-up of grease and deposit can be seen. Some examples of different designs are shown below.

The depth of water in a seal is usually specified: 25 mm is a normal minimum; WC traps are 50 mm.

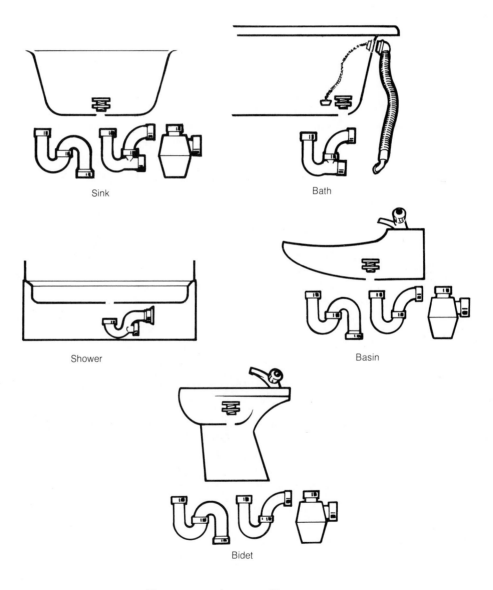

Traps on sanitary appliances

Kitchen Waste   Kitchen waste can be a problem since much of the water contains grease, which can solidify in pipes on cooling. Staff should be instructed to clear as much grease, food, etc., from plates, serving dishes and cutlery before washing up. Tea leaves should not be put down a sink. As a general guide nothing should be sent down a drain unless it will dissolve in cold water.

Grease traps are situated near the outflow of kitchen waste pipes. They consist of a tank which holds cold water in a sufficient amount to cool the flow of hot washing-up water as it passes through on its way to the main drain. The grease contained in the hot water rises to the top of the cold water in the trap, and is then skimmed and collected at intervals. Sludge from potato peeling machines should be caught in a trap, either before it leaves the machine or before it enters the main pipe.

Clearing Obstructions in External Pipes

If uncertain as to the position of the obstruction or the capabilities of a member of staff, ask for expert, professional help. Mistakes are costly, and may cause great inconvenience and damage to the pipework. The first area likely to become blocked is the grating over the trapped gully. Because it is at ground level it can trap leaves and litter. Remove the grating and scrub and scald it; do not throw the debris into the gully. If the blockage still remains, the trap below may be the problem. Use an old spoon tied to a stick and carefully poke around the gully to dislodge the obstruction. Once the dirty water runs free, pour in two or three buckets full of hot water, with a little washing soda added, to finally cleanse the area. Check that the gully is free by running cold water from the taps through the system.

If the obstruction still remains a decision has now to be taken to call in professional help or to continue trying to clear the blockage.

The inspection chamber cover (manhole) should be removed carefully. If the chamber is empty, the obstruction is in the pipes between the chamber and the building. If the chamber is full of waste water, the blockage is further down the drainage system and special rods will be needed to clear it.

Leaks in External Pipes

Leaks in drainpipes, especially those made of stoneware, may be hard to detect. The first indication of a leak may be dampness occurring on internal walls in basements or damage to the foundations.

The fracture can be caused by pressure of tree roots, subsidence of the ground, extremes of temperature or heavy traffic. It may be possible to repair drainpipes if the damage is not too severe, so regular checking is advisable. Branch pipe leaks can be a problem in cold weather, especially in kitchen and bathroom areas, where a constant trickle of water caused by a faulty washer or carelessness makes the pipe freeze. Check taps regularly.

Precautions for Bad Weather

When water freezes in a pipe, its volume can increase by as much as 10%. This increase may cause the pipe to split. When the ice melts water leaks from the split and can cause severe damage and inconvenience. If a frozen internal pipe is suspected, gradually increase the overall temperature of the surrounding area. Do not apply direct heat at this stage.

If the water does not run free after a few hours of extra room heat, place hot cloths or blow hot air (from a hair-dryer) along the pipe. If the pipe has burst already, turn off the water at the main stopcock and drain the system quickly by turning on all the taps. Turn off the water heating system.

Insulation of water pipes is essential; pay attention to the areas around stopcocks and taps. If the area is to be left vacated for any length of time, particularly during winter, leave the heating on a time switch for a few hours each day to keep the overall temperature warm.

To Clear Internal Blockages

- Try pouring hot water and washing soda down the pipe. This may dissolve or remove the blockage.
- If this is not successful, a plunger will be needed. Block the overflow at the top of the appliance with a wet rag to stop air in the pipe escaping. Make sure there is enough water in the appliance to cover the plunger cap. Place the plunger over the waste outlet and pump vigorously. This should clear the blockage. If it does, remove the rag from the overflow and run cold water down the waste flow for a few minutes. If the blockage is still there, then the trap below the appliance will need to be emptied.

SANITARY APPLIANCES

All sanitary appliances should be non-porous, easy to clean and maintain, quiet, suitable for the task required in terms of shape, size and height, and capable of carrying away soil and waste efficiently.

Sanitary appliances fall into the following five groups, each of which has a specific function.
- Carrying away human excreta — urinals, WCs, stop hoppers, bedpan washers (hospitals).
- Personal washing — lavatory basins, baths, showers, bidets.
- Washing of clothes, surfaces, utensils — sinks, cleaners' bucket sink.
- Food preparation — double and single sinks, some combining waste disposal units.
- Special items — for hospitals, clinics, schools, old people's homes, and homes for the disabled.

In selecting items of sanitary ware it is important to consider the following:
- Durability of material used.
- Characteristics and suitability of material.
- Hygiene and ease of cleaning.
- Maintenance.
- Cost.
- Size.
- Noise factor.
- Ease of installing, and weight of item on surrounding surfaces.
- Appearance.
- Rate at which the appliance fills and empties.

Materials Used for Sanitary Appliances

Materials used for appliances are ceramics (fireclay and vitreous china, cast iron, vitreous enamelled steel, stainless steel and plastic.

The following table is intended as a guide only. With new technology and materials, manufacturers are improving and replacing existing models and materials when necessary. For up-to-date details consult trade journals and manufacturers' specifications, and visit local builders' and plumbers' merchants.

A detailed table of materials and their characteristics is shown below.

Sanitary Appliance Materials

BASIC MATERIALS USED	CHARACTERISTICS
CERAMICS *Fireclay*	The widest range of appliances are made in this material. Semi-porous, buff-coloured base with white glaze applied. Suitable for large industrial use, especially hospitals. Very durable, more expensive than vitreous china. Easily cleaned. Appliance may need support as fireclay is heavy
Vitreous china	White base, non-porous. Glaze can be various colours. Impervious to moisture even when unglazed. Should not stain or craze with normal use. Strong, but lighter than fireclay. Suitable for general use. Cheaper than fireclay but each has different properties so a direct cost comparison is difficult. Easily cleaned
Cast iron	Mainly restricted to use in baths. When used as traditional bath material, white or coloured enamel is sprayed or brushed on to the surface, then left to dry and fuse. Strong material, extremely durable, but very heavy. Surface has a high lustre. Colour can be more expensive in this type of material. Easy to clean and has a high resistance to abrasion if correct cleaning agent is used
Vitreous enamelled steel	Steel base with enamel sometimes referred to as porcelain enamel. Relatively light in weight, it is produced in a variety of colours all with a glossy finish. Used for sink tops and baths. Easy to clean, but avoid powder abrasives. Very durable, but severe blows can cause the enamel to chip. The appliance can be noisy in use
Stainless steel	The type of steel used for sanitary appliances contains large amounts of chromium, and is often referred to as 18/8, i.e. 18% chromium, 8% nickel. It can be mirror or satin finish. Mirror finish tends to show scratches and stains more than satin. Extremely hard-wearing, almost absolute resistance to corrosion except in some hospital or swimming pool areas (some acids and chlorinated bleach can cause damage). Very expensive, but hygienic; never cracks; easy to clean with mild detergent or special proprietary cleaner
Plastics (1) Perspex (2) Polypropylene gloss (3) Reinforced plastic (4) Nylon	All have similar characteristics. Colour runs through the article. Smooth gloss finish. Very light. Available in wide range of colours. Hygienic. Not affected by substances that attack metals. Does not chip, can be damaged by use of abrasive powders, lighted cigarettes and hot pans. Tends to be used mainly in domestic areas as life is not as long as other materials

British Recommendations for Sanitary Appliances

These are given in detail on the following three pages.

RECOMMENDATIONS FROM BRITISH STANDARDS CODE OF PRACTICE CP305: Part 1/1974

Hotels

FITMENTS	FOR RESIDENTIAL PUBLIC AND STAFF	FOR PUBLIC ROOMS		FOR NON-RESIDENTIAL STAFF	
		FOR MALES	**FOR FEMALES**	**FOR MALE STAFF**	**FOR FEMALE STAFF**
Water Closets	1 per 9 persons excluding occupants of rooms with WCs 'en suite'	1 per 100 up to 400; for over 400, add at the rate of 1 per 250 or part thereof	2 per 100 up to 200; for over 200, add at the rate of 1 per 100 or part thereof	1 for 1–15 persons, 2 for 16–35 persons, 3 for 36–65 persons, 4 for 66–100 persons	1 for 1–12 persons, 2 for 13–25 persons, 3 for 26–40 persons, 4 for 41–57 persons, 5 for 58–77 persons, 6 for 78–100 persons
Bathrooms	1 per 9 persons excluding occupants of rooms with baths 'en suite'				
Washbasins	1 per bedroom and at least 1 per bathroom in addition to the requirements of Clause 5(a)	*Clause 5(a).* In all buildings it is desirable that there should be a washbasin (or basins) in the vicinity of each WC or range of WCs		1 for 1–15 persons, 2 for 16–35 persons, 3 for 36–65 persons, 4 for 66–100 persons	1 for 1–12 persons, 2 for 13–25 persons, 3 for 26–40 persons, 4 for 41–57 persons, 5 for 58–77 persons, 6 for 78–100 persons
Urinals		1 per 50 persons		Nil up to 6 persons 1 for 7–20 persons, 2 for 21–45 persons, 3 for 46–70 persons, 4 for 71–100 persons	

HOSPITALS (RECOMMENDATIONS FROM HOSPITAL BUILDING NOTES*)

CHILDREN'S WARD

Room	Appliances
Treatment	1 WB with EOT
Clean utility	1 WB with EOT
Dirty utility	1 sink with DB and EOT
Bathroom	1 bath per 10 patients. (At least 1 free-standing bath per ward). 1 WB with hairspray
Ward (or bay)	1 WB with EOT
Patients washing facilities	1 WB per 6 patients+ in multi-bed wards
WC	1 WC per 6 patients with minimum of 3 to be communal. 2 or 3 WB per range
Sluice and test	1 flushing sink, 1 bedpan and pot washer and steriliser 1 small sink unit with EOT
Ward pantry	1 small sink and 1 WB
Cleaners	1 bucket sink and DB
Nurses' station	1 medicine sink with EOT

ADMINISTRATIVE DEPARTMENT

Room	Appliances
Staff sanitary facilities	Male: 1 WC and 1 Ur and 1 WB per 15 persons. Female: 1 WC and WB per 12 persons, plus 1 incinerator per group of WCs. 1 shower per 15 non-residential nurses, dom. staff and porters. 1 WB in each case (male or female)
Rest room	
Cleaners	1 bucket sink and DB 'To be near main waiting space.'
Visitors' sanitation facilities	1 WC and WB and 1 shower to be adjacent
Non-residential matrons' sitting room	Male: 2 shampoo basins
Hairdressing	Female: 2 shampoo basins

OUT-PATIENTS' DEPARTMENTS

Room	Appliances
Consulting	1 WB
Clinical	1 WB with EOT
Dirty utility	1 sink and 1 slop sink and DB
Test room	1 WC and 1 WB per unit
(1 for each sex)	WB per unit
Waiting space (per 4 to 6 consulting rooms per 20–30 patients)	Male: 1 WC and 1 Ur and WB. Female: 1 WC and 1 WB
Staff sanitary facilities	Male: 1 WC and 1 Ur and 1 WB per 15 persons Female: 1 WC and 1 WB per 12 persons
Cleaners	1 bucket sink and DB
Anaesthetic	1 sink and 1 slop sink
Sink room	1 sink and 1 slop sink
Staff changing (ditto for patients)	1 WC and 1 WB and 1 shower in each changing room
Dental surgery	1 WB for dentist with EOT 1 sink and DB for assistant
Dental recovery	1 sink and 1 rinsing bowl
Dental workroom	1 sink

* Published by DHSS (HMSO, 1969).
NOTES: Single bed wards to have separate sanitary accommodation. WB — washbasin, Ur — urinal, EOT — elbow operated taps, DB — draining board.

RECOMMENDATION FOR RESTAURANTS BRITISH STANDARDS CODE OF PRACTICE CP305: Part 1/1974

FITMENTS	FOR MALE PUBLIC	FOR FEMALE PUBLIC	FOR MALE STAFF	FOR FEMALE STAFF
Water closets	1 per 100 persons up to 400; for over 400, add at the rate of 1 per 250 or part thereof	2 per 100 persons up to 200; for over 200, add at the rate of 1 per 100 or part thereof	1 for 1–15 persons. 2 for 16–35 persons 3 for 36–65 persons 4 for 66–100 persons	1 for 1–12 persons 2 for 13–25 persons 3 for 26–40 persons 4 for 41–57 persons 5 for 58–77 persons 6 for 78–100 persons
Washbasins	1 in respect of each WC and, in addition 1, in respect of every 5 urinals	1 in respect of each 2 WC's	1 for 1–15 persons 2 for 16–35 persons 3 for 36–65 persons 4 for 66–100 persons	1 for 1–12 persons 2 for 13–25 persons 3 for 26–40 persons 4 for 41–57 persons 5 for 58–77 persons 6 for 78–100 persons
Urinals	1 per 25 persons		Nil up to 6 persons 1 for 7–20 persons 2 for 21–45 persons 3 for 46–70 persons. 4 for 71–100 persons	

QUESTIONS

1. Describe how you would clean and maintain the following:
   (a) WC,
   (b) bath,
   (c) bidet,
   (d) shower tray?

2. Outline ways in which money and fuel could be saved in heating systems.

3. What are the various methods of arranging for a hot water system to be maintained?

4. Describe, draw and label the various taps available.
   (a) What are the causes of a constantly dripping tap?
   (b) How would you solve the problem?
   (c) If stains from the dripping water have occurred, how can the stains be removed?

5. What preventive measures can you take to stop water in pipes freezing in bad weather?

6. List the colour identification for pipes.

22 Heating and Ventilation

HEATING

Any area must be comfortable for the occupant or worker and the temperature should be high enough to prevent dampness. It is difficult to arrive at a satisfactory general temperature because there can be so many variables (e.g. older people needing extra heat, young children, bad weather, etc.).

The dry bulb temperatures below represent the recommended standards of warmth.

Recommended dry bulb temperatures:
Domestic living rooms 20-21°C
Bedrooms 13-16°C
Kitchens 16°C
Offices, general 20°C
Machine rooms 19°C
Shops 19°C
Classrooms 17°C
Factories, according to type of work 13-18°C
General spaces, entrances, stairs 16°C
Lavatories 18°C
Cloakrooms 16°C
Hospital wards 19°C

HEAT TRANSFER

Heat is transferred in three different ways: conduction, convection and radiation. A summary is given in the diagram on the next page.

Conduction

Heat may be conducted directly through a material. The rate of conduction depends mainly on the density and type of material used. The list below gives common building materials in their order of conductivity.

1 Copper   6 Brick
2 Aluminium   7 Water
3 Iron   8 Wood
4 Glass   9 Cork
5 Concrete   10 Air

Convection

This is the transference of heat in fluids or gases by circulation. When the fluid or gas is in contact with the heated surface it expands and the hot molecules rise. In rising they pass heat on to anything in their path. As warm air moves further away from the initial source of heat it cools and falls back to the lower level. As the air circulates, a convection current is formed.

Radiation   Heat may be transferred directly through space from one body to another by means of radiation. For example, the Sun radiates heat through space, some of which reaches the Earth. Another example is provided by the electric fire, where the reflector behind the element radiates heat into a room.

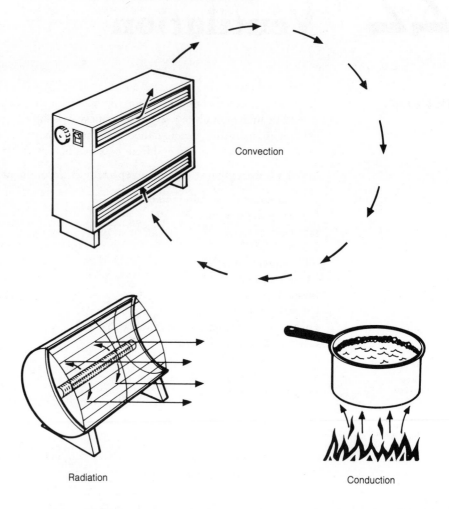

Convection

Radiation

Conduction

Diagram to show the three ways in which heat can be transferred

HEAT LOSS IN BUILDINGS

When heat is passed out of a building through the structure, the three forms of heat transference are used:
- Heat is conducted through solid areas, e.g. floors, walls, roofs.
- Heat is convected from the outside surface by wind.
- Heat is radiated across cavities, and from the outside surface.

The general rate of transmission is known as 'thermal transmittance'. This is defined as 'the heat in watts, that will be transmitted through 1 m^2 of construction when there is 1°C difference between the temperature of the air inside and outside the building'. It is commonly called the 'U-value'.

INSULATION

Conservation of heat in buildings has, over the years, become more important because of rising fuel costs, dwindling world fossil fuel resources and improved standards expected by users. Many new insulating materials have been developed to add thermal properties to the lighter, thinner units of construction built today. Before insulating a large area it may be advisable to check around edges of doors, windows and up chimneys to cure draughts by means of 'weather stripping'.

Insulation will reduce the amount of heat that escapes through a building via walls, floors and roofs. There are a number of types of insulation.

Glass fibre blankets trap air between fibres. They are laid down between roof rafters or around pipes.

Expanded polystyrene and polyurethene are treated plastics which trap air in the cells of the material. They can be used in loft rafters or can be injected into wall cavities. There should be no insulation under water tanks as the heat from below prevents the tank from freezing in bad weather; any insulation should go over the top.

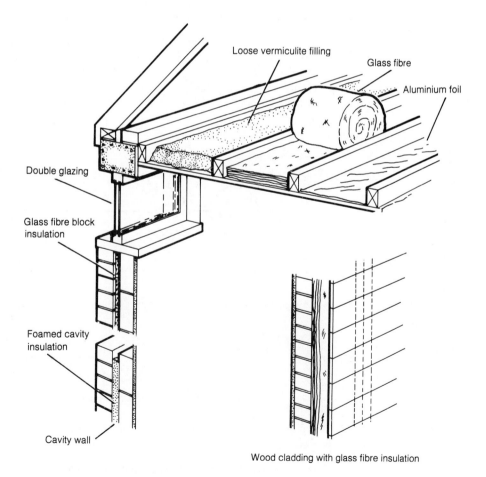

Loose vermiculite filling

Glass fibre

Aluminium foil

Double glazing

Glass fibre block insulation

Foamed cavity insulation

Cavity wall

Wood cladding with glass fibre insulation

Diagram showing some methods of reducing heat loss from buildings

Vermiculite is an exfoliated mineral used in plasters. It is extremely light in weight, and it readily absorbs and retains moisture and air. It can give as much as ten times the amount of thermal insulation as sand and gravel used in the same quantities. It also helps stop condensation and has good acoustic properties.

Double glazing a window enables air to be trapped between two panels of glass approximately 10–20 mm wide. (A heavy lined curtain over windows and doors can also act as a satisfactory insulator.)

Thin sheets of polystyrene veneer can be used to help insulate walls. They are used underneath a normal wallpaper or lining paper.

Thin sheets of aluminium foil placed behind radiators help to reflect the heat back into the room.

Some methods for reducing heat loss from buildings are shown in the diagram on the previous page.

CENTRAL HEATING SYSTEMS

In central heating systems fuel is converted into heat at a central plant. This heat is transferred by a 'heat transfer medium' to emitters in various parts of the building.

The fuel used for combustion is either gas, oil or solid fuel. The heat transfer medium may be water, alcohol, petroleum glycol or air. The distribution system consists of a boiler or mechanism for the production of heat from the fuel, a pump and a system of pipes and/or ducts, to carry the heating medium to heat emitters placed in various parts of the building (see the diagram below). A warm-air system is also shown opposite.

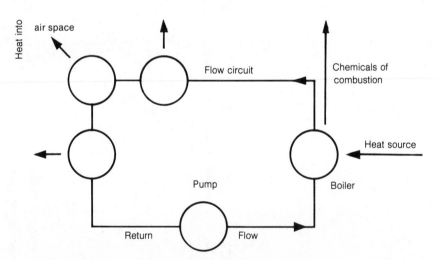

Diagram showing how a basic central heating system operates

When heat reaches the emitters most of it is given off as convected heat, but a small percentage is radiated.

Radiators are often placed underneath windows to provide the best thermal currents, to minimise staining of walls and to use space, but it is advisable to consult a specialist before permanent siting is decided upon. Radiators can be individually controlled. Thermostatically controlled radiators are efficient but expensive initially.

Convectors consist of gilled tubes at low level in a casing. They are quick and easy to control and can incorporate ventilation from outside. Fan convectors rely on air being blown upwards rather than natural convection currents. They have the advantage of quickly heating a room and they require fewer pipe runs than normal convectors; they are suitable for rooms not in constant use. Skirting heaters are shaped convectors, available to take the place of a skirting board. They are neat and unobtrusive.

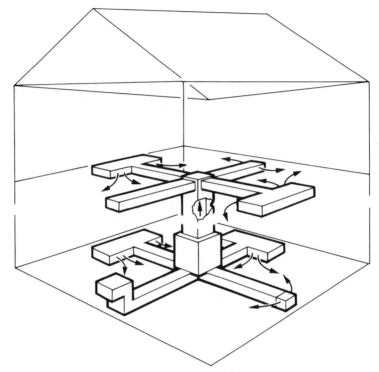

Diagram showing: Warm-air central heating, blowing warm air to all parts of the building

Factors Affecting the Choice of Systems for Heating

- Running costs, including the cost of fuel, electricity for motors, fans, etc., and any labour costs, insurance, etc.
- Capital costs, the cost of installation, cost of building work associated with the system, fuel stove, chimneys, boiler rooms, etc.
- Availability of fuel. Usually there are no problems in urban areas but rural areas may not have gas or oil supplies. Access to the site may be difficult for coal lorries or other fuel tankers.
- Personal choice.
- Clean Air Act 1968. Consult your local authority if considering solid fuel.

VENTILATION

Ventilation is said to be efficient when the air is dry, fresh, pure and comfortable. Comfort is achieved by a combination of the correct temperature, the correct relative humidity, and the correct air movement. The air must also remain at a temperature high enough to eliminate dampness.

To fulfil these criteria ventilation must:

- provide a continuous supply of oxygen for breathing,
- remove fumes, smells and any products of combustion,
- extract bacteria, especially in hospitals, laboratories, etc. — in these situations extra high air-change rates can help; so too can use of disinfectant sprays and ultra-violet rays injected into the extracted air,
- remove excess heat and moisture, especially from bathrooms and kitchens. Heat generated by groups of people needs to be removed for comfort and to combat a feeling of lethargy.
- Prevent condensation.

Laws Governing Ventilation Standards

The Factories Act 1961 does not set out exact standards but inspectors can implement specific levels. The following list recommends air changes per hour:
Kitchens 20–60
Restaurants 10–15
Bathrooms 6 approximately
Cinemas and theatres 6–10
Cloakrooms 2

The Food Hygiene (General) Regulations 1970 state that suitable and sufficient means of ventilation shall be provided and maintained in every food room.

Distribution of Air   In considering a system of ventilation the following points are relevant:

- Air should not strike directly on to the occupant. Positioning of inlet and outlet grilles is important. Ceiling grilles avoid draughts and can be unobtrusive. They can, however, cause ceiling staining. Lower level or floor grilles are easier to clean and maintain.
- Noise from grilles and ducts should be kept to a minimum. Noise is often created by ill-fitting grilles.

Humidity   'Relative humidity' is a measure of the dampness of the atmosphere. A 100% relative humidity would mean that the atmosphere was saturated with as much water as it could hold; a 50% relative humidity would mean the atmosphere was half-saturated; and so on. The actual amount of water that the atmosphere can hold will vary with temperature. Relative humidity determines the rate of evaporation of moisture from the skin. High relative humidity in hot weather causes overheating of the body and a feeling of lethargy. In cold weather it causes a more intense feeling of coldness.

For comfort, the relative humidity of a room should be approximately 40–60%.

Systems of Ventilation

In low buildings it is easier to control air flow and ventilation by opening windows to allow air in. In tall buildings or buildings where it is not advisable to use natural ventilation, some means of mechanical ventilation must be installed.

The following areas may also require extra mechanical ventilation if natural ventilation is not sufficient or available:

- Internal rooms.

- Computer offices, operating theatres.
- Tall buildings where heat rises to the top and leaves the cooler air on the lower floors.
- Kitchen areas, especially above cooking points.
- City centre buildings where the opening of windows is not advisable due to pollution, noise and dust.
- Banqueting or conference rooms.

The basic system of ventilation is usually:
- Natural, where air movement is introduced by wind or temperature differences.
- Mechanical, where air is distributed by fans.

There are also possible combinations using natural and mechanical systems combined.

Examples of Types of Mechanical Ventilation System

Extractor fans are fitted through single glass windows or through walls. They are driven by an electric motor. They are designed to extract contaminated air but are not always efficient at replacing the extracted air with clean air.

Canopies fitted over cooking areas remove heat, moisture and smells. They usually contain a filter for easier cleaning. They can obstruct light on to working areas.

High velocity slots can be used in take-away or fast-food operations. They consist of high-speed extractors connected to ducts that are positioned above the work surface. The extraction rate is not usually sufficient for large kitchens where there is a higher percentage of heat and moisture to be extracted.

Internal ventilation of toilets and bathrooms. Ventilation begins as soon as the light is operated. Fresh air is drawn in via grilles. By law the extracting ducts must be separate from the main plant and a duplicate extractor must be fitted for emergencies. There is no mechanical fresh air input, the fresh air is gained from grilles or gaps under the door.

AIR CONDITIONING

The aim of air conditioning is to deliver clean air and remove impure air, at the same time controlling the temperature to acceptable levels and also regulating the relative humidity to approximately 50%. Air conditioning is installed in new buildings where the use of natural ventilation is limited. It can be in the form of a central system or room mounted unit in the window. Normally all windows are double- or triple-glazed and sealed. The in- or out-flow of air can be directed upwards or downwards but careful consideration of the positioning of grilles is necessary.

Reasons for Air Conditioning
- Human comfort, especially in crowded areas.
- Need to remove airborne dust, e.g. chemical plants, operating theatres.
- The work involved can only be done efficiently when a controlled temperature and humidity is operated, e.g. laboratories, computer rooms.
- Where antique furniture, old documents, etc. are stored, restored or displayed.
- Where the thermal temperature is high due to solar gains, artificial lighting, machinery, etc.
- Where natural ventilation is limited.

All air conditioning systems have the same basic parts. These are:

- filters — for cooling and purifying the air,
- fans — for air movement,
- heating plants,
- refrigeration plants,
- humidity controls.

PART D: PRACTICAL SUPERVISION

23 An Introduction to Supervision

THE SUPERVISOR

A supervisor is a person who is given authority and responsibility for the planning and control of work for a group of people. The duties of a supervisor may be very varied indeed and may differ greatly from one establishment to another, depending on the size and type of the establishment, its structure, staffing and the use of specialists.

Responsibilities of the Supervisor

- Staff recruitment, induction, training, welfare, safety, discipline and morale.
- Work planning, organisation, preparation of duty rosters, setting goals, and supervising work activities of all employees.
- Communications — the ability to operate an effective system of communication between other departments and all staff.
- Cost effectiveness — the requirement to instil in staff the need for economy without reducing efficiency.
- Providing staff with efficient and effective cleaning equipment and materials.
- Acceptance of change and keeping up to date with modern technology.

JOB ANALYSIS

This is the study of all phases of a job including the specific tasks performed, the relationship to other jobs, and the conditions of work. Personal requirements are also considered. It is essential that it is updated from time to time as jobs change with the introduction of new techniques, equipment and materials and changes in conditions. The job analysis provides information for the job description. An example is given below.

Task — Cleaning a toilet
Time allowance — 8 minutes
Equipment/materials required — Lavatory brush   Mop and bucket
2 cloths   Towels, soap
Lavatory cleaner   Toilet rolls
General purpose cleaner

1. Ventilate the room.
2. Flush the toilet.
3. Apply a lavatory cleaner to the toilet pan — base and sides.
4. Remove dirty linen.
5. Sweep floor using mop sweeper.

---

6. Damp-wipe tiled surfaces using a general purpose cleaner and cloth.
7. Thoroughly clean inside of toilet with toilet brush.
8. Flush toilet.
9. Damp-wipe toilet seat, toilet surrounds using a general purpose cleaner and toilet cloth.
10. Clean wash handbasin thoroughly using general purpose cleaner and cloth — paying particular attention to taps, plug, etc.
11. Rinse wash handbasin and dry.
12. Replenish toilet roll (always leave a spare), soap and towels.
13. Damp-mop floor using mop, bucket and general purpose cleaner.
14. Check room, list any maintenance faults and report them immediately to the supervisor. Close door.

JOB DESCRIPTION

This indicates the requirement of the actual job, setting out what is expected of the individual, the responsibilities, limitations and the authority of the particular job. It must be reviewed and revised from time to time as changes occur in the organisation and the running of the establishment. An example is shown below.

Job title Assistant Domestic Service Manager
Hospital General Hospital
Responsible to Domestic Services Manager
Skills and knowledge required Recognised qualifications, e.g. HND, OND, TEC, BTEC Cerfificate. National Health Service Assistant Domestic Services Managers' Course and or relevant experience.
Function The supervision and control of the day-to-day operations of the Domestic Services Department, to meet specified standards, objectives and policy of the department.
Responsibilities
1. The recruitment of staff, within the department, in conjunction with the Domestic Services Manager.
2. To assist with all training of domestic staff.
3. To assist with the general organisation and day-to-day running of the domestic services within the hospital.
4. The preparation of work schedules for the domestic staff in conjunction with the Domestic Services Manager.
5. The maintenance of an acceptable standard of cleanliness throughout the hospital.
6. To control the issuing of cleaning materials and equipment to domestic staff.
7. To prepare staff duty rosters, holiday lists and emergency cover for absentees, etc.
8. To assist with the upkeep of all records within the department.
9. To take control of the domestic services in the absence of the Domestic Services Manager.

JOB SPECIFICATION

A job specification is a summary of the job analysis and job description and outlines the personal requirements for the job, so as to place the right person in the specific position. An example is shown opposite.

> *Job title* Assistant Domestic Services Manager
> *Hospital* General Hospital
> *Function* The supervision and control of the day-to-day operations of the Domestic Services Department to meet specific standards, objectives and policy of the department.
> *Responsible to* Domestic Services Manager
> *Age* 25-35
> *Sex* Male or female.
> *Qualifications* HND, OND, TEC, BTEC or Assistant Domestic Services Manager's Course.
> *Experience* Relevant experience in hospital domestic services or similar.
> *Physical qualities* A clean bill of health, good hearing and vision and good general appearance.
> *Personal qualities* Ability to accept authority, to be able to work with other people and communicate at all levels. To take responsibility and deal with any day-to-day problems as they arise.
> *General intelligence* Ability to use own initative, cope in any emergency and keep up to date with new technology.

WORK SCHEDULE

A work schedule is an outline of the work carried out by the particular member of staff. It will indicate time allocations for specific tasks, stated procedures, type of equipment and materials to be used and any specialised work to be carried out. It will also include break periods for coffee, lunch, tea, dinner, etc. It must be clear, well laid out and simple for it to be effective. For a good example, see below.

Work schedule for an Assistant Domestic Services Manager	
Hours of Work	7 a.m.–4 p.m.
7.00–8.30	Check clock cards to ascertain number of staff on duty. Check number of absentees and re-arrange cover where necessary. Check in tray and deal with any urgent matters.
	Supervision of domestic staff
8.30–12.30	Main duties to include:
	Check with supervisors regarding work routine.
	Deal with any less urgent matters from the previous day.
	Deal with any complaints as they arise.
	Maintenance of records.
10.00–10.30	Coffee.
10.30–12.30	Departmental meetings.
	Preparation of duty rotas, holiday lists.
	Staff training.
	Selection and interviewing of new staff.
	Forward planning of various schemes.
	Purchasing.
	Wages.
12.30–1.30	Lunch.
1.30–4.00	General supervision of staff.
	Inspections.
	Dealing with any other day-to-day matters.

JOB ADVERTISEMENT

A job advertisement gives a summary of the job description and indicates the procedure for applying for a vacancy. An example is given below.

BRIDGEMERE HEALTH DISTRICT
BRIDGEMERE GENERAL HOSPITAL
BRIDGEMERE, BERKS

ASSISTANT DOMESTIC SERVICES MANAGER

We are looking for someone with initiative and enthusiasm to become one of a young team of Managers who are responsible for providing a comprehensive housekeeping and domestic service to a modern 800-bedded General Hospital, a large residential section and community health section. The person appointed would be required to deputise and assist in the day-to-day management of the Hospital and two centres.

Candidates should be able to demonstrate a high level of managerial skills and hold a formal qualification and relevant experience. The post is superannuable and an incentive bonus scheme is in operation.

Salary scale £xxxx — £xxxx
Hours 40 hours per week.
Application form and job description are available from:
Personnel Department
Bridgemere Health District
Bridgemere House
Bridgemere General Hospital
Bridgemere
Berks
Tel: Bridgemere 27272
Ext. 272

RECRUITMENT OF STAFF

The most common methods of recruiting staff are as follows:
- By contacting local employment agencies, Jobcentres.
- By contacting local and national private employment agencies.
- Advertisements in local and national newspapers, trade journals and magazines.
- By contacting the Careers Officer in schools and colleges, especially for temporary, casual or part-time staff.
- By advertisements on notice boards and at works entrances.
- 'Through the grapevine' at work, by asking staff if they know anybody who requires a particular job.
- By contacting former employees.
- Advertisements in local shops, especially for part-time or casual labour.

Whichever method is used, the following information should be made available:

- Type of job.
- Hours and frequency of work.
- Rates of pay.
- Qualifications required.
- Whom to apply to (name, address and telephone number).
- Whether application forms are available and if so, the closing date for return.

Where possible, try not to advertise vacancies for too long a period or too frequently because prospective employees may feel that the establishment has a high turnover of labour for some reason or other.

INTERVIEWING

An interview is a meeting between two or more people to achieve a certain purpose such as filling a vacant position, trying to solve a problem, or an exchange of ideas or opinions.

Who Carries Out the Interview

The person or persons carrying out the interview will depend on:

- type of interview,
- policy of the establishment,
- number of candidates,
- resources available.

The interview may be carried out by the supervisor/manager or an interview panel.

Procedure for Interviewing

Planning the interview

- Be conversant with the job advertisement, job applications, job description and specification.
- Prepare interview report forms, handouts, etc.
- Prepare a short list of candidates.
- Decide on approximate length of individual interviews — do not try to rush through them to finish at a definite time.
- Is only one interview required for each candidate, or do they require more?
- Will all interviews be carried out on the same day — if not over what period of time?
- Select suitable accommodation — quiet, comfortable and private.
- Decide if practical or theoretical tests are necessary for the applicants.
- Follow up any references which may be necessary.
- Expenses for candidates — have forms been prepared?
- Are candidates to be shown around the establishment before or after interview — individually or together?
- Consider the reception of candidates.
- Consider the use of planned questions.
- When will a decision be made about an appointment?

Conducting the interview

- Welcome the candidate and try to put him or her at ease.
- Try to arrange for the interviewer and interviewee to sit at the same level.
- Ask simple and direct questions.
- Try to ask a few searching questions to get the applicant to think.
- Do not ask questions which are negative or require just a yes or no answer.
- Do not criticise the applicant during the interview.
- Try to be a good listener and try not to interrupt when the candidate is answering a question.
- Sum up from time to time.
- Always allow candidates to ask questions if they wish to.
- Try to follow a logical pattern.

Conclusion of interview

- Has sufficient information been given to the candidate?
- If candidate is to be offered a job there and then, when is the starting date?
- Explain the procedure to be taken on completion of the interview:
  - (a) Candidates may be told to wait in the waiting room until all the candidates have been seen. Then a decision may be made and the successful candidate will be called back into the interview room.
  - (b) Candidates may be shown around the establishment.
  - (c) Candidates may be told they can leave and will be informed at a later date if they have been successful.

Making the Appointment

After the completion of the interviews a decision will be made whether to appoint or whether to re-advertise the vacancy. If the former is decided, a letter of appointment will be sent to the successful applicant, as soon as a decision has been made. Unsuccessful applicants will also, in most cases, be notified in writing. If no appointment is made, the vacancy may be re-advertised at a later date.

INDUCTION

Induction is a brief introduction to an establishment, its aims and managerial structure. Its main function is to familiarise new workers with the total work situation and to provide them with general information. It cannot be completed in a few minutes, but is a gradual and continuous process until the new employee is totally accepted by the working group — though some staff may never be totally accepted by all, unfortunately. The first impressions gained are often the ones which stay with you for ever, so it is essential that the new employee gets a good impression. Poor induction can lead to an increase in labour turnover, an increase in costs and reduced productivity, so it is imperative that an induction programme is planned to meet the needs of the individual and the establishment.

An induction programme may include some or all of the following:
- Details of the present organisation structure.
- The type, use and aims of the particular establishment.
- Duties of the job and job title.
- Conditions of employment, e.g.:
  - (a) Hours of work — shifts or straight duties, working week, overtime entitlements.
  - (b) Rates of pay — when and how — incentive bonus schemes.

 (c) Clocking on and off procedures.
 (d) Protective clothing, e.g. uniform, footwear, etc.
 (e) Arrangements for meals — entitlements.
 (f) Holiday entitlement.
 (g) Absence procedure, e.g. illness, personal commitments.
 (h) Termination — length of notice required.
 (Some of these will have been discussed in the interview of course.)

- Promotion prospects.
- Complaints procedure.
- Training opportunities — outline programme.
- General amenities, e.g. cloakrooms, medical services, parking, canteen.
- Social activities.
- Advice on safety and security.
- Name of immediate supervisor and head of department.
- Information on trade unions.
- Familiarisation with the premises — actual place of work and other departments.

The Value of an Induction Programme

To the employer
- More contented staff.
- Less frequent staff turnover.
- Knowledge that the correct methods, materials, etc. are being used.
- Improved quality and efficiency.
- Cost benefits.

To the employee
- More thorough understanding of the organisation as a whole.
- Knowledge of structures, both staffing and communications.
- Understanding of what is expected in the particular job.
- Introduction to all methods, materials and equipment used.
- Security.

TRAINING

The aim of training is to provide a highly efficient, well-motivated work force to do particular tasks to a defined level of performance. Training is a continuous process, and all grades of staff should be given the opportunity to increase their skills and professional knowledge, to enable them to carry out their day-to-day tasks, cope with modern technology and improve promotion prospects.

Training is an essential part of the supervisor's responsibility, and it may be carried out by one specific 'training supervisor' or by individual supervisors in each department. It is important to identify the training needs of the individual and the establishment through appraisal and counselling.

Training Policy

When planning a training policy for an establishment it is essential that the following factors are considered:
- What is the present level of knowledge and skill of employees?
- What skills and knowledge are required for the particular tasks?
- What resources are available, e.g. staff, time, money, etc.?
- Who requires training — in what areas and to what degree of competence?
- The individual's abilities and limitations.

- Frequency of training.
- Type of training — 'on the job', 'off the job', initial, remedial or refresher training.
- Who is responsible for organising the training?
- Who should and will carry out training of staff at all levels?
- What are the benefits of training to the establishment, to the employer, to the employee?
- The need for flexible or multi-skilled staff.

Types of Training

Initial training   takes place at the start of employment. It provides staff with the skills and knowledge they need to do their day-to-day tasks.

Refresher training   enables staff to keep up to date with changes in working methods and equipment. It may also take place to assess the progress of the individual worker and his or her suitability for promotion.

Remedial training   may be necessary to supplement initial training, especially if staff do not prove to be capable of carrying out their tasks or encounter difficulties in a particular area of work.

Methods of Training

Trial and error.   The employee either works on his own, with very little guidance, and learns by his mistakes, or he may learn the job by working with an experienced person — known as 'sitting with Nellie'. This method of training may prove to be successful in some circumstances but it may also present quite a few problems as follows:

- Bad habits may be picked up.
- Training may be very slow, time-consuming and ineffective.
- There may be a clash of personality.
- It may be relatively expensive.
- 'Nellie' may resent being used as a 'training officer'.

On-the-job training   is training which is carried out in the work situation by qualified instructors in a practical or classroom situation. The training programme is planned to provide step-by-step instruction in the particular tasks required. It is essential that training is evaluated from time to time, to make sure it is cost effective, adequate and relevant to the needs of the individual and establishment.

Off-the-job training   offers a planned training programme away from the work situation in the employer's training centre, manufacturer's training centre, residential training centre, or at a local college/hotel on a day release or block release basis. The length of training will depend on the particular grade of staff and the requirements of the training programme.

A COMPLETE TRAINING PROGRAMME

A training programme for domestic assistants is given below.

NUMBER TO BE TRAINED	TYPE OF TRAINING	METHOD OF TRAINING	INSTRUCTOR	DURATION OF TRAINING	REMARKS
All new staff	Induction	Off the job	Training Supervisor	½–1 day	
All staff	Health and safety	On the job, films, off the job, discussions	Safety Officer and Training Supervisor	½–1 day	
All staff	Fire prevention and drills	On the job, off the job, films, discussions, practice	Fire Prevention Officer	½–1 day	
All staff	Security	On the job, off the job, discussions	Security Officer	2 hours	
All new staff	Cleaning methods and procedures	On the job, off the job, discussions, practice, training manual, films	Training Supervisor	} 2–4 weeks	
All new staff	Care, use and maintenance of tools and equipment	On the job, off the job. Demonstrations by manufacturers. Discussions, films, practice, training manual	Training Supervisor, Manufacturers' Training Representative		
All new staff	Types, uses and care of cleaning products	On the job, off the job. Demonstration and talks by manufacturers. Discussions, films, practice, training manual	Training Supervisor, Manufacturers' Training Representative		
As and when required	Remedial training	On the job, off the job. Demonstrations, practice	Training Supervisor	As required	
As and when required	Refresher training	On the job, off the job. Demonstrations, practice	Training Supervisor	As required	

Training Techniques

The training supervisor/instructor may use some or all of the following methods to provide staff with the necessary knowledge and skills:

- Demonstrations — to teach manual skills, etc.
- Practice of skills — continual practice may be necessary until the operator is proficient in the particular skill.
- Lectures, talks — it is essential that these should be short and to the point because the average person retains only 25% of what he or she is told.
- Handouts — to provide back-up information and prevent the need to take notes, e.g. training booklets and manuals.
- Discussions — a pre-set time may be arranged by the instructor to discuss a topic, or discussions may take place on certain topics as and when necessary.
- Audio-visual aids — e.g. films, cassettes, video recordings, film strips, slides and live television programmes, training cards, etc.
- Projects. ⎫ Involving investigation,
- Case studies. evaluation and problem solving
- Role-playing exercises. ⎬ — probably more suitable for
- In-training exercises. training senior operatives,
- Business games. ⎭ supervisors and managers

Teaching a Skill to Employees

Thorough preparation is essential before training staff in new skills. The instructor should be prepared to answer questions whenever they arise to ensure that the trainees understand and benefit from the training sessions.

The major elements of teaching a skill are as follows:

Prepare yourself
- Try to select suitable accommodation to carry out training.
- Define the training objectives.
- Prepare all necessary information, e.g. training manuals/booklets, handouts and visual aids.
- Prepare equipment and materials necessary to carry out demonstration of the particular skills.

Prepare the trainee
- Try to put the trainee at ease — adopt a friendly, confidence-building approach.
- Outline the particular job involved and the skills to be learnt.
- Find out any previous knowledge the trainee may already have.
- Explain the value of training, equipment and materials to be used, safety, standards required and prevention of wastage.

Demonstrate the skill
- The skill should be demonstrated step by step, and each key point should be stressed.
- The skill should first be demonstrated at normal speed.
- Then demonstrate the skill more slowly. The instructor should be certain that all stages are understood.
- Finally, demonstrate the skill at normal speed several times.

Practice of the skill
- When the trainee is ready he or she should do the task slowly. Any mistakes should be corrected immediately.
- Get the trainee to explain what he or she is doing to gain confidence.
- The trainee will then do the task at normal speed until the instructor is satisfied with his or her performance.

Check performance
- The trainee is given a task to do on his or her own — help should be readily available if required.
- Check the work frequently and attend to any problems immediately.

Follow up
- This should be carried out indefinitely to prevent any bad habits occurring and to provide an efficient, well-trained employee.

The Value of Training

To the employer
- Financial savings — more effective use of all resources.
- Improved productivity.
- Improved standard and quality of work.
- Higher standard of efficiency in the industry.
- Reduced accident rate.
- Less machine maintenance.
- Less labour turnover.

To the employee
- Enhanced rates of pay.
- Improved job satisfaction.
- Improved status.
- Better promotion prospects.
- Safe working environment.
- Better equipment and materials to carry out the tasks.
- More confidence in management.

DUTY ROSTERS

Before planning the duty rosters for staff in the department the supervisor should remember the following:
- Consider the amount of cover required — 12, 16 or 24 hours per day; 5 or 7 day week; seasonal, 36 weeks or 52 weeks of the year.
- Consider the number of hours in an average working week, fortnight or month. Is overtime regularly worked?
- Consider the type of shifts — straight, split, rotating or alternating.
- Make sure that all duties are covered.
- Ensure that there is sufficient cover of all grades of staff for each shift.
- Ensure that there is sufficient cover at peak periods during the day and avoid excess of labour at slack periods.
- Try to ensure a fair allocation of weekend work and bank holiday work.
- Examine schemes for off-duty times — e.g. 1 or 2 weekends per month, a long weekend once a month (e.g. Friday, Saturday, Sunday and Monday), 2 consecutive days off per week, etc.
- Take into account variations in work load — e.g. special work activities, conferences, meetings, holidays, sickness.
- Take into account break periods — coffee, lunch, dinner, etc. Consider whether breaks are paid or unpaid.
- Do not ignore the implications of the change over of shifts.

- Make provision for transport to and from work, especially very early in the morning and late at night.
- Avoid arranging rosters to suit individual employees. Rosters must, where possible, be prepared well in advance for everybody's benefit and accepted by all the work force. They should be easy to read and interpret, and readily available for all staff to consult.
- Consider the special requirements for rosters for night duty; staff may present their own problems.

Duty roster for four porters employed in a medium-sized hotel

Examples of duty rosters are shown below.

A.   **The hours to be covered by the porters are from 6.00 a.m. until 11.00 p.m. The porters work a 40-hour week.**

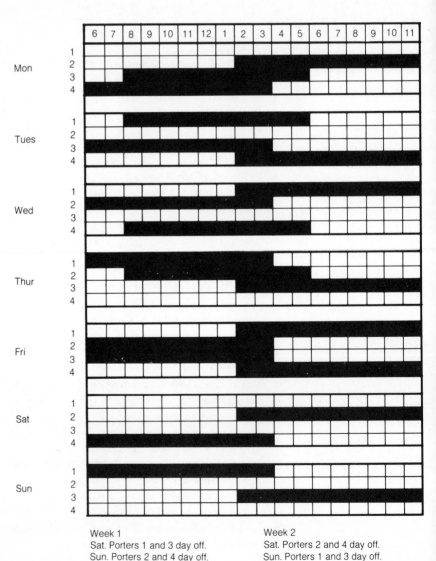

Week 1
Sat. Porters 1 and 3 day off.
Sun. Porters 2 and 4 day off.

Week 2
Sat. Porters 2 and 4 day off.
Sun. Porters 1 and 3 day off.

B.   **Alternative methods of setting out the same roster:**

SHIFTS	A	B	C	D/OFF
	PORTER NO.			
Mon	4	3	2	1
Tues	3	1	4	2
Wed	2	4	1	3
Thur	1	2	3	4
Fri	3 + 2		4 + 1	
Sat	4		2	1 + 3
Sun	1		3	2 + 4

Hours of shifts

A 6.00 a.m.–3 p.m. = 9 hours
B 8.00 a.m.–5 p.m. = 9 hours
C 2.00 p.m.–11 p.m. = 9 hours

1 hour per day deducted for meals

C.

PORTERS	MON.	TUE.	WED.	THUR.	FRI.	SAT.	SUN.	WEEKLY HOURS	MEAL DEDUCTIONS	TOTAL HOURS TO BE PAID
1	D/o	8–5	2–11	6–3	2–11	D/o	6–3	45	5	40
2	2–11	D/o	6–3	8–5	6–3	2–11	D/o	45	5	40
3	8–5	6–3	D/o	2–11	6–3	D/o	2–11	45	5	40
4	6–3	2–11	8–5	D/o	2–11	6–3	D/o	45	5	40

Types of shift

Straight shifts. Staff work a specified number of hours continuously depending on whether they are full-time, part-time or casual, or permanent days, afternoons or nights.

Split shifts are still quite common in some areas of the cleaning and housekeeping departments. Staff normally work a specified number of hours during the peak period, then have a few hours off duty and return to work to cover the next peak period. In all they may not work more than 8 hours, but a shift could cover a 12-hour span during the day.

Rotating shifts. A number of staff will usually cover a work period of 24 hours 7 days per week for 52 weeks of the year. Three shifts of 8 hours rotate in a pre-arranged manner, e.g. 6 a.m.–2 p.m., 2 p.m.–10 p.m. and 10 p.m.–6 a.m. They may work 4 days on duty and 2 days off duty or 7 days on duty and 2–3 days off duty. Then they move on to the next shift and so on. The length of the cycle will depend on the number of staff, the average working hours per week or fortnight and number of working days in relation to off-duty periods.

Alternating shift.   Staff work either a specified number of early and late shifts each week or one week on an early shift followed by one week on a late shift.

The Advantages and Disadvantages of Split, Rotating and Alternating Shifts

Advantages
- Balanced rates of pay, e.g. shift disturbance allowance.
- More 'free time' during the normal working day for personal activities especially on an early or night shift.

Disadvantages
- May interfere with social activities.
- May affect weekend activities, sleep and meal patterns.

OVERTIME

Some staff may have the opportunity to work regular overtime each week or it may be spasmodic depending on demand. Payments for overtime may be made as follows:
- Each week.
- Averaged over a period of 2 weeks or 1 month.
- Days off in lieu to suit both the employer and employee.

STAFF RECORDS

Confidential records of all employees should be kept on cards by the supervisor/ manager in the office to give all up-to-date information on the particular staff as follows:
- Personal details, e.g. sex, address, marital status, next of kin.
- Qualifications.
- Training — amount and type carried out, training needs for the future.
- Grade of staff.
- Hours of work.
- Rates of pay.
- Progress — capabilities, record of promotion.
- Absentees.
- References.
- Any other relevant information.
- Previous employer.
- Date employment terminated.

LABOUR TURNOVER

In some parts of the industry the turnover of staff tends to be very high even in the present economic and job situation. For an establishment to be run efficiently the turnover should be kept to the minimum. Research has shown that labour turnover tends to be highest in the following situations:
- Where a large number of young people, especially under 30 years, are employed.
- With unskilled employees.
- With female employees.
- Where there is a wide range of job opportunities available locally.

Percentage Turnover

To calculate the percentage turnover of staff in a given period of time use the following formula:

$$\frac{\text{No. of staff leaving}}{\text{Average no. of employees}} \times 100$$

e.g. $\dfrac{10}{50} \times 100 = 20\%$

Reasons for Leaving

- Personal reasons, e.g. illness, marriage, pregnancy, moving to another area.
- No job satisfaction.
- Poor working and welfare conditions.
- Poor residential accommodation.
- Job unsuitable for the worker.
- Worker unsuitable for the job.
- Lack of promotion prospects.
- A better job offered elsewhere.
- Poor supervision and communications.
- Clash of personalities.
- Low morale.
- Uncaring attitudes of management.
- Lack of work — poor organisation of work.
- Unacceptable hours — shift work, weekend work, etc.
- Poor incentives, e.g. wages, holiday entitlements.
- Insufficient equipment and materials.
- Transport difficulties.
- Redundancy, retirement.

Ways of Reducing Labour Turnover

- Provide job satisfaction and training.
- Provide promotion prospects.
- Improve supervision.
- Improve morale.
- Improve working and welfare conditions.
- Improve the system of communications.
- Improve work organisation (duty rosters, etc.).
- Try to provide sufficient cleaning equipment and materials for all staff.
- Provide good staff accommodation.
- Introduce incentives, e.g. bonus schemes.
- Arrange transport to and from work, where public transport presents difficulties.

Sometimes in order to introduce new ideas into an establishment it is essential to have some movement of staff, and therefore labour turnover cannot be totally eliminated.

QUESTIONS

1. Define the following terms:
   (a) induction,
   (b) training,
   (c) job analysis,
   (d) job description,
   (e) job specification,
   (f) work schedule.

2. Prepare a short training programme for six new domestic assistants employed by a Local Area Health Authority.

3. Prepare a job analysis for bed-making using:
   (a) conventional linen,
   (b) continental quilt.

4. 'The turnover of staff in my department is so great that it seems to be no use training them.' Discuss this statement, making appropriate recommendations.

5. 'There are so many things to do that I cannot afford the time to train my staff.' Comment on this statement.

6. Discuss the main points which must be considered when preparing duty rosters.

7. Draw up a duty roster for six domestic assistants employed, for general cleaning duties, in a local college. Cover is required 5 days per week from 7 a.m.–7 p.m. inclusive, and staff work an average of 30 hours per week.

8. 'The best way to train a new employee is to put him or her to work with an experienced member of the staff.' Discuss this statement.

9. (a) Outline the main causes of labour turnover.
   (b) Suggest ways in which the supervisor and management can help to overcome this problem.

10. Discuss the importance of planning an employment interview.

11. Prepare an outline interview for a job vacancy.

12. Discuss the ways in which the image of the domestic operator can be improved.

13. Why is it important to have good cooperation between architects, builders and domestic managers at (a) the planning stage, (b) the development stage?

24 Communication

THE IMPORTANCE OF COMMUNICATION

'Communication' means passing on information from one person to another in the right form, at the right time and in the right place. It is the setting up of a dialogue between two or more people and involves human relations just as much as the actual passage of information. Good communications are essential for the smooth running of any operation and act as a link between the worker and the management or between one worker and another. Communication is a two-way process of imparting information to others and attempting to receive a response. Not enough attention is paid to the fact that the information may be misunderstood or misinterpreted.

Why is Communication Necessary?

- In order that a common situation is understood and acted upon.
- To give and receive instructions.
- To give encouragement, support and motivation to staff.
- To give or receive a reprimand.
- To interpret policies of the establishment.
- To delegate authority or responsibility.

Results of Poor Communications

- Reduced productivity, or poor standard of work.
- Duplication of work.
- Neglect of some tasks.
- Increase in the accident rate.
- Poor group feelings, loss of morale, frustration, etc.
- Insecurity and undisciplined staff.

Some managers or supervisors have the mistaken idea that withholding information demonstrates power to subordinates, but often employees do find out the information from other sources. There is a skill in operating the right channels of communications and choosing the correct medium for a given circumstance.

Channels of Communications

Formal channels operate within the structure of the organisation. The larger the organisation the more difficult it is to operate a formal channel successfully. A formal channel nearly always passes information downwards, e.g. from supervisor to worker, and often with the lack of any feedback or response. There should always be a procedure for passing information upwards and from side to side so that employees can be encouraged to use their own initiative and help to participate in the success of the establishment by using suggestion schemes, joint consultation, etc. A procedure is also used for passing information between staff of the same status, e.g. head house-keeper and head receptionist.

If information breaks down along the line there should be a way of putting things right, e.g.

Information ⟶ by sender ⟶ receiver ⟶ action or response taken ⟶ result

There should always be a way of by-passing the system where necessary:

Information ⟶ Manager ⟶ Supervisor ⟶ Chargehand ⟶ Worker

Information ⟶ Worker ⟶ Chargehand ⟶ Supervisor ⟶ Manager

Uses of the formal channel
- For liaison with trade unions.
- For carrying out interviews and counselling.
- Discussion groups.
- Joint consultative committees.
- Informing staff of policy decisions.
- Apart from direct contacts communication can be effected by producing company magazines, literature and posters.

Informal channels   operate by informing staff through 'the grapevine system', the mass media, informal consultation, discussions with trade unions, airing complaints and grievances. The weaker the formal channel of communication, the greater will be the influence of the informal channel. Management tend to dislike the informal method, especially the 'grapevine system', for fear that it may undermine their authority.

CHOICE OF MEDIUM

It is essential to select the correct medium to use in a given circumstance. Communications can involve all the five senses — sight, sound, smell, touch and taste.

Speech.   Approximately 80% of all communication is carried out through the medium of speech, using: telephone, tannoy, tape recorders and video equipment, meetings, interviews and simple conversation.

Advantages	*Disadvantages*
<ul><li>Cost — can be cheaper than post.</li><li>It is quick.</li><li>Lack of formality.</li><li>Emphasis can be placed on right area.</li><li>Feedback is very quick.</li></ul>	<ul><li>It must be articulate — there may be a difficulty with language barriers.</li><li>There may be no record, so information may be distorted when passed on.</li></ul>

- It is easier to attract and hold attention.
- It may be easier to use.

- Words have to be chosen very carefully.
- It may be difficult to try to communicate with a lot of people.
- Snap judgements may be made, especially in interviewing.
- It may be difficult to avoid awkward questions.

Written communications use the following forms: memoranda; notes; notices; reports; letters; bulletins; questionnaires; forms; magazines; specifications; advertising literature; training manuals, including job instruction cards, etc.; records.

Advantages
- They avoid personal contact, which may be desirable.
- They are suitable for conveying long and complex details.
- They are more formal than other media.
- They offer a more convenient method of contacting a large group of people, particularly at a distance.
- They are more permanent, especially where records and references are made.

Disadvantages
- They may be very costly in terms of labour, materials, etc.
- They can be time-consuming to produce.
- There is less room for error or misinterpretation.
- They may be slow to transmit because of difficulties with postage and delivery.
- Sometimes they can create problems because of permanence.

Graphics include: posters; charts; duty rosters; drawings and plans; photographs, etc.; transparencies.

Advantages
- They may be 'international', e.g. road signs.
- They may be easier to follow and understand. ('A picture is worth a thousand words.')
- They can break down language barriers.
- They can have a strong impact on the receiver.
- They can catch people's attention more easily, especially if well displayed.

Disadvantages
- They must be well contructed.
- They must be simple to follow. Some subjects cannot be reproduced by this medium, e.g. ideas, concepts, laws, etc.

Non-verbal and bodily communication includes: facial expressions (e.g. raised eyebrows, smiles, scowls); gestures (e.g. thumbs up or down); posture (by the way we stand, sit, etc.). It is often used to reinforce speech either consciously or unconsciously and as the saying goes — 'actions speak louder than words'.

Advantages	*Disadvantages*
• No material costs involved.	• Snap judgements may be made.
• It is quick.	• It may be difficult to try to communicate with a lot of people.
• Lack of formality.	
• Feedback may be very quick.	• It may cause confusion.

Silence is a medium used for communication. It can be used very efficiently, but it can also in some cases cause the communication process to break down.

Causes of Breakdowns in Communication

External barriers can usually be controlled, but often people are not aware of them and so the problems still exist. Here are examples:
• Excessive heat, cold or noise.
• Tiredness — poor physical and mental health.
• Effects of drugs and alcohol.

Internal barriers may be difficult to control, and this is why it is essential to have a good system of communication operating in the establishment. We need to be aware of industrial differences and causes, e.g.:
• Badly expressed or ambiguous information.
• Wrong information.
• Lack of information.
• Lack of skill and training.
• Personality clashes.
• Language barriers, cultural differences, heavy dialects.
• Speech impediments — unclear speech.
• Hearing difficulties, poor sight, colour blindness.
• Fear of the unknown, lack of feedback.
• Information which is illegible or unclear.
• Incomplete information.
• Impractical information.
• Lack of regular meetings.

How to Prevent a Breakdown in Communication

• Be aware of the importance of a good communication system.
• Select the right channels and media to be used.
• Care of selection and training of staff.
• Policies of establishment must be clearly defined.
• Try to prevent external and internal barriers.
• Improve morale, and good human and industrial relations. Ensure all information is received and understood, reinforced where necessary and suitable feedback is given.
• Give encouragement and motivate staff.
• Introduce a system for by-passing where necessary.

REPORT WRITING

A report is a written account of an event, problem or situation. The person making one must collect relevant information, facts and figures, analyse them and arrive at a logical conclusion where possible, and make recommendations if required. The main purpose is to provide information to those who are concerned with or responsible for taking action.

Personal reports   give an account of a situation dealing with personnel (e.g. accident report, work progress, social disturbances, disciplinary action).

Routine reports   provide information which is passed on to appropriate departments concerned with the day-to-day running of the establishment (e.g. machinery breakdown, maintenance reports, security, lost property, minimising wastage, saving fuel, etc., sales figures, productivity levels).

Special reports   may include very detailed investigations of certain topics (e.g. research programmes, comparative studies, introducing new systems of work, working out reasons for high turnover of labour, and reports from committees and conferences).

Before preparing a report the writer must consider how to tackle it and in what order. He or she must classify the terms of reference and be clear on the main purpose of the report. It is also essential to know to whom the report is to be submitted and by what date. It does not necessarily have to be prepared and submitted in a formal manner so long as it is logical and easy to follow — perhaps in the form of a memorandum, letter, checklist, etc.

The Essential Requirements of a Report

- Layout is very important and it should be logical and easy to read and stimulate interest.
- It should be accurate.
- It should be concise and clear, with good grammar and correct spelling.
- It should fulfil the terms of reference — the amount of details included should be consistent with the type of subject.
- It should be unbiased and tactful.
- It should contain up-to-date relevant facts, figures and general information.
- It should contain suitable conclusions and recommendations where appropriate.

Collecting, sorting, and arranging information

Information can be gathered first-hand or second-hand, and often first-hand information is overlooked. Be very selective and look at the relevant importance of the information collected. All sources of information should be identified and acknowledged. They may include the following:

- Material from the work situation (e.g. records, costs, systems and techniques used, observations and personal experiences).
- Library books, textbooks and reference books — some may be out of date.
- Information from manufacturers and suppliers of equipment, plant, materials, etc.
- Trade journals — they are likely to have more relevant up-to-date information than books.
- Information from other similar establishments, associations, etc.

Contents of a Report

Terms of reference.   These include the guidelines to the report and should be set out very clearly at the beginning of every report. The guidelines should set the scene and give background and historical information, the purpose, scope and limitations.

Summary.   This provides a brief outline of the problem, findings, conclusions and recommendations — supporting facts are kept to a minimum.

Findings.   This section usually forms the main part of the report and should be presented in a logical manner. It is a good idea to tabulate the facts so that they are clear and easy to follow — using the conventional method.

Conclusions.   Facts are discussed and analysed and certain deductions are made about them. Conclusions are then made and put forward in a clear, concise, logical manner.

Recommendations.   These are based on the findings and conclusions. If there are several recommendations they should be submitted in order of priority with arguments for and against. In some cases the report may recommend short-term and long-term changes or the need for future planning and change. It is also very important to keep up to date with changes in systems, products, technology, etc.

THE MEMORANDUM (Memo)

A memo is a written note which is usually sent through the internal post to convey, confirm or request information or to act as a reminder. It is usually prepared on the sender's initiative and does not have to result from a specific request. It is the most widely used form of written communication. Unfortunately there are often too many to deal with and they are too long in content especially when another form of communication would have been more suitable.

The following items must be included in any memo:
- Name, department and position of the sender.
- Name and department of the person to whom it is to be sent.
- Date.
- Subject — outline details.
- Initials or signature of the sender.

An example is given below.

To: All Domestic Supervisors   Date: 12 February 19–

From: The Training Officer   Subject: Crime Prevention

Please inform all your staff that a local Crime Prevention Officer will be giving a talk on 'Crime Prevention' in the Lecture Theatre on Wednesday 7 April 19– from 2.30 to 4.00 pm. Please ensure as many of your staff as possible can attend.

P M Williams

QUESTIONS

1. Explain in detail why a good system of communications is necessary in the housekeeping department.

2. Briefly outline the main channels of communication.

3. Indicate the main causes of a breakdown in communication and suggest ways of preventing such a breakdown.

4. What is the 'grapevine system'?

5. List the media which can be used to communicate information to the staff and suggest advantages and disadvantages of each type of medium.

6. Why do supervisors and operators often misunderstand information which is given to them?

7. Outline the main types of report.

8. Why is it essential that a report should be clear, concise and brief?

9. List the essentials of a report.

10. What is a formal report and how should it be submitted?

PART E: GLOSSARY & APPENDICES

GLOSSARY OF TECHNICAL TERMS

ACCELERATOR
A substance which is used in a two-pot surface coating material (e.g. paint, seal, etc.) to increase the speed of a chemical reaction. It is also known as a 'hardener' and is added to the 'base' product before use.

BASE
The main component of a two-pot surface coating material, e.g. paint, seal etc. It will not, by itself, form a film and requires the addition of an accelerator.

BLOCK METHOD OF CLEANING
The same task is carried out in all the rooms of a section before moving on to the next task.

BUFFABLE FLOOR WAX
A floor wax which must be buffed to provide a gloss and harden the surface. It can be re-buffed from time to time to produce a good appearance.

CALENDER
A series of heated, well-padded rollers which iron flat items, e.g. sheets, pillowcases. After ironing the items can be folded by an automatic device on the machine or by hand.

CANTILEVERED FURNITURE
Items of furniture, e.g. bookcases which project from a wall, resting on brackets.

CAUSTIC
A material which is corrosive or destructive to living tissue, e.g. caustic soda and caustic potash which are two very strong alkaline materials.

CLEANING AGENTS
Materials used in the cleaning and maintenance process, e.g. detergents, abrasives, solvents, seals, polishes, etc.

CONCENTRATED WEIGHT
The total weight of the floor maintenance machine is borne on the brushes/pads.

CONTRA-ROTATING
Usually refers to a floor maintenance machine which has a reversible drive to provide more even wear on the brushes/pads.

CONVENTIONAL CLEANING METHOD
The work involved is carried out in a given sequence. When completed the worker moves on to the next area until all the allotted work has been completed.

DEEP CLEANING
A thorough or periodic cleaning process carried out in a particular area.

DEW POINT
The temperature at which water vapour in the air changes to liquid.

DILUTE
To reduce the strength of a product by the addition of water or other appropriate solvents to assist in the ease of use or application. The correct dilution rate is essential for various reasons.

DIVIDED WEIGHT
The weight of the floor maintenance machine is distributed between the brush/pad head and the wheels.

DRUGGETS
Made of plastic, canvas or coarse linen in the form of a runner or square and used to protect the floor surface against excessive wear especially in very heavy traffic areas and bad weather.

DRY-BRIGHT FLOOR WAXES
When applied to the floor surface they dry to a high initial gloss without buffing. Buffing will produce very little, if any, increase in gloss.

DRY RISER
Runs on the outside of a building over 45 m high and is connected to a water hydrant in case of fire.

DUSTING
Usually associated with the disintegration of the surface layer of concrete into very fine particles of dust.

DUVET
A duvet is a continental quilt which is filled with down or synthetic fibres and used on a bed instead of blankets and bedspread.

EMULSION WAX
A blend of water/wax emulsion and an alkali-soluble resin or shellac. It can be buffed depending on type.

ERGONOMICS
The study of the relationship of the worker to the environment, tools and equipment so as to avoid unnecessary strain and tension and as a result make the best use of human resources.

FLASH POINT
The temperature at which vapour from a liquid will ignite when exposed to a small flame or spark. The lower the temperature at which ignition takes place, the more flammable is the liquid.

FRASS
Fine granular boredust found near exit holes of woodworm.

HUE
Another name for colour.

HYDROEXTRACTOR
A machine which is used to extract or remove water, etc., from the laundry after it has been through the washing process — similar to a spin dryer.

INDUCTION
A brief introduction to an establishment, its aims and managerial structures, conditions of employment, etc.

INITIAL CLEAN
Cleaning which is carried out after an area has been redecorated, opened, updated, etc.

IN SITU

'On site' or 'on the spot': e.g. if a carpet is shampooed 'in situ' it is cleaned on the spot within the establishment.

INSULATORS

Poor or non-conductors of heat or electricity. Used to stop heat loss and as insulation on wire (plastic).

INTER-COAT ADHESION

The bonding together of two or more coats, on top of each other, of surface coating material, e.g. seals, polishes, paints, etc.

JOB ANALYSIS

Process of studying all phases of a job including the specific tasks performed. The relationships to other jobs and the conditions of work.

JOB DESCRIPTION

Details of the specific job, what is expected of the worker, the responsibilities and limitations.

JOB SPECIFICATION

An outline of the personal requirements for the job to fit the right person into the specific job. It may also include an outline of the job itself.

LEVELLING

It is the ease with which a surface coating material, e.g. seal or polish will flow out and spread evenly over a surface, without leaving marks.

LINEN BANK

A central area, usually attached to a group laundry, where clean linen is stored until required by the individual wards, departments, etc.

LINEN HIRE

Clean linen is supplied to the establishment, on a contract basis, by a firm offering a rental service.

LUMINOUS FLUX

Flow of light emitted per second in a cone of a certain size by a point source of known intensity.

LUX

A unit of illumination. One lumen per square metre.

MEMO

A written note, usually sent through the internal post to convey, confirm or request information or to act as a reminder.

METHOD STUDY

The systematic recording and critical examination of existing and proposed ways of doing work, as a means of developing and applying easier and more effective methods and thus reducing costs.

MOTION ECONOMY

Is concerned with the economy of movement. Fatigue will be reduced and time fully utilised if movements can be eliminated, reduced or simplified.

ONE-POT PRODUCTS
Materials which are packed into a single container, ready for use without any additives being necessary, e.g. one-pot seal, polish, etc.

OPL
On premises laundry or laundry on site.

pH SCALE
The pH scale indicates the acidity or alkalinity of a product. The scale ranges from 1–14; 1–6 is acid, 7 is neutral and 8–14 alkali.

PIGMENT
A material which is added during manufacture to give colour to a product.

POT LIFE
It refers to two-pot materials and is the period during which the material is usable once the base and the accelerator have been blended together. After a certain period of time it may become unusable.

PREVENTIVE AND PLANNED MAINTENANCE
A detailed scheme of work for the daily, weekly and occasional cleaning and servicing of plant, premises, furnishings, fittings, etc., to ensure maximum efficiency, comfort and cleanliness.

REFURBISH
To improve the appearance of a room by redecoration, renewing soft furnishings, carpets, furniture, etc.

RE-SHEETING
The complete renewal of clean linen for beds.

SEAL
Is a semi-permanent material which is applied to a surface to prevent the entry of dirt, stains, liquids, etc.

SEMI-BUFFABLE FLOOR WAX
The wax dries to a subdued gloss which can be increased if required by buffing. Buffing will help to harden the surface and increase durability.

SHELF-LIFE
The life expectancy of a product, stored under ideal conditions. After a certain period the product may deteriorate or be unsuitable.

SOFT FURNISHINGS
Include curtains, loose covers, cushions, bedspreads, but not carpets.

SOLVENT
A liquid which will dissolve a solid is known as a solvent.

STANDARD TIMES
Average times which have been worked out for particular cleaning operations. They are dependent on various factors, e.g. the worker, the surface to be cleaned and the working conditions.

STOCK ROTATION
A system of stock control whereby old stock is issued before new stock. The new stock is stored at the back of shelves and old stock is brought to the front.

STOCKTAKING
A physical check on all items in stock which is carried out on a regular basis, e.g. monthly, 6 monthly, etc. Any discrepancies are noted and investigated.

SWEEPING COMPOUND
Blends of organic and inorganic fillers, e.g. sand, wood flour, etc., mixed with oil or wax. Applied to a floor surface to absorb oils, fats, etc., and then swept up to remove build-up and dry dust.

SYNTHETIC
Refers to items, products which are artificial.

TARE WEIGHT
Weight of an empty gas cylinder.

TEAM CLEANING
Cleaning carried out by two or more people in a given area. They either work together or carry out different tasks in one area.

TEROTECHNOLOGY
The science of maintenance.

THERMAL TRANSMITTANCE
Overall rate of transmittance of heat by either conduction, convection or radiation.

THINNERS
A liquid added to a paint, seal, etc., to facilitate application.

TOG VALUE
The measurement of warmth to be found in continental quilts. The higher the value the warmer the quilt.

TOXIC
Poisonous. Toxicity is the degree to which a substance is poisonous.

TRAINING
Training is a continuous process used to impart skills, knowledge, etc., to the employees.
- On-the-Job Training which is carried out in the actual work situation by demonstrations, talks, practice, etc.
- Off-the-Job Training which is carried out away from the normal work situation, e.g. in a training centre, college, etc.

VENEER
A covering of fine wood for chipboard, laminates, etc.

VISCOSITY
The resistance of a liquid to flow — the greater the resistance the higher is the viscosity. Viscosity decreases considerably with the increase in temperature.

WET RISER
A water pipe that runs vertically through the inside of a building. Used in the event of a fire.

WORK STUDY
A general term for those techniques which are used in the examination of human work in all its contexts and which lead systematically to the investigation of all factors, which affect efficiency and economy of the situation being reviewed, in order to effect improvement.

APPENDIX I

FLOOR MAINTENANCE CHART — DETERGENTS

TYPE OF FLOOR	DETERGENTS TO USE	DETERGENTS TO AVOID
Wood Wood composition Cork	Solvent-based detergents. Neutral detergents	Alkaline detergents. Abrasive powders. Detergent crystals
Magnesite	Solvent-based detergents. Neutral detergents	Strong alkaline detergents. Abrasive powders. Detergent crystals
Concrete Granolithic	Neutral detergents. Alkaline detergents. Detergent crystals. Solvent-based detergents	None
Terrazzo Marble	Neutral detergents. Mild alkaline detergents. Mild abrasive detergents	Strong alkaline detergents. Detergent crystals. Solvent-based detergents. Oily materials

Natural stone:
  Granite
  Limestone
  Sandstone
  Quartzite
  Slate
	Neutral detergents.
	Alkaline detergents.
	Abrasive powders.
	Detergent crystals.
	Solvent-based detergents
		Oily materials

Clay (quarry) tiles	Neutral detergents. Alkaline detergents. Mild abrasive powders	Solvent-based detergents. Oily materials
Brick	Neutral detergents. Alkaline detergents. Solvent-based detergents	Oily materials
Cement latex	Neutral detergents. Mild alkaline detergents	Solvent-based detergents. Oily materials
Mastic asphalt Pitchmastic	Neutral detergents. Alkaline detergents. Detergent crystals	Solvent-based detergents. Oily materials
Linoleum	Neutral detergents. Mild alkaline detergents. Solvent-based detergents	Strong alkaline detergents. Abrasive powders. Detergent crystals

TYPE OF FLOOR	DETERGENTS TO USE	DETERGENTS TO AVOID
Cork carpet	Neutral detergents. Solvent-based detergents	Strong alkaline detergents. Detergent crystals
Thermoplastic tiles PVC (vinyl) asbestos Flexible PVC Rubber	Neutral detergents. Mild alkaline detergents	Strong alkaline detergents. Oily materials. Detergent crystals. Abrasive powders (on flexible PVC)
Iron and steel	Neutral detergents. Solvent-based detergents	None
Aluminium	Neutral detergents. Solvent-based detergents	Strong alkaline detergents
Glass	Neutral detergents. Mild alkaline detergents. Mild abrasive powders	Strong alkaline detergents. Coarse abrasive powders. Oily materials

Plastic seamless:
  Screeded
 	
  Self-levelling
  Decorative
	Neutral detergents.
	
	Alkaline detergents.
	Solvent-based detergents
		Abrasive powders (on
		decorative floors)
		Oily materials

Antistatic:
  Terrazzo
  Magnesite
  Linoleum
  Rubber
  Flexible PVC
	Neutral detergents.
	Mild alkaline detergents.
	Fine Abrasive powders
		Strong alkaline detergents.
		Detergent crystals.
		Oily materials

FLOOR MAINTENANCE CHART — FLOOR SEALS

TYPE OF FLOOR	FLOOR SEALS TO USE	FLOOR SEALS TO AVOID
Wood Wood composition Cork	Solvent-based clear seals	Water-based seals
Magnesite	Solvent-based clear seals. Water-based seals (coloured if required)	Silicate dressing
Concrete Granolithic	One- and two-pot polyurethane clear and pigmented seals. Synthetic rubber pigmented seal. Silicate dressing. Water-based seals	Conventional seals liable to be affectd by alkali
Terrazzo Marble	Water-based seals	Solvent-based seals. Silicate dressing

Natural stone:
  Granite
  Limestone
  Sandstone
  Quartzite
  Slate
	Generally none; but
	water-based seals can be used
	on some floors if necessary
		Solvent-based seals

Clay (quarry) tiles	Generally none, but water-based seals can be used if necessary	Solvent-based seals
Brick Cement latex	Generally none, but water-based seals can be used if necessary	Solvent-based seals
Mastic asphalt Pitchmastic	Water-based seals (coloured if required). Two-pot polyurethane pigmented seals. Synthetic rubber pigmented seal	Solvent-based clear and pigmented seals (except two-pot polyurethane and synthetic rubber seals). Silicate dressing
Linoleum	Water-based seals	Solvent-based seals. Silicate dressing
Cork carpet	Generally none, but solvent-based clear seals can be used if necessary	Water-based seals. Silicate dressing
Thermoplastic tiles PVC (vinyl) asbestos Flexible PVC Rubber	Water-based seals	Solvent-based seals. Silicate dressing

TYPE OF FLOOR	FLOOR SEALS TO USE	FLOOR SEALS TO AVOID
Iron and steel Aluminium	None	Conventional solvent and water-based seals
Glass	None	Solvent-based and water-based seals

Plastic seamless:
  Screeded
  Self-levelling
  Decorative
	None	Conventional solvent-based seals.
		Silicate dressing

Anti-static:
  Terrazzo
  Magnesite
  Linoleum
  Rubber
  Flexible PVC
	None	Solvent-based and water-based seals.
		Silicate dressing

FLOOR MAINTENANCE CHART — FLOOR WAXES

TYPE OF FLOOR	FLOOR WAXES TO USE	FLOOR WAXES TO AVOID
Wood Wood composition Cork	Solvent-based waxes. (*NB* If floor is well sealed a water emulsion floor wax can be used)	If unsealed, avoid water emulsion floor waxes
Magensite	Solvent-based waxes. (*NB* If a floor is sealed a water emulsion floor wax can be used)	If unsealed, avoid water emulsion floor waxes
Concrete	Water emulsion floor waxes. Solvent-based waxes	None
Terrazzo Marble	Water emulsion floor waxes	Solvent-based waxes

Natural stone:
  Granite
  Limestone
  Sandstone
  Quartzite
  Slate
	Generally none, but water emulsion floor waxes can be used if necessary	Solvent-based waxes

Clay (quarry) tiles	General none, but water emulsion floor waxes can be used if necessary	Solvent-based waxes

TYPE OF FLOOR	FLOOR WAXES TO USE	FLOOR WAXES TO AVOID
Brick Cement latex	Generally none, but water emulsion floor waxes can be used if necessary	Solvent-based waxes
Mastic asphalt Pitchmastic	Water emulsion floor waxes (coloured if required)	Solvent-based waxes
Linoleum	Solvent-based waxes. Water emulsion floor waxes	None
Cork carpet	Solvent-based waxes	If unsealed, avoid water emulsion floor waxes
Thermoplastic tiles PVC (vinyl) asbestos Flexible PVC Rubber	Water emulsion floor waxes	Solvent-based waxes
Iron and steel Aluminium	None	Solvent-based waxes and water emulsion floor waxes
Glass	None	Solvent-based waxes and water emulsion floor waxes

Plastic seamless:
  Screeded
  Self-levelling
  Decorative
	Generally none, but water emulsion floor waxes can be used, particularly on decorative floors, if required	Solvent-based waxes

Antistatic:
  Terrazzo
  Magnesite
  Linoleum
  Rubber
  Flexible PVC
	None	Solvent-based waxes and water emulsion floor waxes

APPENDIX II

FAULTS, CAUSES AND REMEDIES

Quality control of products is a very important function in any manufacturing organisation. In order to achieve this aim, once products have been delivered it is essential that they are stored under ideal conditions to prevent deterioration which causes problems when being used. It is also very important that surfaces are correctly prepared before treatment to prevent flaking off, streaking, slow drying and poor adhesion, etc.

Detergents

Faults	Causes	Remedies
1. Excessive foaming or difficulty in rinsing away foam.	(a) Too much detergent being used.	(a) Check dilution rate.
	(b) Sponge used as an applicator.	(b) Use a different type of applicator.
2. Lack of foam (check to see that the detergent is not a low foaming product).	Too little detergent being used.	Check dilution rate.
3. Harsh on skin.	Too frequent contact with the skin.	Try to avoid contact with the skin; if necessary wear rubber gloves.

Seals

Faults	Causes	Remedies
1. Slow drying.	(a) Floor incorrectly prepared.	(a) Make sure floor is clean, neutral and free from wax, etc.
	(b) Seal applied too thickly.	(b) Apply several thin coats. Allow time for the seal to dry — good ventilation and warmth will help.
	(c) Poor ventilation.	(c) Improve ventilation.
	(d) First coat may not have dried out before second coat is applied.	(d) Each coat should be allowed to dry hard before further coats are applied.

Faults	Causes	Remedies
2. Poor adhesion.	(a) Floor incorrectly prepared.	(a) Make sure floor is clean, neutral and free from wax, etc.
	(b) Seal may be incompatible with previous seal on floor.	(b) Remove all seal and reapply new seal.
3. Poor finish, e.g. streaky, patchy rough.	(a) Floor incorrectly prepared.	(a) Clean off floor thoroughly using abrasive pads or sanding, mop with appropriate solvent and apply new coat as soon as solvent has evaporated.
	(b) Seal applied too thickly.	(b) Lightly sand or machine with abrasive pads — damp mop —leave to dry and apply new seal.
4. Poor durability.	(a) Insufficient coats of seal applied.	(a) Thoroughly clean floor and apply more coats of seal.
	(b) Seal applied too thinly.	(b) Thoroughly clean floor and apply more coats of seal.
	(c) Scrubbing too frequently.	(c) Check frequency and standard of cleaning. Thoroughly clean floor and apply more seal.
	(d) Grit carried in on the floor from outside.	(d) Remove source of grit or provide effective mats. Thoroughly clean floor and apply more seal.

Solvent-based Waxes

Faults	Causes	Remedies
1. Floor appears slippery.	(a) Build up of wax over a period of time. Too frequent application. Too much wax applied to surface.	(a) Strip off old wax using a solvent-based detergent wax remover. Reapply a thin coat of wax and buff well.

Faults	Causes	Remedies
	(b) Insufficient buffing of wax. Buffing hardens wax and improves anti-slip properties.	(b) Buff wax regularly, particularly after new application.
	(c) Underfloor heating causing wax to soften.	(c) Where possible use water emulsion waxes with under-floor heating.
	(d) Water, oil or solvents carried on to the floor by footwear.	(d) Provide effective matting: remove water, oil or solvents immediately they appear.
2. Machine marks left on floor.	(a) Floor still wet when buffing began.	(a) Apply a thin coat of wax, allow to dry and buff up.
	(b) Too much wax applied to floor.	(b) Change pads frequently. Apply only thin coats of wax.
	(c) Incorrect grade of pad used.	(c) Use only five grades of pads.
	(d) Machine brush or pad dirty.	(d) Clean brush or pad and re-buff.
3. Slow drying.	(a) Inadequate ventilation or low temperature.	(a) Provide adequate ventilation and heat if possible.
	(b) Wax applied too thickly.	(b) Allow time for wax to dry. Buff surface, change pad and repeat operation.

Water Emulsion Floor Wax

Faults	Causes	Remedies
1. Floor appears slippery.	(a) Emulsion wax applied too frequently and too heavily. Build-up of wax.	(a) Strip off wax using an alkaline detergent. Rinse thoroughly, neutralise and apply new coat of wax.
	(b) Insufficient buffing.	(b) Buff floor regularly particularly after a new application of wax.

Faults	Causes	Remedies
	(c) Wrong type of wax used.	(c) Make sure correct type of wax is used.
	(d) Oil, water or solvent wax may be carried by traffic from adjoining floor.	(d) Prevent entry of oil, water or solvent on to the floor. Provide effective matting.
2. Poor dry-bright qualities.	(a) Floor incorrectly prepared. (Check that wax is a dry-bright emulsion.)	(a) Strip off wax using alkaline detergent, rinse, neutralise and apply fresh coat of wax.
	(b) Dirty equipment used to apply wax.	(b) Make sure all equipment is clean before being used.
	(c) Emulsion applied too thinly.	(c) Check coverage rate and dilution rate. Apply a fresh coat of wax.
	(d) Insufficient number of coats applied.	(d) Apply further coats of wax.
	(e) Second coat applied before first coat is dry.	(e) Strip off wax, rinse, neutralise and apply a fresh coat of wax.
3. Poor flow — appearance patchy or streaky.	(a) Floor incorrectly prepared. Alkaline detergent may still be deposited on surface, and is likely to attack fresh coat.	(a) Strip off old wax, rinse, neutralise and apply a new coat or buff and apply a new coat.
	(b) Dirty equipment used to apply wax.	(b) Make sure all equipment is clean before using it. May not need to strip off wax, but just buff and apply a fresh coat of wax.
	(c) Emulsion wax applied too thickly.	(c) Either strip off old wax or buff surface and apply a thin coat of wax.
	(d) Second coat applied before first coat is dry.	(d) Strip off old wax as before or, if the appearance is not too bad, buff and apply a new coat of wax.

Faults	Causes	Remedies
4. Slow drying.	(a) Damp floor.	(a) Provide a good damp-proof course.
	(b) Poor ventilation, high humidity, low temperature.	(b) Adjust temperature and if possible humidity — provide good ventilation.
5. Poor durability.	(a) Incorrect detergent or solution too concentrated.	(a) Use correct detergent and appropriate dilution rate.
	(b) Incorrect pads being used.	(b) Use fine grade pads to achieve the desired result.
	(c) Emulsion wax applied too thinly.	(c) Apply a further coat or coats of emulsion wax.
	(d) Floor incorrectly prepared.	(d) Strip off old wax using alkaline detergent. Rinse thoroughly, neutralise and apply fresh coat of wax.
6. Poor removability.	(a) Wrong detergent used for stripping.	(a) Use correct detergent at the recommended concentration.
	(b) Excessive build-up of wax.	(b) Prevent build-up of wax. Strip floor wax using alkaline detergent or a fortified detergent with solvent.
	(c) Incorrect pads used on machine.	(c) Use the correct pads for stripping off old wax.

Index